VHDL AND AHDL DIGITAL SYSTEM IMPLEMENTATION

FRANK A. SCARPINO, PH.D.
University of Dayton

Prentice Hall PTR
Upper Saddle River, New Jersey 07458
http://www.phptr.com

ISBN 0-13-857087-6

9 780138 570873

90000

Library of Congress Cataloging-in-Publication Data

Scarpino, Frank.
  VHDL and AHDL digital system implementation/
  Frank A. Scarpino.
    p. cm.
  Includes index.
  ISBN 0–13–857087–6
    1. Electronic digital computers—Circuits—Design and
  construction—Data processing. 2. VHDL (Hardware description
  language) 3. System design—Data processing. 4. Logic circuits—
  Design and construction—Data processing. I. Title.
  TK788.4.S24 1998
  621.39'2—dc21   97–44778
                                                              CIP

Acquisitions editor: Bernard M. Goodwin
Cover designer: Design Source
Cover design director: Jerry Votta
Manufacturing manager: Alexis R. Heydt
Marketing manager: Betsy Carey
Compositor/Production services: Pine Tree Composition, Inc.

Prentice Hall books are widely used by corporations and government agencies for training, marketing, and resale.
The publisher offers discounts on this book when ordered in bulk quantities. For more information contact:

Corporate Sales Department
Phone: 800-382-3419
Fax: 201-236-7141
E-mail: corpsales@prenhall.com

Or write:

Prentice Hall PTR
Corp. Sales Dept.
One Lake Street
Upper Saddle River, New Jersey 07458

The author and publisher of this book have used their best efforts in preparing this book. These efforts include the development, research, and testing of the theories and programs to determine their effectiveness. The author and publisher make no warranty of any kind, expressed or implied, with regard to these programs or the documentation contained in this book. The author and publisher shall not be liable in any event for incidental or consequential damages in connection with, or arising out of, the furnishing, performance, or use of these programs.

Printed in the United States of America
10 9 8 7 6 5 4 3 2

ISBN: 0-13-857087-6

Prentice-Hall International (UK) Limited, *London*
Prentice-Hall of Australia Pty. Limited, *Sydney*
Prentice-Hall Canada Inc., *Toronto*
Prentice-Hall Hispanoamerican, S.A., *Mexico*
Prentice-Hall of India Private Limited, *New Delhi*
Prentice-Hall of Japan, Inc., *Tokyo*
Simon & Schuster Asia Pte. Ltd., *Singapore*
Editora Prentice-Hall do Brasil, Ltda., *Rio de Janeiro*

Dedicated to Christina, Katie, Carolyn . . . and all those who follow. May they live in peace.

CONTENTS

**Part II   Introduction to Applications
in VHSIC Hardware Description Language**

INTRODUCTION

A NEW PARADIGM FOR HARDWARE DESIGN

In modern design practice, the process of digital design has recently taken a major departure from the processes of the recent past as well as from the distant past. Traditionally, digital design has been accomplished with the time-honored tools of block diagrams, wiring lists, Boolean equations, and schematic diagrams as the key elements. These time-honored methods have produced countless designs over the past half-century . . . designs of immense complexity and sophistication. The designers who produced significant designs using the traditional tools have contributed to significant change in the digital technology world and in the world as a whole. As with all such accomplishments, correspondingly vital changes have accompanied these recent accomplishments. Digital designers have produced very high-speed computing equipment which, in turn, has produced essential change in the science and art of digital design itself. These changes have helped produce a digital design world that is more productive and dynamic than at any time in the past. Until the present revolution, a relatively clear distinction existed between hardware and software. However, in more recent years, with the advent of programmable logic and the associated design tools, this distinction has begun to erode.

In recent years, the traditional methods have given way to development processes involving hardware description languages (HDL)—the primary topic of this book. The use of HDL involves the use of tools reminiscent of the tools commonly used in software development. These tools include text editors, compilers, debuggers, and simulators. This modern hardware design approach, based upon HDL, produces a design environment that encourages productivity and creativity and yet helps to produce fully tested, reliable digital products. Yet these same tools, as commonplace as they are in the software world, are creating significant changes in the hardware world.

The HDL approach incorporates a level of abstraction in the digital process that is essentially not present in traditional design methodologies. In the traditional approaches, the logical descriptions implicitly (or even explicitly) contain descriptions of the components of which the digital system is to be constructed. These implicit descriptions are contained in the schematic diagrams, wiring diagrams, and wiring lists that form the essential components of the design. By contrast, in the HDL approach, the designs are created in a lexical format that describes the essence of the design in some combination of a structural, functional, or behavioral form. The behavioral or functional design descriptions may be overlaid onto component descriptions after a compilation process on the lexical file representing the hardware design. However, the compiler output is prepared in the form of an interconnection list or "netlist" which readily lends itself to both an implementation process and a simulation process. Simulation is the recommended next step since debugging of complex logic is much more straightforward in a simulation environment. After simulation, when functional performance has been verified, the logical description contained in the source file text description may be overlaid onto a hardware implementation. In the current text, the logical description will be implemented in a programmable logic array. Programmable arrays are prefabricated logical arrays within which electronic interconnections may be either enabled or disabled. The rapid and inexpensive enabling and disabling of data paths within the internal structure of available chips permits the logical designer to readily implement logical designs with a high level of sophistication. If desired, implementation of the logical design into a programmable hardware array may be accomplished literally within a matter of minutes.

While the logical design process and the implementation practice have both taken new turns in the recent past, the combination of new design methodology, such as text-based design utilizing an HDL, and new implementation methodology, such as programmable logic arrays, together have produced an entirely new era in which the traditional lines between hardware and software have been blurred. Hardware has traditionally been viewed as difficult and expensive to produce while it has also been viewed as even more difficult to modify. In a modern world, HDL is used to design and/or redesign hardware, and programmable logic chips are used for implementation. The corresponding conceptual notions including difficulties in design, implementation, and subsequent alteration are radically different in a modern environment than in the environment of even the recent past.

Software has been traditionally viewed as relatively simple to design and produce. Lexical-based design for software is the norm. Compilers and linkers readily produce object files and executable files from designer produced text files (source files). Software is viewed as relatively simple to design because text files may be easily edited, recompiled, and relinked. The resulting executable files are readily loaded into a computer as a final implementation step.

However, now that hardware may be produced with tools comparable to the tools successfully used for software design and implementation, hardware may be viewed as substantially less costly and difficult to design and implement . . . and, in turn, substantially less difficult and costly to modify. As a collateral effect, much more sophisticated processing hardware can be produced economically and efficiently.

IMPACT OF THE NEW HARDWARE PARADIGM

The ramifications of the elimination of many of the clear traditional hardware-software distinctions are probably many in number. Perhaps, as with any significant paradigm shift, the technologists of the world will spend a considerable length of time discovering the resulting impacts.

Traditional texts on logic design are replete with techniques on design methodology. Methodologies explored typically include Boolean-function simplification techniques, including Karnaugh mapping and Quine-McClusky tabular simplification methods. Traditional books also cover methods for the design of and implementation of counters, state machines, arithmetic units, and a complete array of the important logical building blocks. Necessarily, in traditional texts, designs of significant implementation detail are avoided in favor of designs stressing methods the designer might employ in more complex designs. This perspective is perhaps, to some extent, motivated by the pure volume of documentation required to explore more pragmatic implementations. This emphasis on design methods continues to be important even with a significant paradigm shift in the digital-system design process. It is highly recommended that the designer acquire a substantial basis in the traditional design principles.

On the other hand, the traditional design methods are not the primary topics of the current text. The current text places an emphasis on the implementation of modern digital systems using HDL and programmable arrays. This approach affords more latitude in the presentation of implementation details because HDL provides a substantially more efficient and compact means of system representation. For example, as the reader progresses through the current text he or she might consider the traditional means of representing systems that are developed as illustrations in HDL. The traditional means including block diagrams and/or schematic diagrams are often far more cumbersome and ambiguous than the compact means consisting of source language files. As experienced designers are well aware, the devil is often in the details. The luxury of a more compact and explicit system representation permits a more detailed study of digital system implementation than would otherwise be reasonably possible. This more detailed level of study is also facilitated because the assumption is made here that the reader already has some familiarity with the traditional paradigms of logic design and implementation.

In many ways, the reader may observe that the current text reads more like a classical software book than a hardware book. While this may initially feel awkward to the reader, it is the opinion of the author that this is the future of digital system design. Furthermore it is not difficult to adapt to the new paradigm and the motivation is quickly generated by the rapid pace at which the reader will soon acquire proficiency using the lexical approach.

The current book may well be utilized either as a text for classroom use, a means of casually becoming acquainted with HDL implementation, a tool for learning the details of HDL implementation, or as a reference to be used while implementing designs. Whatever the motivation of the reader, the excursion is sure to be interesting. Every attempt has been made to select complete illustrations. Each illustration has been successfully compiled and simulated. Illustrations have been selected to be large enough to provide sufficient design detail, but small enough to be fully understood and absorbed in a reasonably short length of time. Each illustration contains at least one simulation fragment providing additional insight—insight not only into the logical functionality involved but also into the implementation using programmable logic arrays.

With the increasing interest in HDL, many languages or language dialects are emerging and evolving. The approach taken in the current text is to concentrate on two of the available languages. The language occupying the central theme of the first chapters is the Altera hardware description language (AHDL) which is a straightforward, easy-to-learn, yet very powerful language. The language occupying the later chapters in the text is the very powerful and complex language called VHDL. VHDL is the language that is rapidly growing into an internationally recognized standard language for system representation. The approach of using the selected two languages is to permit the reader to learn in an effective and efficient manner. The student may rapidly progress through the early chapters while acquiring the formidable capabilities in the art of modern logic design. This approach is facilitated using AHDL. In the latter chapters, the student is exposed to VHDL which is a powerful and complex language. VHDL contains more modes and styles of design than does AHDL. Attending the additional power is a level of complexity that may be intimidating at times. Nevertheless, the power and utility of VHDL makes it an attractive candidate for design and standardization. The exploration of digital system design utilizing the combination of AHDL and VHDL provides an interesting and informative perspective into modern digital-system implementation.

It is my earnest desire to convey basic information concerning this new and exciting technology with a minimum of confusion and obfuscation. I have attempted not only to be clear and cogent in my writings, but also to be concise . . . perhaps too much so. My worst fear, is that I may not have succeeded in clarity and brevity. In the time it has taken to write this text, I have never viewed the manuscript without wanting to modify major portions. Perhaps major revisions would yet be the best course of action, but for the current time, it is no longer possible. Please feel free to provide written comments concerning the text. All comments will be welcomed.

To avoid the problem of typing the included examples into a text editor, Prentice Hall has made the source files available on the internet. The URL for accessing the examples is: http://www.phptr.com/scarpino. As available, new examples will be added to the site and examples may be modified due to feedback provided from readers. All of the examples in the text were compiled and simulated using the Altera Max+plus II software development system (version 6.2). This software was generously provided by Mr. Joe Hanson[1] of Altera Corporation. Several version upgrades have evolved since the development of examples included here. The software system worked smoothly and responsively throughout the development. Altera has recently released an educational version of the software which is provided without charge for educational purposes only. The reader wanting to duplicate example results and work end-of-chapter problems will have to obtain the required software. My sincere good wishes are extended to readers pursuing this course of action. Stress the illustrations. See how they work. Find their limits and force them to fail. Consider sharing your results.

---

[1]Altera Corporation, 101 Innovation Drive, San Jose, CA 95134.

ACKNOWLEDGMENTS

I would like to express my sincere thanks to the Altera Corporation and particularly to Joe Hanson of Altera. They supplied the software on which all of the examples were designed and simulated. The software was straightforward to use and worked smoothly throughout the project. Altera also supplied the chips which were used to implement both the VHDL and the AHDL receivers as well as a significant number of the other examples. All of the EPLD implemented projects worked precisely as the simulations had performed. I would also like to thank Trina Zimmerman, Russ Hall, and Bernard Goodwin of Prentice Hall. Trina supplied the initial idea for the undertaking and Russ Hall and Bernard Goodwin made it happen. Trina has an exuberant personality. Some day I hope to meet Russ and Bernard. Pine Tree Composition, particularly Patty Donovan, provided brief periods of tranquillity during the final hectic days. Thank you.

Frank Scarpino

PART I

THEORY AND APPLICATIONS IN ALTERA HARDWARE DESCRIPTION LANGUAGE

CHAPTER 1

AN INTRODUCTION TO COMBINATIONAL LOGIC AND HARDWARE DESCRIPTION LANGUAGE (AHDL)

1.1 INTRODUCTION

In this chapter, we review some basic combinational logic design by example. We also introduce the representation of digital systems by a means known as hardware description language (HDL). The particular form of HDL employed in this chapter is Altera Hardware Description Language and is abbreviated as AHDL. AHDL bears the name of the corporation (Altera) which produced the language. AHDL may perhaps best be described as a dialect of HDL. A number of HDLs or language dialects currently exist. While all of the dialects contain certain advantages, we will concentrate on only AHDL in the current chapter. Once the process of digital system design has been acquired using one of the available languages, it is a relatively small step to learn additional languages. Hardware description language as a digital system design representation is fundamentally different from the usual representations used in classical design.

The illustrations in this chapter are designed to review some basic characteristics of combinational logic and also review several classical theorems and rudimentary building blocks often used in digital systems. In each case, the theorems are shown to be correct by conventional means. Then the Altera hardware description language is utilized to develop a particular implementation. The HDL implementation text file is then compiled and the resulting simulation net file (a file with extensions of .SNF) is used to drive a digital system simulation. The simulation may be used to verify the correctness of the theorem. The user of the simulation may choose to execute the simulation utilizing all combinations of the input variables. Since the digital simulation process produces all combinations of the output signal, the correctness of the implemented logical operations may be verified by inspection. The inclusion of HDL in the current context serves to verify the correctness of the theorems but more importantly, for our purposes, it serves to present the essential characteristics, operations, and operators which are a part of the AHDL design process.

In each case where source code listings are shown, they have been "cut-and-pasted" directly from correctly operating programs. Therefore the program code may be taken directly from the text, modified, and utilized. The reader is welcome to use the code freely in formulating future design implementations.

1.2 A COMBINATIONAL LOGIC THEOREM

A straightforward and often useful theorem for reducing logical expressions is given below by equation (1.1). Proving the correctness of theorems is helpful in understanding basic logical processing. We now proceed to prove (1.1).

$$w + \bar{w}y = w + y \qquad (1.1)$$

The validity of (1.1) may be illustrated by perfect induction through the use of a truth table. The truth table below provides the required enumeration of all of the combinations of (1.1). After enumerating all possible combinations of the input variables, w and y, a brief inspection of the table easily verifies the logical equivalence of the fourth and fifth columns. This clearly demonstrates the correctness of (1.1).

Truth Table for Example 1.1

w	y	$\bar{w}y$	$w + \bar{w}y$	$w + y$
0	0	0	0	0
0	1	1	1	1
1	0	0	1	1
1	1	0	1	1

Theorem (1.1) is now proven. We therefore proceed to an HDL implementation of (1.1).

1.2.1 Combinational Theorem Using HDL

Equation (1.1) may be implemented using HDL and an appropriate, compatible simulator. Below we demonstrate the use of the AHDL and the Altera logic simulator to examine the perfect induction proof of the combinational logic theorem contained in (1.1).

The program shown below (program 1.1) indicates one way of coding a solution to the task of proving theorem (1.1) in an HDL format. Program 1.1 is coded using the AHDL language.

```
1   Subdesign 'example1'
2   %A design to show that w + wbar · y = w + y %
3   % This is theorem (1.1) %
```

PROGRAM 1.1 AHDL Code to Implement a Combinational Theorem

```
4    % Percent signs bracket comment lines %
5    (
6    % Within the Subdesign section parenthesis, declare the
     I/O %
7    % The I/O variables are in a comma separated list %
8    % A colon separates the variable from the I/O keyword %
9    w, y    :Input;
10   z1, z2  :Output;
11   )

12   Begin
13   % The logical processing occurs between Begin and End %
14   % # is a binary logical OR operation symbol %
15   % ! is a unary logical inversion operator symbol %
16   z1 = w # !w & y ;
17   % z1 is the LHS of the logical equation, (1.1) %
18   z2 = w # y ;
19   % z2 is the RHS of the logical equation, (1.1)%
20   End;
```

PROGRAM 1.1   *Continued*

The line numbers shown in program 1.1 are not part of the source code, but are merely included for discussion purposes. In the following paragraphs, the discussion is organized by line number groupings. For the purposes of the current discussions, assume that the Altera program for compiling and simulating digital systems is running on an IBM compatible personal computer.

Lines 1–11: "Subdesign" is a keyword of the Altera system. The subdesign section of the source code describes the input and output sections of the digital system design. The name of the source file directly follows the subdesign keyword and may be contained in single quotations as shown or the single quotation marks may be omitted. The source file name must be the same as the file name used to save the source file to disk. The source file is called a "text design file" in Altera terminology and is saved using a .TDF extension. As an illustration, the source file of program 1.1 is saved in a file named example1.tdf. The input variables, w and y, appear in a comma separated list followed by a colon and the keyword input. The output variables z1 and z2 also appear in a comma separated list followed by a colon and the keyword output. Note that each line is terminated in a semicolon following the tradition of the C and Pascal software programming languages.

Lines 12–20: Lines 12 and 20 of program 1.1 frame the processing body in the keywords begin and end. These two keywords delineate the procedural or processing body of the source code. In the case of this example, the body is the region of the source in which the combinational logical statements are implemented. The logical statements in lines 16 and 18 implement the left hand side (LHS) and right hand side (RHS) of the combinational logic of equation (1.1) respectively. The binary value resulting from the LHS expression is assigned to variable z1. The binary value resulting from the RHS expression is assigned to variable z2. In the processing body, unlike the counterpart for software languages, no sequential nature of the processing is implied by the ordering of the statements. The logical implementation and results are unaffected by the ordering of source commands. This will become more obvious and more important in later illustrations. For the present, we will not dwell on this matter.

The program file is processed by compiling the source much as would be accomplished in an analogous software design implementation. Once the code has been successfully compiled, then a simulation may be performed with various combinations of input variables. The outputs of the simulation may be inspected to verify the correctness of the implemented logic. Since the inputs consist of user-specified values, the user must provide the input values by some means. Several means are available for providing input values (for example, vector files which have a .VEC extension). Using the Altera simulation tools, an array of input alternatives may also be applied by selecting a set of menu alternatives. These various means will be elaborated in subsequent examples, but for now we simply show the results of one selected simulation.

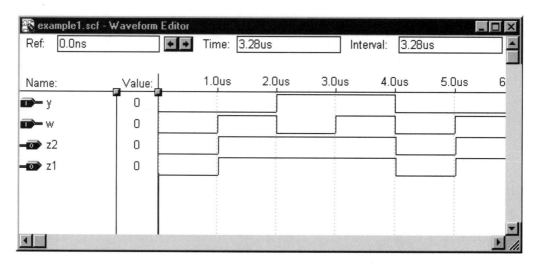

Simulation Results for Program 1.1: A Combinational Theorem

From the simulation results shown above, it is readily apparent that the time scale is divided into grid markings at a spacing of 1-μsec. The input values are initialized and at 1-μsec intervals, the input values are modified so that every combination of the input variables is provided. As before, inspection of the two output signals, z1 and z2 in this case, indicates that they are identical regardless of the input variable combination. This proves the theorem using the simulation approach.

Careful inspection of the input and output variables indicates that some small delay exists between the instants when the input values change and when the corresponding output values change value. The delay is difficult to observe at the selected timing scale and is certainly no problem at the selected simulation speed. Of course, if the input variables were permitted to change value in a shorter interval, then the circuit delay could be a problem. Matters involving time delay will be considered more carefully in subsequent illustrations, but for the present, we consider theorem (1.1) to be verified.

1.3 DEMORGAN'S THEOREM

Another well known and extraordinarily useful theorem is the DeMorgan's theorem. Simply stated, the theorem is:

$$\overline{w + y} = \overline{w}\,\overline{y} \tag{1.2a}$$
$$\overline{wy} = \overline{w} + \overline{y} \tag{1.2b}$$

Again we examine the theorem and show its validity through the use of the enumeration or "perfect induction" method. The truth table below corresponds to (1.2). The truth table lists the left-hand-side and right-hand-side Boolean functions along with intermediate variables (for example, $\overline{w}$ and $\overline{y}$) to assist in reading the table.

Truth Table for Example 1.2

w	y	$\overline{w}$	$\overline{y}$	$\overline{w + y}$	$\overline{w}\,\overline{y}$	$\overline{wy}$	$\overline{w} + \overline{y}$
0	0	1	1	1	1	1	1
0	1	1	0	0	0	1	1
1	0	0	1	0	0	1	1
1	1	0	0	0	0	0	0

With all combinations of the input variables, w and y, enumerated, it is clear from a comparison of columns 5 and 6 of the table, which correspond to the left-hand side and right-hand side of (1.2a) respectively, that the validity of (1.2a) is verified (proven). Similarly, comparison of the seventh and eighth columns, verifies (1.2b). We now proceed to the examination of DeMorgan's theorem using an HDL approach.

1.4 DEMORGAN'S THEOREM AND HDL

The HDL program below illustrates one program which can be used to explore and verify DeMorgan's theorem. The Boolean values corresponding to columns 5, 6, 7, and 8 of truth table 1.2 are assigned to z1, z2, z3, and z4 respectively.

```
1    Subdesign 'DeMorgan'
2    (
3    w, y                 :Input;
4    z1, z2, z3, z4       :Output;
5    )
6    Begin
```

PROGRAM 1.2   AHDL DeMorgan's Theorem

```
7    % ***** equation 1.2a ***** %
8    z1 = not(w OR y);
9    z2 = not w AND not y;
10   % ***** equation 1.2b ***** %
11   z3 = not (w And y);
12   z4 = not w Or not y;
13   End;
```

PROGRAM 1.2   *Continued*

Program 1.2 presents one solution to verifying the combinational logic theorem (1.2). Additional comments, similar to those shown in program 1.1, have not been included in the source code listing to reduce the source code clutter, but a description of the program is given below for the purpose of clarification.

Lines 1–5: The subdesign section of the program declares two input variables, namely w and y. This section also declares four output variables, z1, z2, z3, and z4. The output variables are not explicitly required in the truth table implementations but are required to generate chip outputs for the programming approach.

Lines 6–9: The body of the program, framed between "begin" and "end" statements, contains the logical structure of the digital system. These lines form the variables corresponding to equation (1.2a). The variable z1 corresponds to the LHS and z2 to the RHS of (1.2a). The reader might compare the slightly different use of keywords and symbols between program 1.1 and program 1.2. In program 1.2 the binary logic operator keywords AND and OR are used instead of the directly corresponding binary operator symbols & and #. Either approach is acceptable. Similarly, the programs differ in their use of the unary complement operator. Program 1.2 uses the unary logical operator keyword "not" whereas program 1.1 uses the corresponding unary logical operator symbol !. The language permits the keywords and symbols to be mixed in any combination, but good programming practice and the desire for readability and program maintenance should mitigate arbitrary combinations of the words and symbols.

Lines 10–12: These lines correspond to equation (1.2b). The variable z3 corresponds to the LHS of (1.2b) and z4 to the RHS of (1.2b).

A simulation based upon program 1.2 is shown on the next page. The results of the simulation verify the truth table for this example as might be expected. The simulation approach may appear an unnecessarily elaborate extension of the truth table/perfect induction method. However, as the designs we examine evolve, the desirability of such methods will become obvious. Certainly, when circuit implementations are involved, the advantages of an HDL methodology with simulation are more apparent. Visual comparison of z1 and z2 verifies the form of equation (1.2a) given by DeMorgan's theorem and comparison of z3 and z4 verifies (1.2b).

1.5   IMPLEMENTATION OF A ONE-BIT FULL ADDER

We now consider a slightly more complex case and consequently enjoy a bit more freedom in the design implementation. In the current example, the following symbols and associated meanings apply.

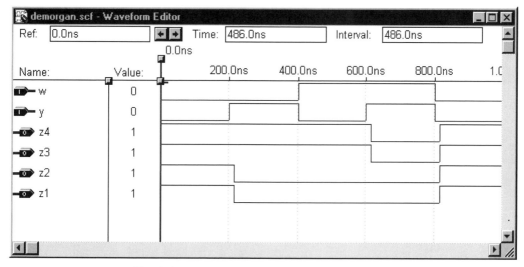

Simulation for Program 1.2: DeMorgan's Theorem

Symbol	Meaning
S	Sum
C_{in}/C_{out}	Carry In/Carry Out
A_1/A_2	Addend One/Addend Two

We begin the design of the adder with the development of the desired truth table. The sum and carry-out terms are formed from the binary addition of the A_1, A_2, and carry-in terms.

Truth Table for Full Adder

A_1	A_2	C_{in}	S	C_{out}
0	0	0	0	0
0	0	1	1	0
0	1	0	1	0
0	1	1	0	1
1	0	0	1	0
1	0	1	0	1
1	1	0	0	1
1	1	1	1	1

From the Truth Table for the full adder, the Karnaugh map (K map) for the sum term may be drawn as shown in K Map for the Sum Term.

K Map for the Sum Term

	$\overline{A}_1\overline{A}_2$	$\overline{A}_1 A_2$	$A_1 A_2$	$A_1\overline{A}_2$
$\overline{C}_{in}$	0	1	0	1
C_{in}	1	0	1	0

By inspection, the sum term of the full adder may be written directly from the truth table as

$$S = \overline{C_{in}}\,(A_1 \oplus A_2) + C_{in}(\overline{A_1\ A_2} + A_1 A_2) \tag{1.3a}$$

It is clear after inspecting (1.3a), that it can be rewritten as

$$S = \overline{C_{in}}\,(A_1 \oplus A_2) + C_{in}\,\overline{(A_1 \oplus A_2)} \tag{1.3b}$$

Which, in turn, can be written as

$$S = C_{in} \oplus A_1 \oplus A_2 \tag{1.3c}$$

The circuit diagram for the sum term (1.3c) is shown below.

Combinational Circuit for the Sum

Similarly, we develop a K map for the carry-out term.

K Map for Carry-Out Term

	$\overline{A}_1\overline{A}_2$	$\overline{A}_1 A_2$	$A_1 A_2$	$A_1\overline{A}_2$
$\overline{C}_{in}$	0	0	1	0
C_{in}	0	1	1	1

Incorporating the obvious three logical terms from the K map yields the following Boolean equation as a representation of the carry-out term of the full adder.

$$C_{out} = C_{in}A_2 + C_{in}A_1 + A_1 A_2 \tag{1.3d}$$

Further factoring may be applied to simplify (1.3d) to the form given by

$$C_{out} = A_1 A_2 + C_{in}\,(A_1 \oplus A_2) \tag{1.3e}$$

Either (1.3d) or (1.3e) may be employed as an implementation of the carry-out term, but (1.3e) is slightly more efficient in terms of the number of gates utilized for implementation. We therefore show the final implementation logical circuit as (1.3e) below.

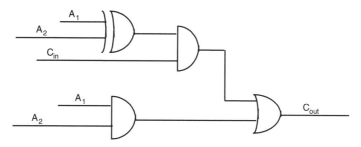

Logical Circuit Diagram for the Carry Output

A reasonable approach to verifying the one-bit full adder is a proof by perfect induction as applied above in the verification of combinational theorem (1.1) and DeMorgan's theorem (1.2). The procedure would involve enumerating all combinations of the input variables and assuring that the equations given as (1.3c) and (1.3e) evaluate to the correct binary values intended by the original design truth table. The reader may choose to follow this approach to gain additional practice and dexterity with Boolean functions. Because we are primarily pursuing an introduction to HDL, we follow, instead, the programming methodology shown below.

1.6   AN HDL SOLUTION FOR A ONE-BIT FULL ADDER

The program below contains an implementation of the full adder design above. The source code helps clarify that the text development method is a powerful, straightforward means of producing a logical implementation.

```
1      Subdesign 'Adder'
2      (
3      Cin, A1, A2      :Input;
4      Sum, Cout        :Output;
5      )
6      Variable
7      Temp             :Node;
8      Begin
9      Temp = A1 XOR A2;
10     Sum = Cin XOR Temp;
11     Cout = A1 & A2 # Cin & Temp;
12     End ;
```

PROGRAM 1.3   AHDL Implementation of a One-Bit Full Adder

The description of program 1.3 is given below.

Lines 1–5: As in prior examples, the subdesign section is employed to declare the input and output variables. The carry input, C_{in}, and the two addends, A_1 and A_2, are declared as binary input variables for the full-adder circuit. The input and output variables are assigned, by the compiler, to input and output circuits respectively. These I/O circuits are elements of the programmable chip on which the simulation is based. These variables will be assigned to I/O pins in the eventual hardware implementation of the system.

Lines 6–7: In the current illustration, the "variable" section of the source code file contains the explicit declaration of variables which are neither input nor output variables. As such, the variable Temp is declared an internal node of the digital system (in other words, full adder). The Temp variable will not be assigned to an input or output circuit but will be maintained as a distinct internal node of the programmable logic implementation.

Lines 8–12: The main body of the program is framed, as usual, in a Begin-End pair. The logical equations in the main body are observed to be an implementation of equations (1.3c) for the sum term and (1.3e) for the carry-out term.

The compilation process conducted on the source file of program 1.3 produces a simulation netlist file (.SNF extension). A simulation based upon the .SNF file has been conducted and the results are shown below. The eight combinational inputs have been presented to the digital system inputs for 1-μsec intervals and the output values of the full adder have been recorded. Therefore the full simulation has taken 8 (simulated) μsec. A brief inspection of the sum and carry-out system outputs reveals that the simulation has produced the same outputs as predicted by the truth table, which of course is the expected outcome.

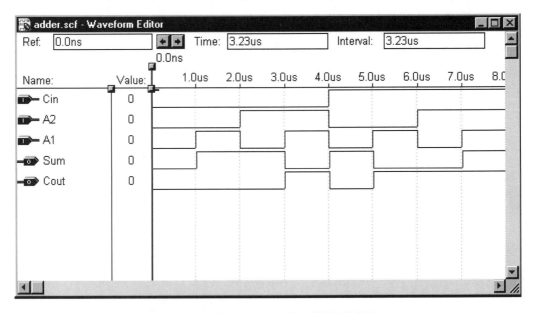

Simulation of Program 1.3: One-Bit Full Adder

1.7 AN ALTERNATE HDL SOLUTION FOR A ONE-BIT FULL ADDER

From the illustrations given above, it is probably becoming clear that the HDL approach to digital system design has significant advantages over conventional design approaches. However, the full power and flexibility has not been demonstrated, by any means. This is largely because, up to this point, we have not significantly leveraged productivity and documentation features of the text design approach. To begin exploring productivity advantages, we now present an alternate solution to the one-bit full adder presented earlier. Program 1.4 represents the source code for such an alternative solution.

```
1     Subdesign 'Adder2'
2     (
3     Cin, A1, A2          :Input;
4     Sum, Cout            :Output;
5     )
6     Begin
7     Table
8     A1,   A2,   Cin =>  Sum, Cout;
9     0,    0,    0   =>  0,   0;
10    0,    0,    1   =>  1,   0;
11    0,    1,    0   =>  1,   0;
12    0,    1,    1   =>  0,   1;
13    1,    0,    0   =>  1,   0;
14    1,    0,    1   =>  0,   1;
15    1,    1,    0   =>  0,   1;
16    1,    1,    1   =>  1,   1;
17    End Table;
18    End;
```

PROGRAM 1.4   An Alternate AHDL One-Bit Adder

Note that the variable names in program 1.4 are identical to the variable names in program 1.3 (with the exception of the node variable, Temp, which is not required for program 1.4). This selection of variable names should facilitate a comparison of the two listings. We next describe program 1.4 in some detail.

Lines 6–18: The body of the program contains the main implementation description, as in the prior example, framed between Begin-End pair statements. The main body contains a new programming construction. Instead of implementing the logical system design in Boolean statements as in prior examples, the body of this illustration contains a truth table description. The truth table in the body of program 1.4 is functionally identical to the truth table of example 1.3 which represents the conventional design. The only differences are: (1) the truth table in program 1.4 is bracketed by Table-End Table separators; (2) the input variable list is separated from the output variable list by the => symbol; and (3) the input variables and output variables are each contained in distinct, comma-separated lists. These differences are clearly necessitated by the need for a syntactical representation in the formal HDL grammar.

On the next page is the result of executing a digital simulation based upon the program 1.4. Comparison of this result with the simulation from program 1.3 clearly shows that the two results are functionally identical. This serves to illustrate not only productivity improvements, but also a variety of alternative source language offerings from which the designer may make preferential selections.

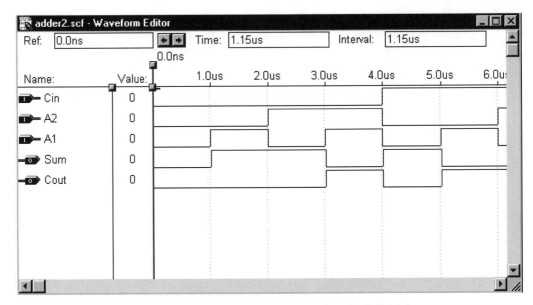

Simulation Results from Program 1.4: One-Bit Full Adder

1.8   AN HDL FOUR-BIT RIPPLE-CARRY ADDER

In a typical digital system, elementary building blocks are often combined into more complex units by making essentially duplicate copies of the elementary building blocks and combining them. The composite systems are formed by interconnecting the elementary building blocks to provide more complex and capable subsystems. We will now demonstrate the combining of one-bit full adders into a four-bit adder by using a hierarchical design technique. The design method utilizes the one-bit full adder developed above as an essential building block in the process of producing a four-bit adder.

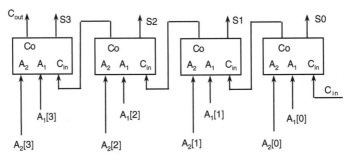

A Four-Bit Ripple-Carry Adder

The process we employ to design the four-bit adder using HDL is as follows.

- First we use the compiler along with the source file, adder.tdf (program 1.3), to create an include file. The source file is compiled into an include file. The resulting include file is named adder.inc.
- We then create a four-bit adder utilizing the one-bit full adder as an essential building block. The link in the process is the include file, adder.inc, which represents the essence of the one-bit, full adder.
- The four-bit adder is created as a text design file. The text design file follows the usual recipe which we have developed over the last few illustrations. A minimum number of additions to this recipe are required and are described briefly below.
- Four instances of the elementary building block adder, as described in adder.tdf are created. The four instances are created using a classical, software-type declaration statement.
- The four instances of the one-bit adder are combined logically in a new building block which we formulate as a new text design file called 4bitadd.tdf.

We now proceed directly to design the four-bit adder. The source code for the four-bit adder is shown as program 1.5 below.

```
1     include "adder.inc";
2     Subdesign '4bitadd'
3     (
4     A1[3..0], A2[3..0], Cin              :Input;
5     Sum5[4..0]                           :Output;
6     )
7     Variable
8     Adder4[3..0]                         :Adder;
9     Begin
10    % ***** series of carry assignments ***** %
11    Adder4[0].Cin=Cin;
12    Adder4[1].Cin=Adder4[0].Cout;
13    Adder4[2].Cin=Adder4[1].Cout;
14    Adder4[3].Cin=Adder4[2].Cout;
15    % ***** Addend #1 assignments ***** %
16    Adder4[0].A1=A1[0];
17    Adder4[1].A1=A1[1];
18    Adder4[2].A1=A1[2];
19    Adder4[3].A1=A1[3];
20    % ***** Addend #2 assignments ***** %
21    Adder4[0].A2=A2[0];
22    Adder4[1].A2=A2[1];
23    Adder4[2].A2=A2[2];
24    Adder4[3].A2=A2[3];
25    % ***** assign output sums ***** %
```

PROGRAM 1.5   A Four-Bit Ripple-Carry Adder

```
26    Sum5[4]=Adder4[3].Cout;
27    Sum5[3]=Adder4[3].sum;
28    Sum5[2]=Adder4[2].sum;
29    Sum5[1]=Adder4[1].sum;
30    Sum5[0]=Adder4[0].sum;
31    End;
```

PROGRAM 1.5 *Continued*

The program for the four-bit ripple-carry adder contains several new features. These additions include: (1) the use of subscripted variables in a format which is very similar to the Pascal software programming language; (2) the use of an include file; and (3) the instantiation of a hardware entity. The instantiation is accomplished similar to the manner in which a user-defined data type is instantiated in a modern software programming language.

We now discuss the details involved in the source file of program 1.5.

Line 1: The compiler is being instructed to include the source file, adder.tdf (in the incarnation of the include file, adder.inc), which contains the definition of the one-bit full adder which has been designed, analyzed, and simulated above. The one-bit adder therefore becomes a user-defined hardware entity. Multiple instances of this user-defined hardware entity may be generated and utilized within the currently active file, 4bitadder.tdf in this case.

Lines 2–6: As usual, the subdesign section of the source file contains the declarations of input and output variable names. In this case however, the names consist of subscripted variables. The input variable declaration, A1[3..0] declares a 4-bit variable which is the first addend. This addend will eventually consume four input pins on the chip which is used to implement the four-bit adder. Therefore, since A1[3..0] and A2[3..0] each define four-bit input data buses, the two addends together will utilize eight input pins in the eventual implementation. The range of each addend is 0 through 15 (decimal) or 0 through F (hexadecimal). Cin is a single carry-input line which will consume an additional input pin. Similarly, the variable Sum5[4..0] constitutes a 5-bit bus which is the result of adding two 4-bit numbers (plus a possible carry-in). Therefore, the maximum output value can be 31_{10}. That is, if A1[3..0] = F_{16}, A2[3..0] = F_{16}, and Cin = 1, then the output term, Sum5[4..0] will be $1F_{16}$ which is a decimal 31. The Sum5[4..0] output variable will therefore require five output pins on the implementing chip. Note that we have now planned for the utilization of ten I/O pins. It is not unusual for the designer to consume a large number of I/O pins in any realistic implementation.

Lines 7–8: The keyword "variable" defines the beginning of the variable section of the source file. The variable section may be used to: (1) declare any variables to be used, (2) declare the existence of an internal node, or it may be used to make an instance declaration. In line 8, an instance declaration is used. The inclusion of the file adder.inc establishes the existence of a user-defined hardware element which is a one-bit full adder. This may be thought of as a user-defined type in a software language such as C or Pascal. The phrase "user-defined type" implies that the compiler or language does not contain an intrinsic or built-in hardware element type, "Adder." However, we have created and defined the Adder type and established the type through the proper processes (creating the source file Adder.tdf, compiling the source file, creating the Adder.inc file, and finally incorporating the statement, 'include "Adder.inc" ', at the beginning of the source file 4bitadd.tdf). The instance declaration then creates four instances of the adder since the user-declared variable Adder4[3..0] is an array variable of length four. The array declaration further permits the four one-bit full adders to be referenced as an array if so desired. Alternatively, each member of the hardware array may be accessed individually. For example, the reference to Adder4[3] refers only to the high-order member of the array, while a reference to Adder4[0] refers to the low-order member of the array. References to Adder4[3..0] refer to the collective group of the four one-bit adders. Since the original source file which defines the one-bit adder declares the existence of single-bit inputs, Cin, A1, A2, and single-bit outputs Sum and Cout, these declarations are carried forward as ports of the newly declared instance of the user-defined type. These ports are accessed through the use of the fully qualified name of the port. The fully qualified name of the port consists of the name of the instantiated object, followed by a dot, in turn followed by the name of the port (for example, Adder4[0].Cin or Adder4[3..0].Cin).

Line 9: The word "begin" starts the main body of the source file.

Lines 10–14: These program lines incorporate the carry chain. First we route the carry-in logic line into the four-bit ripple-carry adder (line 11). Then lines 12–14 route the carry-out lines from low-order bits into the next higher order adders.

Lines 15–19: The four input data lines, A1[3] through A1[0], for the first addend (four pins on the implementation chip) are being routed into addend bits for the four-bit adder.

Lines 20–24: The four input data lines, A2[3] through A2[0], for the second addend (four pins on the implementation chip) are being routed into addend bits for the four-bit adder.

Lines 25–30: The output result of the four bit add, Adder4[3] through Adder[0], are being routed to output pins, Sum5[4] through Sum[0], of the implementation chip. The output carry is also being routed.

The results of one particular simulation run are shown on the next page. It should be clear that debugging the logic using a simulator is much more convenient and powerful than attempting to debug at the hardware level. Of course, debugging at the hardware level is inevitable, but the preparation achieved by first producing (relatively) error-free logic at the simulator level is extremely compelling.

Many other input combinations may be provided to complete the simulation testing for the adder, but the current illustration is now complete. The reader is encouraged to simulate other data sequences to verify that the logical implementation is correct.

1.9   AN ALTERNATE FOUR-BIT HDL FULL ADDER

We now modify program 1.5 above to make use of the subscript variables in logic assignments. This capability is inherent in the Altera language and compiler. The current modification makes the program substantially more compact and, in many ways, improves the

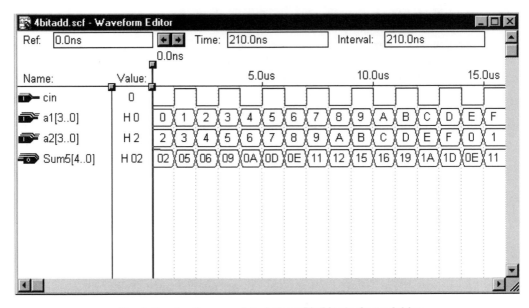

Simulation for Program 1.5: A Four-Bit Ripple-Carry Adder

"readability" of the program. The modified program is shown as program 1.6 below. Note that the variables containing subscripts may be moved in groups by single HDL commands. This capability alone provides a design capability and concurrent documentation capability which provides a great deal of productivity improvement over classical design methods.

```
0       include "adder.inc";
1       Subdesign '4bitadd2'
2       (
3       A1[3..0], A2[3..0], Cin          :Input;
4       Sum5[4..0]                       :Output;
5       )
6       Variable
7       Adder4[3..0]                            :Adder;
8       Begin
9       % ***** series of carry assignments ***** %
10      Adder4[0].Cin=Cin;
11      Adder4[3..1].Cin=Adder4[2..0].Cout;

12      % ***** Addend #1 assignments ***** %
13      Adder4[3..0].A1=A1[3..0];
```

PROGRAM 1.6   A Modified Four-Bit Ripple-Carry Adder

```
14    % ***** Addend #2 assignments ***** %
15    Adder4[3..0].A2=A2[3..0];


16    % ***** assign output sums ***** %
17    Sum5[4]=Adder4[3].Cout;
18    Sum5[3..0]=Adder4[3..0].sum;
19    End;
```

PROGRAM 1.6   *Continued*

A simulation of the modified four-bit adder of program 1.6 is shown below. The reader should verify that the functional performance is correct as expected. The modification accomplished in this section illustrates some alternatives and simplifications available to the designer. Not only are the methods valuable to the designer, but the documentation inevitably required of either research or product designs is greatly enhanced as well.

The description of the source code for program 1.6 is given below in terms of the corresponding source code of program 1.5.

Lines 1–5: As usual, the subdesign (recall that the language is not case sensitive) section of the program declares the chip input and output logical terms. In this illustration, the input and output terms consist of array variables which may be subsequently accessed either individually or in groups by using the appropriate subscript groupings.

Lines 9–11: The carry chain is generated with the assignment of individual and sub-groupings of carry terms. The carry terms which are members of the various adder objects are accessed using the fully qualified names though the object-oriented dot notation. These program lines correspond directly to lines 10–14 in program 1.5.

Lines 12–13: The first addend is routed from the input pins on the chip to the logical corresponding addend input of the four-bit adder. These program lines correspond directly to lines 15–19 in program 1.5.

Lines 14–15: The second addend is routed from the input pins on the chip to the corresponding logical addend input of the four-bit adder. These program lines correspond directly to lines 20–24 in program 1.5.

Lines 16–18: The final sum is routed to the appropriate "Sum" output pins on the implementation chip. These program lines correspond directly to lines 25–30 in program 1.5.

A simulation which has been conducted using the netlist of program 1.6 is shown below. It is a slight variation from the input data used to demonstrate program 1.5 and simply serves as a variation of the test case. It should be noted that the output variables are displayed in hexadecimal notation as indicated by the H in the value column of the simulation figure. Unless there are extenuating circumstances, the variables will be displayed in either hexadecimal notation or decimal notation, whichever is the most appropriate for the particular test condition or examination under consideration.

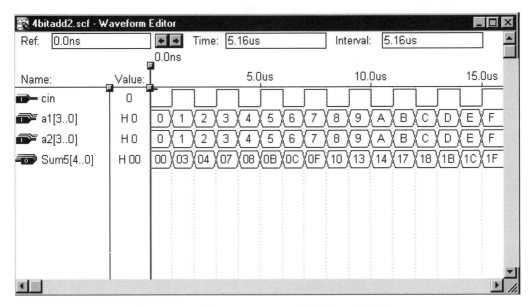

Simulation of Program 1.6: Modified Four-Bit Adder

1.9.1   Timing Analysis of a Four-Bit Adder

A matter of some significance, in the performance of digital systems, is the system speed performance. While functional performance is obviously paramount, the matter of system speed performance may make the difference between success and failure as well. With combinational circuits, the system speed (or inversely delay) performance is a function of the measured time delay through the combinational logic elements. The propagation delay is a measure of how often the circuit in question can be asked to produce a result. A frequently coined phrase is the number of decisions per second which a circuit may be expected to produce. In the current example, it is this system propagation delay which will indicate how many additions per second can be accomplished. While it is conceptually possible to measure the propagation performance of the system through measurement made directly from the presented simulation waveforms, the Altera automation software (and other software) will extract the time delays and place them into a performance matrix. The matrix for the current illustration is presented on the next page. The left-hand column represents the source of the signal. Subsequent column headings indicate the signal destination. In each of the matrix elements, a propagation is given between the associated source and destinations. Typical case and worst case delays are listed if they are different. Otherwise, only a single performance is listed in the matrix entry. Directly below is the delay matrix presentation for the four-bit adder. Note that the lowest order bits of the adder exhibit the least propagation delay (in other words, sum5[0] has a delay of the order of 15 ns).

Delay Matrix

Destination

	Sum50	Sum51	Sum52	Sum53	Sum54
a10	15.0ns	15.0ns/23.0ns	23.0ns/24.0ns	24.0ns	15.0ns
a11		15.0ns	23.0ns/24.0ns	24.0ns	15.0ns/23.0ns
a12			23.0ns	23.0ns/24.0ns	15.0ns/23.0ns
a13				23.0ns	15.0ns/23.0ns
a20	15.0ns	15.0ns/23.0ns	24.0ns	24.0ns	15.0ns/23.0ns
a21		15.0ns	23.0ns/24.0ns	24.0ns	15.0ns/23.0ns
a22			23.0ns	23.0ns/24.0ns	15.0ns/23.0ns
a23				23.0ns	15.0ns/23.0ns
cin	15.0ns	15.0ns/23.0ns	23.0ns/24.0ns	24.0ns	15.0ns/23.0ns

Delay Matrix for Four-Bit Adder

It is clear from the presentation, that the worst case pin-to-pin delay is 24 ns. Therefore, the adder circuit presented here is capable of performing 41.6 million additions per second. If this calculation rate is satisfactory, the design is complete. If on the other hand, an increased computational rate is desired, the designer must seek alternative design solutions. Of course, the total arithmetic process must be considered to provide an accurate computational performance estimate. For example, the transportation time involved in movement of the respective operands to the inputs of the adder must be taken into account to provide a complete picture of the implementation. The time required to assure that the operands provide suitably stable inputs to the adder before the adder can reasonably produce a reliable output must also be considered. For the present time, we consider the current design satisfactory for the purposes of illustration and will not consider alternative design strategies in the interest of pursuing speed. However, later we will discuss in greater detail the process of achieving alternative design techniques in the interest of performance improvements. It may however be of interest to the reader to perform a timing analysis on the basic components of the four-bit adder to try to uncover some of the basic causes of the delays in the aggregate four-bit adder system. We leave this as an exercise for the reader.

1.10   AN HDL ADDER/SUBTRACTOR

We conclude our study of arithmetic units in this chapter with an example AHDL design which is a variation on the four-bit adder which was developed earlier in this chapter. The source code for the adder/subtractor on the next page implicitly provides a tutorial guide demonstrating capabilities. Before presenting the program, we briefly discuss the mechanics provided by the source code.

1.10.1 Additional Adder Hierarchy

The adder portion of the code which follows is exactly as provided in program 1.6. In fact, by way of the include commands and files, the exact four-bit adder has been provided. The adder/subtractor source code file is named AdderA in the subdesign section of the source file and is saved in a file named AdderA.tdf. AdderA includes the file 4BitAdd.inc which, in turn, includes the file Adder.inc. This means that both the file Adder.tdf and the file 4BitAdd.tdf have been compiled into corresponding .inc files. This hierarchical design method avoids repeating code in the final implementation file. In the current case, it means that this example is built upon the immediately preceding example, which, in turn, is built on even earlier illustrations in this chapter. This method illustrates a completely encapsulated set of examples which may be utilized and/or modified as desired. To provide the subtraction process, the number to be subtracted is converted to a 2's complement representation. Recall that adding the 2's complement of a given number provides the same solution as subtracting. Therefore we convert the appropriate number to a 2's complement form and then add, using the adders developed earlier in this chapter. We now present the source code for an adder/subtractor program. Recall that the ports implicit in the design of the four-bit adder are carried forward in the hierarchical design procedure. For example, the current four-bit adder will contain ports as defined in the previous source code files (in other words, .Sum5[4..0], .A1[3..0], .A2[3..0], and .Cin are ports carried forward in the hierarchical design process). We have also defined a control signal named PlusMinus. If PlusMinus is equal to a logic 1, the digital system will subtract one argument from another. If PlusMinus is equal to a logic zero, the digital system will add the two arguments provided.

```
1       include "4bitadd.inc";
2       Subdesign 'AdderA'
3       (
4       Sum[4..0]                           :Output;
5       TwosComp[3..0]                      :Output;
6       Arg1[3..0], Arg2[3..0],Cin          :Input;
7       PlusMinus                           :Input;
8       )

9       Variable
10      AdderA                              :4BitAdd;

11      Begin
12      % ***** Handle Addition ***** %
13      if(!PlusMinus) Then
14          TwosComp[3..0] = H"0";
```

PROGRAM 1.7 An Adder/Subtracter

```
15        Sum[4..0] = AdderA.Sum5[4..0];
16        AdderA.A1[3..0]=Arg1[3..0];
17        AdderA.A2[3..0]=Arg2[3..0];
18        AdderA.Cin = Cin;
19     end if;
20     % ***** Handle Subtraction ***** %
21     if(PlusMinus) Then
22         Sum[4..0] = AdderA.Sum5[4..0];
23         TwosComp[3..0]=(PlusMinus Xor Arg1[3..0]) + 1;
24         AdderA.A1[3..0] = TwosComp[3..0];
25         AdderA.A2[3..0]=Arg2[3..0];
26         AdderA.Cin = Cin;
27     end if;
28     End;
```

PROGRAM 1.7 *Continued*

Line 1: This line provides for the inclusion of the file 4BitAdd.inc, and consequently the source code from the file 4BitAdd.tdf into the current file AdderA.tdf.

Lines 2–8: The subdesign section, as usual, provides the declaration of chip input and output signals.

Lines 9–10: The variable section of the source code instantiates an entity of type 4BitAdd, named AdderA.

Lines 12–19: When the input control signal PlusMinus is a logic zero, the code simply routes the input signals, namely arg1[3..0], arg2[3..0], and Cin in this case, to the input terminals of the instantiated adder named AderA.

Lines 20–27: When the input control signal PlusMinus is a logic one, the 2's complement value of arg1[3..0] is calculated and routed to the appropriate input port of the adder, AdderA. The value of arg2 is merely routed directly to the appropriate port, unmodified. In line 23, observe that the 2's complement is formed by inverting each of the bits in the subject operand and then adding one.

Below, a simulation is presented (admittedly incomplete) which demonstrates the functional performance of the system for a particular set of input variables. The input signals in the simulation are modified every half-microsecond and the results corresponding to the signals in program 1.7 are presented.

To assist with the interpretation of the simulation results, the mathematics for the first few computational periods is demonstrated immediately below.

Period 1:   Decimal $1 + 3 = 4$
             Binary $0001 + 0011 = 0100$

Period 2:   Decimal $2 + 5 = 7$
             Binary $0010 + 0101 = 0111$

Period 3:   Decimal $3 - 7 = -4$
             Binary $0011 - 0111 = 0011 + 1001 = 1100 \xrightarrow{2's\ comp} 0100$

Period 4:   Decimal $4 - 9 = -5$

Binary $0100 - 1001 = 0100 + 0111 = 1011 \xrightarrow{2's\ comp} 0101$

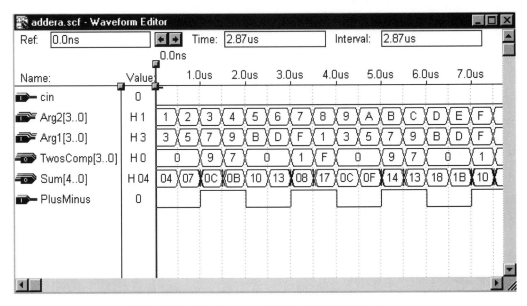

Simulation for Program 1.7: An Adder/Subtracter

1.11   TWO-LEVEL LOGIC FUNCTIONS

Digital systems typically employ two-level Nand-Nand logic or two-level Nor-Nor logical forms. These forms tend to be less intuitive for the infrequent designer or the beginning designer. However, a brief review of the classic two-level forms will readily reinforce the intuitive "feel" which is fundamental to design. In this section, we review the basic two-level forms which have been utilized productively in medium-scale integrated (MSI) circuits for quite some time. The illustrations are selected additionally because they are short and can readily reinforce the design utility of the HDL approach.

1.11.1   Two-Level Nand-Nand Forms

In this section, we consider the fundamental logical equations with terms of the general form given by

$$f(\cdot) = g(w,x,y,z)$$

where the function contains terms with Nand-Nand constructions. There is no loss in generality in considering the simple equation

$$f = \overline{(\overline{wx})(\overline{yz})} \tag{1.4}$$

where w and x provide the inputs to one Nand gate while y and z provide the inputs to a second Nand gate. In turn, the outputs of the two Nand gates provide the input signals to a third Nand gate.

The term, $\overline{wx}$, represents the output of a first-level Nand gate with inputs w, x. The term, $\overline{yz}$, represents a second Nand gate with inputs, y, z. The outputs of these two "first-level" Nand gates are connected to a second-level Nand gate which, in turn, produces the output function, f.

Equation 1.4 represents the logical circuit shown in the figure below.

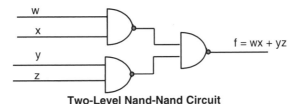

Two-Level Nand-Nand Circuit

Using DeMorgan's theorem on (1.4) we see that

$$f = wx + yz \tag{1.5}$$

Equation (1.5) is the desired result and demonstrates that two-level Nand-Nand logic is functionally equivalent to And-Or logic. The equivalent And-Or logic configuration is shown directly below.

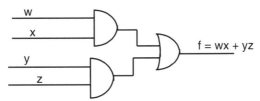

Two-Level And-Or Circuit

The popularity of And-Or or, equivalently, Nand-Nand logical forms is that many Boolean functions are written directly in a sum-of-products form during development or logic simplification. We now proceed to present an AHDL source file listing which may be used to verify the equivalence of And-Or and Nand-Nand logical forms.

```
1    Subdesign 'Nand'
2    (
3    w, x1, y, z                    :Input;
4    f1, f2                         :Output;
5    )
6    Begin
```

PROGRAM 1.8   Two-Level Nand-Nand/And-Or

```
7    % ***** first the nand-nand form ***** %
8    f1 = !( !(w & x1) & !(y & z) );
9    % ***** second the And-Or form ***** %
10   f2 = w & x1 # y & z;
11   End;
```

PROGRAM 1.8   *Continued*

Program 1.8 is a straightforward portrayal of the equivalence of equations (1.4) and
(1.5) respectively. The details are as follows.

Lines 1–5: The subdesign section of the source file declares the four required input
variables in line 3 and the two required output variables in line 4.

Lines 5–11: The body of the implementation portion of the source code is contained
in lines 5–11 inclusively. Line 8 is a direct implementation of equation (1.4) and line 10 is
a direct implementation of equation (1.5).

The simulation of the netlist corresponding to program 1.8 is shown below. Each of
the fifteen possible combinations of the four variables w, $x1$, y, and z are given in the simulation file. For convenience of visual inspection, the fifteen logical combinations are
grouped as a composite variable $wxyz$. Inspection of the simulation results clearly demonstrates the equivalence of (1.4) and (1.5).

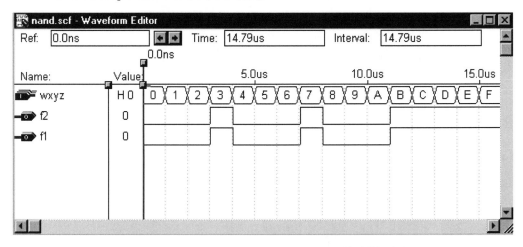

Simulation of Program 1.8: Two-Level Nand-Nand/And-Or

1.11.2   Two-Level Nor-Nor Logic Forms

In a manner directly analogous to the discussion of Nand-Nand forms, it is often convenient to express logical implementations in the so-called Nor-Nor form. For example, we
write the two-level Nor-Nor mechanization of four variables as

$$f = \overline{(w+x) + (y+z)} \tag{1.6}$$

Equation (1.6) represents the logical circuit diagram shown below.

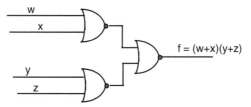

Two-Level Nor-Nor Logical Circuit

Applying DeMorgan's theorem directly to (1.6) we arrive at the conclusion that

$$f = (w + x)(y + z) \qquad (1.7)$$

Equation (1.7) is the desired result and represents a product-of-sums form. Program 1.9 below is used to demonstrate the use of AHDL and verify that the two-level logic forms given by (1.6) and (1.7) are logical equivalents.

```
1     Subdesign 'Nor'
2     (
3     w, x1, y,z                    :Input;
4     f1, f2, ErrTest               :Output;
5     )

6     Begin
7     % ***** first the nor-nor form ***** %
8     f1 = !( !(w # x1) # !(y # z) );

9     % ***** second the And-Or form ***** %
10    f2 = (w # x1) & (y # z);

11    % ***** ErrTest Signal ***** %
12    ErrTest = f1 Xor f2;
13    End;
```

PROGRAM 1.9 Two-Level Nor-Nor/Or-And

The description of the details of program 1.9 is now presented.

Lines 1–5: The subdesign section declares inputs w, x1, y, and z (line 3). In addition, the output of equation (1.6), f1, the output of equation (1.7), f2, and a error test signal (ErrTest) is given by line 4.

Lines 6–13: The implementation body is contained here. Line 8 provides implementation of equation (1.6) and line 10 supplies the implementation of equation (1.7). The outputs of the two equations is exclusive OR'ed so that if at any time the two output signals are not identical, the ErrTest signal will generate a Boolean true output which will draw attention to the unequal comparison.

In the simulation below, it is clear that the two outputs, f1 and f2, are identical and the ErrTest signal remains low as expected in this case.

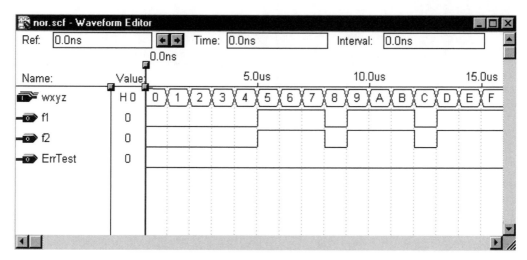

Simulation of Program 1.9: Two-Level Nor-Nor/And-Or

1.12 RETROSPECTIVE

In this chapter, we have shown some of the basic combinational forms traditional to the subject of digital systems. These forms constitute important combinational building blocks of current digital systems. We have also shown some straightforward alternatives for the implementation of combinational Boolean logical forms using the text design option of the Altera hardware description language. In addition, we have shown initial demonstrations of hierarchical design implementation in the form of basic arithmetic processing for digital systems.

CHAPTER 1 EXERCISES

1. The function shown in the K-map below is: $f = \bar{a}\,\bar{c} + ac$

	cd			
ab	00	01	11	10
00	1	1		
01	1	1		
11			1	1
10			1	1

The function, f, as given is written in product-term (sometimes called the sum-of-products) form.

a) Write the sum-term (product-of-sums) form of the expression for f by using the given K-map.

    b) Verify the functional equivalence of the product-term and sum-term forms by algebraic manipulation.

    c) Verify the functional equivalence of the product-term and sum-term forms by perfect induction.

    d) Write an HDL program which verifies the equivalence of the product term and sum term forms. Define a signal named "equal" which is true when the two binary numbers are equal and is false otherwise. Define an additional signal named abGTcd which is true when the binary number represented by ab is greater than cd and is false otherwise.

    e) Create a simulation which will compare the sum-term and product-term forms and verify the comparator designed above.

2. Consider the function, $f = a + \bar{a}b$.

    a) Simplify the expression for f by using a K-map.

    b) Verify the simplification of (a) using perfect induction.

    c) Simplify the function using algebraic methods.

3. Two two-bit, binary numbers, *ab* and *cd* are to be compared for equality. If they are equal, a digital output line, *f*, indicates the equality by asserting a true value. Otherwise, the output is false.

    a) Make a four-variable K-map and indicate the elements of the solution on the K-map.

    b) Write the product-term solution directly from the K-map entries.

    c) Write the solution using sum terms by indicating the elements of the solution on the K-map.

    d) Verify that the product-term and sum-term solutions are equivalent.

    e) Select the "best" solution considering the following parameters.
- performance
- cost

    f) Write an HDL program which solves the comparison problem.

CHAPTER 2

D-TYPE MEMORY, BASIC APPLICATIONS, AND HDL

2.1 BASICS OF D-TYPE, ONE-BIT MEMORIES

In this chapter, we begin to explore the basic properties of memory elements. The application and implementation of memory elements and the associated digital design alternatives will be presented. We begin with the definition of one of the most basic forms of memory element, the D-type element. This element is often referred to as a D-type flip-flop. The D flip-flop (in other words, one-bit memory) structure is defined as follows. The device has two inputs named "clock" and "D" respectively. The D-memory element has two outputs, referred to as Q and $\bar{Q}$ respectively. For simplicity, we define the clock as a periodic rectangular waveform containing only two states in the idealized incarnation. For a positive edge-triggered element, the output, Q, copies the D input on the positive edge of the clock. In other words, the truth table for the D flip-flop is:

Truth Table for D-Memory Element

Input		Output
D^n	Q^n	Q^{n+1}
0	0	0
0	1	0
1	0	1
1	1	1

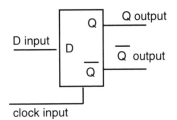

Schematic Representation of D Flip-Flop

The transitions in the output occur only in response to positive transitions of the clock signal, for a positive-edge-triggered flip-flop, and only on negative transitions of the clock signal for negative-edge-triggered flip-flops. Unless otherwise specified, this text will assume that positive-edge-triggered flip-flops are utilized. We now proceed directly to an AHDL implementation demonstrating the use of D-type flip-flops and some associated concepts.

In program 2.1, a D flip-flop is employed and various temporal relationships of the D control input and clock signal are examined to illustrate the properties of the D flip-flop.

```
1    Subdesign 'DMem'
2    (
3    Qout                    :Output;
4    DIn, Clock              :Input;
5    )
6    Variable
7    Mem1          :DFF;
8    Begin
9    Mem1.clk = Clock;
10   Mem1.d = DIn;
11   Qout = Mem1.q;
12   End;
```

PROGRAM 2.1   Demonstration of D Flip-Flop

In program 2.1, a single memory element is instantiated and is responsive to a single input signal, DIn. The single memory element's output is connected to a chip output signal named Qout. A more detailed description follows.

Lines 1–5: The subdesign section of the source code declares, as in previous examples, the input and output signals as specified in lines 3 and 4 respectively. Recall that the file should be saved with the designation Dmem.tdf when using the Altera system. Other design systems have variations in file-naming conventions.

Lines 6–7: The variable section of the program contains a single statement allocating one of the available flip-flops on the implementation chip and directs that the memory element's configuration be that of a D flip-flop. The logic designer may select other memory element configurations such as JKFF, but, for now, we simply utilize the D-type for the current example. This process is similar to the declaration of a "built-in" data type such as an integer- or a float-type variable in a software programming language such as C. Whereas the declaration of the built-in variable type allocates memory for the variable in a software language, the implementation of AHDL allocates one memory element on a chip containing essentially a fixed number of memory elements. Each memory element contains predefined ports. For example the ports defined for a D flip-flop are given in the table below.

D Flip-Flop Ports

Port	Use
D	Input terminal
Q	Output terminal
prn	Active low preset
clrn	Active low clear
clk	Clock

In the current example during the instantiation of the memory element, it is given the name Mem1 which may be used to access the object and its various ports.

Lines 8–12: The body, framed in the Begin-End statement pair provides structural connections between the I/O ports and the D flip-flop. The ports are accessed using the fully qualified port name utilizing the dot notation often associated with object-oriented programming. The D-type memory element with the given name Mem1 may be thought of as an object, whose various ports are accessed through the fully qualified name notation.

The result of a simulation for the D flip-flop control is shown below. Note that the D flip-flop has the characteristic of storing the data which resides on the input line (in other words, D) on the positive transition of the clock. The stored information, which is displayed as the output data Qout, remains fixed until the clock signal presents an additional positive-going transition (and the power supply voltage, Vcc, remains within tolerance).

The system above performs as expected. The simulation provides additional insight into the D flip-flop performance, including the impact of timing delays. To articulate another important characteristic of memory elements, we next consider a slightly different arrangement of the input signal timing.

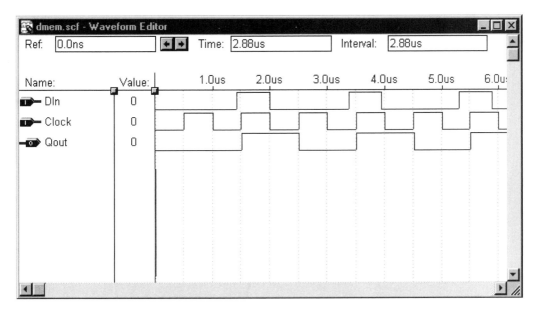

Simulation of program 2.1: D Flip-Flop Management

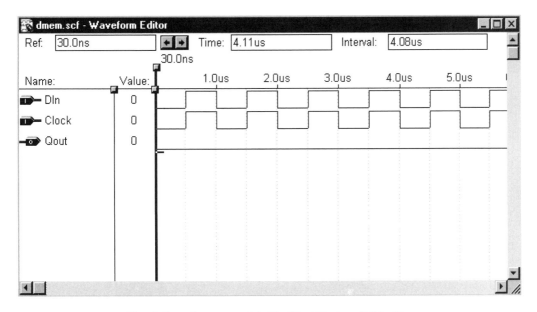

Simulation of program 2.1: Modified Timing, D Flip-Flop

Note that in the modified simulation above, the Qout signal remains low although the input signal goes high synchronously with the clock. Since the input signal goes high at the same instant that the clock goes high, the conditions violate the setup time requirement. Setup time is defined as follows. The input signal to any memory element must be present and stable for the setup time, prior to the transition of the clock on which the memory element executes its read operation.

In the first simulation diagram above, Simulation for D Flip-Flop Management, the data input signal, DIn, occurs just prior to clock signal and consequently the flip-flop reads and stores the data correctly.

In the second simulation, Simulation for Modified Timing, setup times are violated and consequently information is not registered into the memory element. The setup time in modern memory elements typically ranges from 2 to 10 ns.

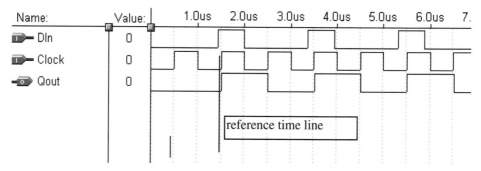

Timing Diagram Indicating Setup Time Requirement

In practical design implementations, setup time is usually a major factor in determining maximum allowable clock speed for a digital system.

2.2 ASYNCHRONOUS INPUTS

The input signal of the previous section is referred to as a "synchronous" input signal. That is, the signal effectively is synchronous with the clock. This means that the input signal is only effective during the positive transition of the clock signal, subject to the setup time constraint described above. Two classical signals which effect the output of the flip-flop any time they are asserted are the active low preset signal (prn) and the active low clear signal (clrn). The effect of these signals is not dependent on the clock signal in any way.

```
1     Subdesign 'DMem2'
2     (
3     Qout                              :Output;
4     DIn, Clock, Prn, Clrn             :Input;
5     )

6     Variable
7     Mem2          :DFF;

8     Begin
9     Mem2.clk = Clock;
10    Mem2.prn = Prn;
11    Mem2.clrn = Clrn;
12    Mem2.d = DIn;
13    Qout = Mem2.q;
14    End;
```

PROGRAM 2.2   D-Memory with Asynchronous Clear

Program 2.2 reinforces the notation that is used to access the various ports on the memory elements. It also provides a demonstration of the utility of the asynchronous pre-set and clear signals. A description of program 2.2 is given below.

Lines 1–5: The subdesign section of the source code declares the input and output signals respectively.

Lines 6–7: The variable section of the source file is used to instantiate the memory element of type DFF and assign the name, Mem2.

Line 9: The externally supplied clock is routed from the input pins on the chip to the clock port on the instantiated memory element, Mem2.

Lines 10–11: The externally supplied asynchronous clear and asynchronous pre-set lines are routed from the input pins to the clear and preset ports on the allocated flip-flop.

Line 12: The input signal is routed from the chip input pin to the D port on the allocated flip-flop.

Line 13: The q output of the flip-flop is routed from the flip-flop .q port to the chip output pin.

Two simulations are given below to illustrate the use of the asynchronous signals.

In the simulation of the D flip-flop employing the use of the asynchronous clear signal, once the clear signal is asserted, the flip-flop remains in the zero or cleared memory state regardless of the activity related to the input signal or the clock signal.

In contrast to the use of the asynchronous clear, the asynchronous preset results in the flip-flop achieving the set state, regardless of the activity on the input or clock lines as can be observed directly.

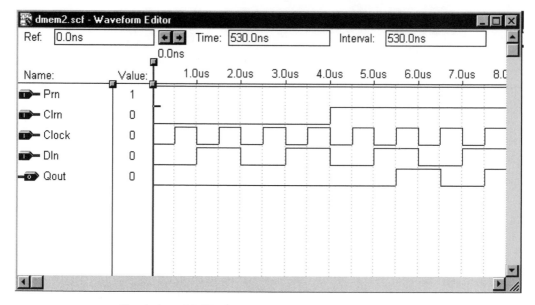

Simulation of D Flip-Flop with Asynchronous Clear Signal

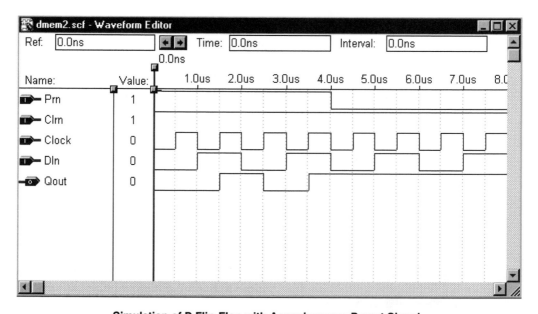

Simulation of D Flip-Flop with Asynchronous Preset Signal

2.3 BUILDING A TWISTED RING COUNTER WITH D FLIP-FLOPS

The twisted ring counter, or Johnson counter as it is sometimes called, is created by making a slight modification to shift register. Assume that we have a three-bit, right-shift register. Using the Altera language, the memory elements may be declared in a declaration statement contained in the variable section of a source file as:

```
DMem[2..0]   :DFF ;
```

This statement allocates an array of three memory elements from the available resources on a programmable chip. The right-shift register is then formulated with the straightforward command:

```
DMem[1..0].d = DMem[2..1].q;
```

The output (q port) of the high-order shift-register bits are connected to the input ports (d ports) of the next lower order bits as shown in the figure below. In this figure, notice that the *negative* side of the low-order flip-flop is fed back to the D input of the high-order flip-flop. The remaining interconnections constitute a right-shift register.

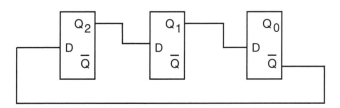

A Three-Bit Twisted Ring Counter

Once the designer becomes facile with the language constructs, the need to make drawings and schematics is vastly reduced. The HDL language is not only useful for design level activities but also provides a convenient, highly productive means of communicating among designers. To complete the twisted ring, we now connect the negative side of the least significant bit of the register to the input of the most significant bit.

```
Dmem[2].d = ! DMem[0].q ;
```

We now present the source code for a three-bit, twisted ring, or Johnson counter. The program "twist3", is shown below. Note that the complete counter code is very brief including the declaration of memory components, connection of clocks and generation of the counter itself through the interconnecting structural "wiring diagram".

```
1      Subdesign 'twist3'
2      (
3      clock           :Input;
4      Mem[2..0]       :Output;
5      )
6      Variable
7      Mem[2..0]       :DFF;

8      Begin
9      Mem[2..0].clk = clock;
10     Mem[1..0].d = Mem[2..1].q ;
11     Mem[2].d = !Mem[0].q ;
12     End;
```

PROGRAM 2.3   A Three Bit Twisted Ring

The simulation below indicates that the three bit twisted ring counter contains six unique and sequential states. The states are, in decimal, zero, four, six, seven, three, one.

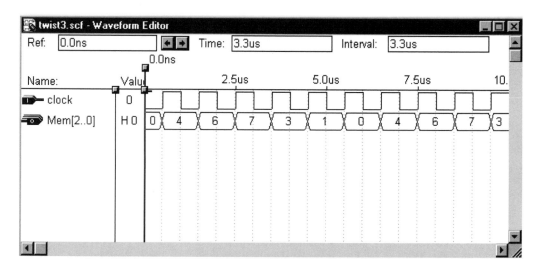

Simulation of Program 2.3: Twisted Ring Counter

A truth table description of the counter states is presented below. Since the least significant bit is always inverted and placed into the most significant bit location, this digital machine is limited to only six states although three binary bits are actually capable of producing 2^n unique states or 2^3 unique states in this case. Twisted ring counters are capable of producing only 2n sequential states.

Truth Table, Twisted Ring

Current State	Next State
$Q_1 Q_2 Q_3$	$Q_1 Q_2 Q_3$
0 0 0	1 0 0
1 0 0	1 1 0
1 1 0	1 1 1
1 1 1	0 1 1
0 1 1	0 0 1
0 0 1	0 0 0

In general, for a twisted ring counter, there are $2^n - 2n$ states which are not *legal*. In the current example, there are two *illegal* states. For example, if the counter were to get into the 010 state the machine would operate as follows.

Illegal State Sequence

Current State	Next State
0 1 0	1 0 1
1 0 1	0 1 0

2.4 A RELIABLE TWISTED-RING COUNTER USING A CASE CONSTRUCTION

If the twisted-ring state machine were to enter one of the illegal states, it would not produce the desired sequential cycle. If a noise voltage or some other disturbance temporarily stimulates the digital system into one of the illegal states, then the machine would malfunction permanently (or until induced by another random or deterministic event back into a legal state). We, therefore, now illustrate an additional language construction and a means of assuring a transition back from an illegal state, into one of the legal states.

```
1      Subdesign 'twist3'
2      (
3      clock          :Input;
4      Mem[2..0]       :Output;
5      )
6      Variable
7      Mem[2..0]       :DFF;

8      Begin
9      Mem[2..0].clk = clock;
10     CASE Mem[2..0] IS
```

PROGRAM 2.4   A Reliable Twisted Ring

```
11              WHEN H"2" =>
12                  Mem[2..0].d = H"0";
13              WHEN H"5" =>
14                  Mem[2..0].d = H"0";
15              WHEN OTHERS =>
16                  Mem[2].d = !Mem[0].q ;
17                  Mem[1..0].d = Mem[2..1].q ;
18      END CASE;
19      End;
```

PROGRAM 2.4 *Continued*

Program 2.4 contains the usual program structure and in addition introduces the Case language construct. The keywords of the Case structure are:

- CASE
- IS
- WHEN
- OTHERS
- END CASE

The expression written between the CASE and IS keywords is examined by the construct. If the examined expression evaluates to the constant value listed after any of the WHEN statements, the language statements directly following the subject WHEN statement are executed. END CASE, as might be expected, terminates the CASE IS clause.

We now describe the content of program 2.4 in greater detail.

Lines 1–5: The usual subdesign section declaring the I/O variables are contained here.

Lines 6–7: These lines constitute the usual variable section, instantiating the resources.

Line 10: The expression Mem[2..0] is evaluated.

Lines 11–12: When the expression of line 10 is found to be 2_{16}, then the D control inputs of all flip-flops are set equal to logic zero.

Lines 13–14: When the expression of line 10 is found equal to 5_{16}, then the D control inputs of all flip-flops are set equal to zero.

Lines 15–17: When the expression of line 10 is found to be anything other than 2_{16} or 5_{16}, then the D control inputs of the twisted-ring counter are set to mechanize the twisted-ring process.

2.5   A RELIABLE TWISTED-RING COUNTER WITH STATE DECODER

We now present a slight variation of the twisted ring sequential circuit of the previous section. In the following example, a combinational logic subsystem has been added to the sequential circuit. It is often necessary in digital systems, to keep track of the state of a sequential circuit by decoding the state or to otherwise create a sequence of pulses with which to control a "sequence domain" process. A traditional logic diagram for a decoder which decodes the six legal states of the twisted ring is presented for convenience and comparison with the source code file.

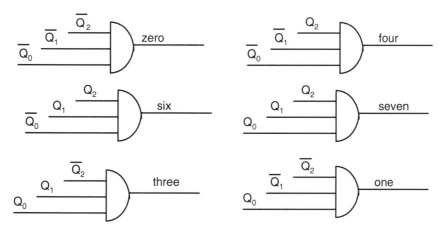

**Full Decoder for Legal States
of a Three-Bit Twisted Ring**

The source file listed below, program 2.5, provides an illustration of such required signal generation capability.

```
1     Subdesign 'twist3D'
2     (
3     clock                                        :Input;
4     Mem[2..0], Zero, four, six, seven, three, one :Output;
5     )
6     Variable
7     Mem[2..0]      :DFF;
8     Begin
9     Mem[2..0].clk = clock;
10    CASE Mem[2..0] IS
11        WHEN H"2" =>
12            Mem[2..0].d = H"0";
13        WHEN H"5" =>
14            Mem[2..0].d = H"0";
15        WHEN OTHERS =>
16            Mem[1..0].d = Mem[2..1].q ;
17            Mem[2].d = !Mem[0].q ;
18    END CASE;
19    % ***** decoder function ***** %
20    zero = !Mem[2]&!Mem[1]&!Mem[0];
```

PROGRAM 2.5   Reliable Twisted Ring and Decoder

```
21    four = Mem[2]&!Mem[1]&!Mem[0];
22    six = Mem[2]& Mem[1]&!Mem[0];
23    seven = Mem[2]& Mem[1]& Mem[0];
24    three = !Mem[2]& Mem[1]& Mem[0];
25    one = !Mem[2]&!Mem[1]& Mem[0];
26    End;
```

PROGRAM 2.5   *Continued*

In the hardware description source file of program 2.5, a decoder for all legal states has been added to the reliable twisted-ring counter of program 2.4. We now provide a detailed description of program 2.5.

Lines 1–18: These source lines are identical to the source lines of program 2.4. Refer to the detailed description of program 2.4.

Lines 19–25: These source lines describe the combinatorial logic of the decoder. The decoder is a set of combinational gates which are connected to the memory element outputs and therefore provide six discrete output logic lines. Only one output logic line of the decoder will be asserted at any one period of time, which is consistent with the fact that the twisted ring state machine can only be in one state during any one period of time. Below is presented the simulation showing the functional performance of the counter and decoder.

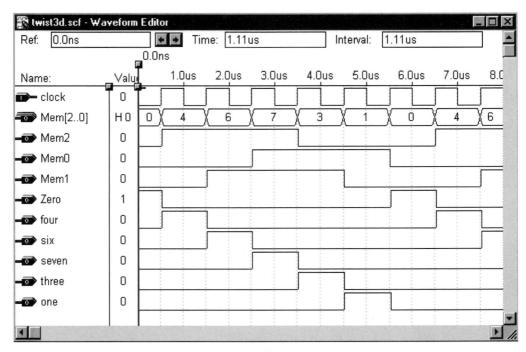

Simulation for Program 2.5: Reliable Twisted Ring and Six-Line Decoder

We have concentrated on the specific structure of the twisted-ring counter thus far. It is instructive if we now step back and look at the general structure of the counter. The twisted-ring counter above consists of three memory elements which record and store the state of the counter. The interconnecting wires (lines 12, 14, 16, and 17 in program 2.5), constitute an elementary combinational logic circuit which determines the next sequential state of the digital system. The output signals of this combinational logic system, which terminate on the D inputs of the memory elements are transferred into the respective memory elements on the positive transition of the clock. This is the means by which the sequential digital circuit acquires its next state.

The digital system above (three-bit twisted-ring counter) is capable of running at a substantially faster rate than 1.0 MHz. We simply have performed this simulation to demonstrate functional performance. As the counter proceeds through its natural twisted ring cycle, the decoder repeats a "waterfall" sequence of pulses which indicate the state of the counter and may be used to control a sequence of logical processes if so desired. This demonstrates the desired result and so we proceed to another illustration. We next examine the maximum clock rate performance of a simple digital system.

2.6   A HIGH-SPEED TWO-BIT TWISTED-RING (JOHNSON) COUNTER

The subject of clock speed almost always arises in high-performance digital systems. There is, apparently, a continuing need for more speed. Observing the rapid growth rate of desktop computers from their infancy speeds in the few tens of megahertz not long ago to the hundreds of megahertz range today certainly illustrates this point. We often think of speed as synonymous with performance. Although it is not strictly true that clock speed equals performance, there is an inevitable link. We therefore examine a two-bit twisted-ring (Johnson) counter in the interest of pursuing the speed issue.

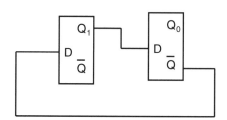

A Two-Bit Twisted-Ring (Johnson) Counter

In the three-bit twisted-ring system discussed above, the system was tested at a clock rate of only 1 MHz. The relatively short delays involved in high-performance circuits which composed the system were not obvious. We now consider a two-bit twisted ring with a much higher clock rate. We restrict our consideration to a two-bit system for the sake of convenience. There is no loss in generality for the speed considerations, since a twisted ring of any size would illicit the same basic considerations. In fact, any cyclic state machine would require inclusion of the same considerations, along with, potentially, additional considerations. Program 2.6 is the AHDL description of a two-bit twisted ring which will be the basis of our discussions.

```
1    Subdesign 'twist2'
2    (
3    clock          :Input;
4    Mem[1..0]       :Output;
5    )
6    Variable
7    Mem[1..0]       :DFF;

8    Begin
9    Mem[1..0].clk = clock;
10   Mem[0].d = Mem[1].q;
11   Mem[1].d = Not Mem[0].q;
12   End ;
```

PROGRAM 2.6   Two-Bit Twisted Ring

2.7 MAXIMUM CLOCK RATE FOR A TWO-BIT JOHNSON COUNTER

Program 2.6 above is selected since the combinational logic is straightforward and we can therefore concentrate on the basic speed issue. We define the largest time required to transfer the information from the Q output ports of the memory elements to the corresponding pins of the implementation chip as:

$$\text{Clock-to-Output propagation time} = T_{Clk-Out} \tag{2.1}$$

We define the largest propagation time from the output of the memory through the combinational logic system back to the D input of the memory elements as:

$$\text{Combinational Logic propagation time} = T_{P-Comb} \tag{2.2}$$

Recalling that the logic signal must be stable at the input terminal of the memory element for T_{Setup} prior to the arrival of the rising edge of the clock waveform, it is clear that for a well-behaved operation, the clock period, T_{Clk}, is defined by:

$$T_{Clk} \geq T_{P-Comb} + T_{Setup} + T_{Clk-Out} \tag{2-3}$$

Therefore the maximum frequency at which the counter may be clocked is:

$$f_{Max-Clk} = \frac{1}{T_{Clk}} \tag{2.4}$$

Since the combinational logic, in this case, consists only of wires (actually, minia-ture transmission lines) in the case of the three-bit twisted ring, we may assume that T_{P-Comb} is negligibly small (recall that the speed of light, 186,384 m/s provides a propa-gation delay of approximately 85 ps/in.). Even at a velocity factor[1] of 0.5 (surely it will be higher than that) we arrive at only 170 ps/in. propagation delay for the transmission paths which carry the signals between flip-flops. Since the chip which will be used to imple-ment the current system is very small compared with 1 in., the combinational propagation time will be much less than .17 ns. Therefore we neglect this portion of equation (2.3). If we implement the two-bit twisted ring counter using the Altera MAX 7000 series pro-grammable array, the published specifications may be used to find the remaining two pa-rameters of equation (2.3). The specifications for a 5.0 volt MAX 7000 series device are listed as

$T_{SetUp} \leq 7.5$ ns for a -7 speed grade device
$T_{SetUp} \leq 6.0$ ns for a -6 speed grade device
$T_{SetUp} \leq 5.0$ ns for a -5 speed grade device

Similarly, for the clock-to-output signal propagation we see from the specifications

$T_{Clock-Out} \leq 6.0$ ns for a -7 speed grade device
$T_{Clock-Out} \leq 5.0$ ns for a -6 speed grade device
$T_{Clock-Out} \leq 4.0$ ns for a -5 speed grade device

Therefore if we use the slowest of these devices we get from (2.3):

$T_{Clock} \geq 7.5$ ns

And if we use the fastest of these devices we get from (2.3):

$T_{Clock} \geq 4$ ns

The resulting clock rates (2.4) reveal that we can expect to clock the device some-where between 133.3 and 250 MHz. The output will appear at the respective pins of the implementation chip in the range of 4 to 6 ns after the respective state is reached, depend-ing upon which device is selected for implementation.

The simulation shows a two-bit twisted ring running at a clock rate of 200 MHz as one particular implementation utilizing a MAX 7000, -6 speed grade device. The simu-lated clock is running at a rate of 200 MHz as can be readily seen by inspecting the simu-lation. Note that there is a 4-ns delay between the rising edge of the clock and the change of state of the counter. This is consistent with the -6 speed grade, MAX 7000 device

---

[1]Velocity factor is defined as v/c, where c is the speed of light. Therefore the velocity factor is in the range [0, 1]. The velocity of electrical signals along a digital transmission line is slowed by the inductance, ca-pacitance, resistance, and conductance of the transmission line. A velocity factor of .6 to .7 is usual in the cir-cumstances currently under consideration.

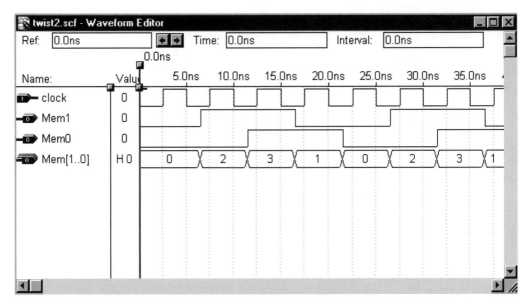

Simulation for Program 2.6: High-Speed Two-Bit Twisted Ring

specifications. An automated timing analysis, executed by the Altera Max+PlusII software package indicates that the clock-to-mem[0] and clock-to-mem[1] delays are each identical and equal to 4 ns when utilizing a 7000 series part. This indicates that the counter, as designed, may be expected to run at a maximum of 250 MHz.

2.8   BUILDING A J-K FLIP-FLOP FROM A D-TYPE FLIP-FLOP

In this section, we consider an exercise of marginal practical utility, but perhaps useful in the demonstration of differences between a D flip-flop and a J-K flip-flop. It also provides some insight into the logic design process utilizing systems with flip-flop memory.

We now present the truth table of a J-K flip-flop as a reminder of the functional performance of a J-K device.

Truth Table for J-K Flip-Flop

Input		Output	
J	K	Q^n	Q^{n+1}
0	0	0	0
0	0	1	1
0	1	0	0
0	1	1	0
1	0	0	1
1	0	1	1
1	1	0	1
1	1	1	0

The essential objective of this section is, given a D-type flip-flop, how do we create a J-K flip-flop using the D flip-flop as a fundamental building block? In the diagram presented below, we see that a D flip-flop is shown as a primary building block. In the design of a "new" element from the "old" element, the designer's responsibility is simply to provide the logical design of the combinational logic in the diagram as shown.

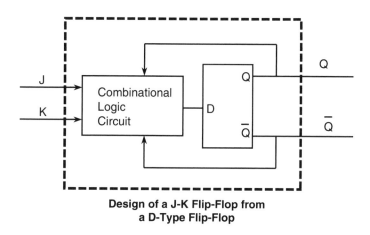

**Design of a J-K Flip-Flop from
a D-Type Flip-Flop**

We begin by creating a truth table for the desired behavior of the J-K flip-flop, including the D flip-flop as an essential building block element.

**Truth Table for J-K Flip-Flop
Created from a D Flip-Flop**

	Input			Output
J	K	Q^n	D^n	Q^{n+1}
0	0	0	0	0
0	0	1	1	1
0	1	0	0	0
0	1	1	0	0
1	0	0	1	1
1	0	1	1	1
1	1	0	1	1
1	1	1	0	0

The K-map corresponding to the truth table is developed as shown directly below.

K-Map for D^n or Q^{n+1}

	$\bar{J}\bar{K}$	$\bar{J}K$	JK	$J\bar{K}$
$\bar{Q}^n$			1	1
Q^n	1			1

Writing the terms directly from the derived K-map we see that

$$D^n = Q^{n+1} = J\,\overline{Q^n} + \overline{K}\,Q^n \qquad (2.5)$$

To examine the result, we now create a source file implementing equation (2.5). The required source program is presented directly below as program 2.7.

```
1     % ***** J-K from a D ***** %
2     Subdesign 'D2JK'
3     (
4     D2JK                        :Output;
5     J, K, clock                 :Input;
6     )
7     Variable
8     D2JK                        :Dff;
9     Begin
10    D2JK.clk = Clock;
11    D2JK.d = J & !D2JK # !K & D2JK;
12    End;
```

PROGRAM 2.7   A J-K Flip-Flop from a D Flip-Flop

The source code is relatively straightforward to follow. The design equation (2.5) is implemented as line 11. Note that the flip-flop is declared in line 8 as a D-type flip-flop but, as implemented, it behaves as a J-K flip-flop. This fact is evident by examining the behavior of the device as exhibited in the simulation given.

2.9   RETROSPECTIVE

We have examined the behavior of the single-bit D-type memory element (otherwise referred to as a D-type flip-flop). After examining the behavior of the D flip-flop this basic building block was utilized to build two-bit and three-bit twisted-ring counters. Functional behavior was examined for the twisted-ring counters. Finally, speed performance and propagation delay were examined by discussing various timing parameters. We concluded the chapter by briefly discussing control logic in the form of D flip-flop to J-K flip-flop conversion.

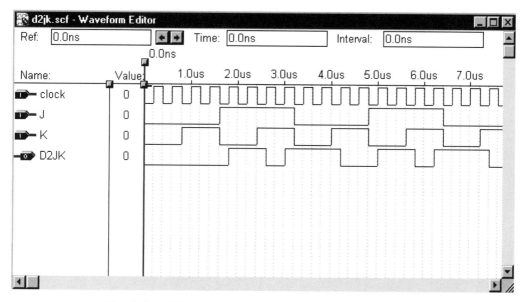

Simulation of Program 2.7: A J-K Flip-Flop from a D Flip-Flop

CHAPTER 2 EXERCISES

1. Design a five-bit twisted ring counter using only D-type flip-flops (in other words, connect the $\bar{Q}$ output of the least significant bit to the D input of the most significant bit).

   a) Assuming that the counter is initialized to the state [0,0,0,0,0], make a truth table showing the count sequence.

   b) Design the counter without regard to illegal states; make a logic diagram of the counter.

   c) List at least three fundamental parameters which will conceptually limit the maximum clock rate at which the system will perform properly.

   d) Add the logic required which will provide for reliable operation of the twisted ring.

   e) Perform a simulation of the counter and estimate the maximum operational clock rate from the simulation. Use the timing analyzer, if available, to verify your observations from the simulation.

   f) Replace the feedback loop of the previous design with a connection from the Q output of the least significant bit, through an inverter, back to the D input of the most significant bit. Describe the effect, if any, on the operation of the system.

   g) Perform an additional simulation on the system as modified in part (f) and verify your estimation of effects in system operation. Explain your observations.

2. Design a four-bit binary counter using only D-type flip-flops.
   a) Make a truth table describing, sequentially, the "current state" and "next state" for each state which the system assumes.
   b) Implement the counter using a "Table" HDL declaration as the primary means of implementing the count sequence.
   c) Perform a simulation of the counter and estimate the maximum operational clock rate from the simulation. Use the timing analyzer, if available, to verify your observations from the simulation.
   d) Compare the speed performance of the binary and twisted-ring counters. Discuss the two counters, contrasting their performances and describing basic reasons for the contrast and/or similarities.

3. Write the truth table for a J-K flip-flop
   a) Using a J-K flip-flop as the basic building block element, design a D flip-flop by providing the requisite combinational logic.
   b) Write an HDL program to verify the performance of your D flip-flop.
   c) Create a simulation of the D flip-flop and verify the functional performance of the resulting design.

4. Write the truth table for an R-S flip-flop
   a) Using an R-S flip-flop as the basic building block element, design a J-K flip-flop.
   b) Write an HDL program to verify the performance of your J-K flip-flop.
   c) Create a simulation of the J-K flip-flop and verify the functional performance of the resulting design.

5. For the five-bit twisted-ring system of exercise 1b, create a simulation which initializes the counter into its illegal states.
   a) Perform a simulation for each of the illegal conditions to determine if any of the illegal states are self-correcting.
   b) Summarize your observations concerning the illegal states.

CHAPTER **3**

ELEMENTS OF CONTROL LOGIC

3.1 LOOKING BACK: CONTROL LOGIC FOR TWISTED-RING COUNTERS

The word "control," applied to a digital system, essentially means the control of the state of the digital system. Recall that the current system state is defined by the content or state of the system memory. Controlling the state refers to the process of determining, unambiguously, the next sequential state to be assumed by the system. The current state of the system is determined from the contents of the memory portion of the digital system under consideration. In digital counting circuits as presented in the previous chapter (with more to come later), the control logic was such a natural and implicit mechanism of the design, that we paid little or no attention to the essential process of control. In these counters, the current state is resident in the memory portion of the system. The current state is utilized as a driving function for a set of combinational logic which generates a combinational output. The combinational output is reached and remains stable only after (a) the input driving functions (output of the memory elements) have reached steady state and (b) a propagation delay. The propagation delay is dependent upon the combinational logic and the clock-to-output propagation delay of the memory elements. In counters, outputs of the combinational logic terminate on input terminals of the memory elements. Therefore, the next sequential state of the system is entirely determined from the current state. In particular, the twisted-ring counters of the previous chapter contained the most trivial (or conversely, elegant) form of combinational logic, namely data paths or transmission paths. Although they certainly consist of wires, these transmission paths are more properly referred to as transmission lines. The twisted-ring counters were formed by creating a right-shift register where the output of each memory element was routed to the input of the element directly to its right. Since we envision the register arrayed with the left-most position as the most significant bit position, this right shift moves each bit to a less significant position. The inverse of the least significant bit was routed to the input of the most significant (left-most) bit position. Since the routing is accomplished with *wires*, it is clear that the combinational logic is of the simplest form. Of course, the logical arrangement nevertheless creates a useful cyclic sequence of states and the twisted ring counter is often a useful state machine in practical systems. We have examined the notion of control logic in an implicit sense by exploring simple counting methods. We next focus on the explicit control of a single D-type memory element.

3.2   A BASIC FORM OF CONTROL LOGIC FOR D-TYPE FLIP-FLOPS

In this section, we examine the control (in other words, setting and resetting) of a single D-type flip-flop at arbitrary times determined by a designer. A D-type memory simply reads its input on the rising edge of the clock and then retains the specified input value until the next clock arrives, at which time the process is repeated. The periodic clock signal repeats its transitions every cycle and the memory read process simply repeats ad infinitum.

3.2.1   An Eight-State Timing Generator

We begin the process by designing a four-bit twisted-ring counter which will provide a series of pulses, which we name T_0 through T_7. The series of pulses defines a "sequence domain" within which we will control the state of a D-type flip-flop. Recall that a twisted-ring counter generates 2n unique sequential states where n is the number of memory elements contained in the twisted ring. Below, we show the text design file listing for the four-bit twisted ring. The construction of the "logical-if" of the AHDL is also introduced in this program and will be elaborated upon below. If the designer is acquainted with any of the classical software languages such as C or Pascal, the logical-if construction should be intuitive. Since the reader has seen the design of a twisted-ring counter in previous examples, we proceed immediately to the source file for the four-bit counter.

```
1    Subdesign 'twist4'
2    (
3    clock                              :Input;
4    Mem[3..0]                          :Output;
5    T7, T6, T5, T4, T3, T2, T1, T0     :Output;
6    )
7    Variable
8    Mem[3..0]    :DFF;
9    Begin
```

PROGRAM 3.1   A Four-Bit Twisted Ring

```
10    Mem[3..0].clk = clock;
11    CASE Mem[3..0] IS
12          WHEN H"2" =>
13                Mem[3..0].d = H"0";
14          WHEN H"5" =>
15                Mem[3..0].d = H"0";
16          WHEN H"4" =>
17                Mem[3..0].d = H"0";
18          WHEN H"6" =>
19                Mem[3..0].d = H"0";
20          WHEN H"9" =>
21                Mem[3..0].d = H"0";
22          WHEN H"A" =>
23                Mem[3..0].d = H"0";
24          WHEN H"B" =>
25                Mem[3..0].d = H"0";
26          WHEN H"D" =>
27                Mem[3..0].d = H"0";
28          WHEN OTHERS =>
29                Mem[2..0].d = Mem[3..1].q ;
30                Mem[3].d = !Mem[0].q ;
31    END CASE;
32    % ***** Generate T0 ***** %
33    If(Mem[3..0] = = H"0") Then
34          T0 = VCC;
35    Else
36          T0 = GND;
37    End If;
38    % ***** Generate T1 ***** %
39    If(Mem[3..0] = = H"8") Then
40          T1 = VCC;
41    Else
42          T1 = GND;
43    End If;
44    % ***** Generate T2 ***** %
45    If(Mem[3..0] = = H"C") Then
46          T2 = VCC;
47    Else
48          T2 = GND;
49    End If;
50    % ***** Generate T3 ***** %
51    If(Mem[3..0] = = H"E") Then
52          T3 = VCC;
53    Else
54          T3 = GND;
55    End If;
```

PROGRAM 3.1   *Continued*

```
56   % ***** Generate T4 ***** %
57   If(Mem[3..0] = = H"F") Then
58         T4 = VCC;
59   Else
60         T4 = GND;
61   End If;
62   % ***** Generate T5 ***** %
63   If(Mem[3..0] = = H"7") Then
64         T5 = VCC;
65   Else
66         T5 = GND;
67   End If;
68   % ***** Generate T6 ***** %
69   If(Mem[3..0] = = H"3") Then
70         T6 = VCC;
71   Else
72         T6 = GND;
73   End If;
74   % ***** Generate T7 ***** %
75   If(Mem[3..0] = = H"1") Then
76         T7 = VCC;
77   Else
78         T7 = GND;
79   End If;
80   End;
```

PROGRAM 3.1   *Continued*

A detailed explanation of program 3.1 follows. Most of the program includes constructions that have been used before so that elaborate discussions of constructions or program structure is not required.

Lines 1–6: The subdesign section, as usual, declares the chip input and output signals.

Lines 7–8: The variable section of the file reserves the four required memory elements for the twisted-ring counter

Lines 11–31: The twisted ring is formed with the "WHEN OTHERS" clause. All of the other lines in this segment handle the illegal members of the state possibilities and assure that the counter will not become *beached* in the series of illegal states. The number of illegal states is $2^n - 2n$, which is $16 - 8 = 8$ in this case. The number of *illegal* states is a definite drawback of the twisted ring. The drawback is especially serious for long sequences. The error states must be decoded as means to an error correction method.

Lines 32–79: These lines of the source code handle the decode function and output function. Each of the legal states of the counter generates a unique decoder output line. Note that the if-then construction is used simply for introductory purposes. The double-equal relational operator as utilized in the C programming language is required. The reader may want to rewrite these lines to use the CASE command and to see how much of a simplification in the source code results. Perhaps a truth table approach might also be applied to see if even further simplification results.

The simulation of the twisted-ring sequence-domain generator, with a clock rate of 500 kHz is shown below. As stated earlier, T_0 to T_7 define a sequence domain within which the control process in question will be conducted.

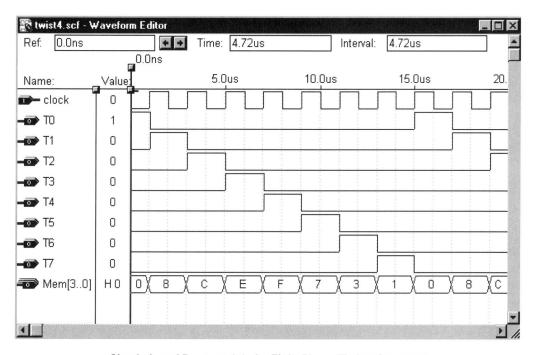

Simulation of Program 3.1: An Eight Phase Timing Generator

3.2.2 Controlling the State of a One Bit, D-Type Flip-Flop

We now consider a straightforward control problem applying control signals to the input of the D-type flip-flop to set and reset the flip-flop at arbitrarily determined, discrete times which are in the discrete time-space defined by T_0 through T_7. Remember that the D flip-flop reads its input each and every time that the applied clock signal achieves a positive transition. In this sense, the D flip-flop has only a one clock-period memory and at the beginning of each clock time it must be distinctly instructed which state it must assume at the clock signal transition. Although this is conceptually straightforward, in practice it rapidly becomes impractical and therefore an improved, more formal method is sought. We define set and hold signals which are responsible for providing the appropriate controlling function.

In a manner similar to that used for the development of a J-K type flip-flop from a D-type flip-flop (see Chapter 2), we develop the logical design for the set or hold form utilizing the following diagram.

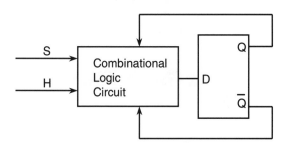

Set or Hold Logical Control Form

Referring to the diagram, we seek the design equations for the combinational logic circuit shown. The operation we desire is revealed in the following truth table.

Truth Table for D Flip-Flop Control

Set	Hold	Q^n	Q^{n+1}
0	0	0	0
0	0	1	0
0	1	0	0
0	1	1	1
1	0	0	1
1	0	1	1
1	1	0	x
1	1	1	1

The symbol x implies a "don't care" condition in the truth table. We next create a standard K-map for the truth table.

K-Map for Q^{n+1}

	$\bar{S}\bar{H}$	$\bar{S}H$	SH	$S\bar{H}$
$\bar{Q}^n$			x	1
Q^n		1	1	1

Writing the logic equation implied by the K-map for Q^{n+1} yields

$$Q^{n+1} = S + HQ^n \qquad (3.1)$$

Equation (3.1) reveals that a suitable manner for control of the desired element is to use the *S* input term to set the memory. Then as long as the *H* or hold term is asserted, the memory will hold its current value. Therefore, we may simply assert the two signals, *S* and *H*, to set or hold a value in the memory. The schematic representation of (3.1) is shown.

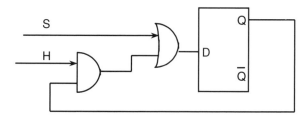

Set or Hold Implementation Form

This form often simplifies the control of the desired element as we show through an illustration below. We now proceed to incorporate this logical form into an illustration program and then to demonstrate the utility through the execution of a simulation.

For the demonstration of the set-or-hold logical implementation, we desire to utilize the entire source code of program 3.1. To avoid repeating the code which generates the discrete sequence domain (in other words, to avoid repeating program 3.1), we merely compile program 3.1 into an include file named twist4.inc. We then prepare the source file given below as program 3.2 and we "include" the twist4.inc file as the first line of program 3.2. Program 3.2 provides the timing-pulse generation through an invocation of the code of program 3.1. The functionality of program 3.1 is achieved through the process of generating an "instance" of the required timing generation program. We are then at liberty to utilize the timing signals generated for control of the D-type memory element. The utilization of the timing pulses for control is demonstrated in program 3.2. Without further discussion, we now proceed to the presentation of program 3.2 and the corresponding detailed discussion.

```
1      include "twist4.inc";
2      Subdesign 's_h1'
3      (
4      Clock                              :Input;
5      Flag                               :Output;
6      t[7..0]                            :Output;
7      )
8      Variable
9      Flag                               :DFF;
10     twister                            :twist4;
```

PROGRAM 3.2   Simple Control of a D Flip-Flop

```
11   Begin
12   twister.clock=clock;
13   Flag.clk=clock;
14   t[7..0]=twister.t[7..0];
15   Flag.d = (t0 # t3) # (!t2 & !t6 & Flag.q);
16   End;
```

PROGRAM 3.2   *Continued*

Line 1: This include statement provides all of the functionality of program 3.1 (which has been compiled into the file twist4.inc) and places this functionality at the disposal of commands within the source file s_h1.

Lines 4–6: As usual, the subdesign section of the source file declares the chip input and output signals.

Lines 8–10: Line 9 reserves one of the available D-type memory elements of a programmable chip under the declared name Flag. The variable Flag now contains all of the ports befitting a one-bit D-type memory. That is the ports Flag.d, Flag.q, Flag.clrn, and Flag.prn are all available ports belonging to the element Flag. Line 10 instantiates or declares an instance of a "module" of type twist4. The instantiated module twister now contains all of the ports befitting an object of type twist4. That is, twister.clock, twister.t0, twister.t1, twister.t2, ... twister.t7, twister.Mem[3..0] are all sanctioned ports belonging to the object twister.

Lines 12–13: The externally supplied clock signal is connected to the two entities which are each a part of the current system. Line 12 supplies the clock to the timing generator which has been included with the include twist4.inc of line 1 and then instantiated under the name twister in line 10. Line 13 applies the clock signal to the D flip-flop which is reserved in the variable section of the source file.

Line 14: This line routes the timing generator outputs to pins on the implementation chip. These signals may not be required at the chip output in any particular design. In other examples, they may be referred to as internal nodes using the node keyword.

Line 15: This logical form implements equation (3.1). Following the timing cycle, T_0 to T_7, it is clear from the simulation below that the timing signal, T_0, sets the memory element and T_2 releases the memory content. Then the assertion of T_3 sets the memory element once again and, in turn, the timing signal, T_6 releases the memory content. The student is encouraged to try other combinations of the Set-or-Hold control format. As a final note we observe that the timing signals operate on a one-clock delay.

In the simulation below, we note that the Flag memory element is in the logical one state from T_1 to T_2 inclusive and from T_4 to T_6 inclusive. Note particularly that the "don't care" condition of the design K-map is avoided. However, it should be noted that since the logic one alternative of the "don't care" was selected in the development of equation (3.1), the input conditions are completely specified. The reader is encouraged to examine the control logic equation of program 3.2, line 15 and compare the control terms with the timing diagram below.

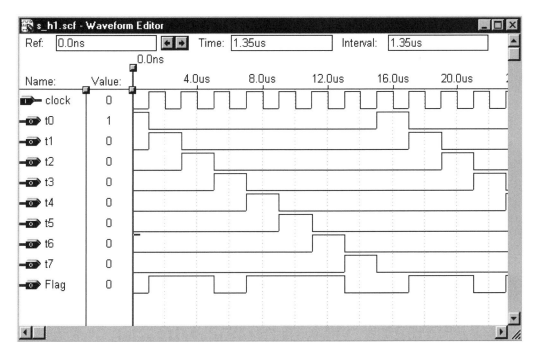

Simulation for Program 3.2: Simple Control of D Flip-Flop

3.2.3   A Three D Flip-Flop Illustration

To elaborate, slightly, we provide program 3.3 (below), which presents three different control equations for D-type flip-flop elements. The memory elements are named Flag1, Flag2, and Flag3, respectively. The reader is encouraged to write the set-or-hold logical control forms which apply for the three Flag variables corresponding to the simulation diagram shown below. (In other words, a reasonable exercise consists of inspecting the simulation results for program 3.3 and then writing sample source code before inspecting the content of program 3.3.) Then examine program 3.3 to compare the result achieved with the source code which generated the netlist from which the simulation was produced. Line 17 of the source code controls the Flag1 variable, line 18 of the source code controls Flag2 and line 19 controls Flag3.

```
1      include "twist4.inc";
2      2Subdesign 's_h1'
3      (
4      Clock                          :Input;
```

PROGRAM 3.3   Three D Flip-Flop Control Logic

```
5     Flag1, Flag2, Flag3              :Output;
6     t[7..0]                          :Output;
7     )

8     Variable
9     Flag1, Flag2, Flag3      :DFF;
10    twister                          :twist4;

11    Begin
12    twister.clock=clock;
13    Flag1.clk=clock;
14    Flag2.clk=clock;
15    Flag3.clk=clock;
16    t[7..0]=twister.t[7..0];
17    Flag1.d = (t0 # t3) # (!t2 & !t6 & Flag1.q);
18    Flag2.d = t0 # !t5& Flag2.q;
19    Flag3.d = t4 # !t2&Flag3.q;
20    End;
```

PROGRAM 3.3   *Continued*

3.3   A LOADABLE, LEFT-RIGHT SHIFT REGISTER

We now undertake the design of a shift register which can be loaded from an external data source, can be commanded to shift left or right or may be required to hold the register contents in place. In this illustration, left and right shifts are limited to a single bit for any

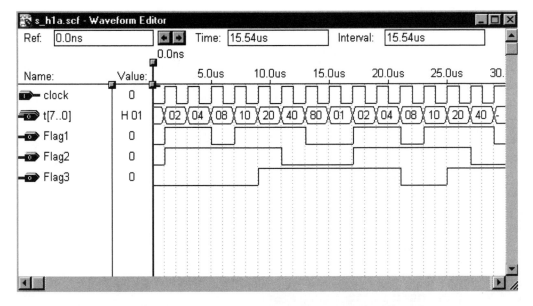

Simulation for Program 3.3: Three D Flip-Flop Control Logic

single clock period. We specify shifts as circular in the present example. The input control lines which we define are named, appropriately, Load, LShift, RShift and Hold, where the assertions of these control lines must be mutually exclusive. It is the designer's problem to assure that one and only one of the input control lines is asserted during any given interval. The set-or-hold logical form (equation 3.1) will be adapted for this purpose. The data input to the chip will be named Ldata[7..0]. The program below (program 3.4) employs a slight variation of the set-or-hold form which is quite useful for generalized control, especially when employing D-type memory elements.

```
1     Subdesign 'LSHRegx'
2     (
3     Clock                                            :Input;
4     LData[7..0]                                      :Input;
5     Load, Hold, SRight, SLeft    :Input;
6     Reg[7..0]                                        :Output;
7     )
8     Variable
9     Reg[7..0]                              :dff;
10    Begin
11    Reg[].clk = Clock;
12    Reg[6..1].d = Load & Ldata[6..1] #
13                  Hold & Reg[6..1].q #
14                  SRight & Reg[7..2].q #
15                  SLeft & Reg[5..0].q;
16    Reg[7].d =    Load & LData[7] #
17                  Hold & Reg[7].q #
18                  SRight & Reg[0].q #
19                  SLeft & Reg[6].q;
20    Reg[0].d =    Load & LData[0] #
21                  Hold & Reg[0].q #
22                  SRight & Reg[1].q #
23                  SLeft & Reg[7].q;
24    End;
```

PROGRAM 3.4   Load/Hold/L-R Circular Shift Register

The description of program 3.4 will now be given.

Lines 1–7: This section of the source code is the normal subdesign section of the source code, in which input and output signals are defined.

Lines 8–9: This section is the variable section of the file, which reserves an array of eight flip-flops, on the implementation programmable logic chip, configured as D-type memories.

Lines 12–15: This logic controls the loading, holding, left- and right-shifting of the register array elements. When loading, all internal elements of the array (in other words, Reg[6..1]) are loaded from the LData input pins of the chip. When holding, all of the contents of the register array elements must be held *in place*.

Lines 16–19: These source lines control the high-order memory bit content. The value of Reg[7] is determined in the same manner as the internal register content for loading and holding. When the register is being shifted right (circular right in this case), the most significant seven bits are shifted to the right. The least significant (right-most) bit is shifted into the most significant (Reg[7]) bit position.

Lines 20–23: These lines control the low-order memory bit content. Reg[0] is determined in the same manner as the internal register content for loading. The value of Reg[0] is determined from the previous value of Reg[1] when right circular shifting and from the previous value of Reg[7] when left circular shifting.

The simulation directly below exhibits that the control processes for the shift register of program 3.4 behave in the manner directed by the control equations and, in fact, control the actions of the register as desired. The load signal line is high during the initial time segment shown. This action causes the value 0x88 to be loaded into the register. During the next time slice, load returns to a false position and the hold control line is asserted. This accounts for the back-to-back time slices where the register maintains the value 0x88. The left-shift line is then asserted for a period of five clocks. The register consequently assumes the values 0x11, 0x22, 0x44, 0x88, and 0x11, in sequence. The right-shift line is finally asserted and the register contents reverse the previous pattern and assume the sequence 0x88, 0x44, 0x22, 0x11, ... as shown in the simulation waveform.

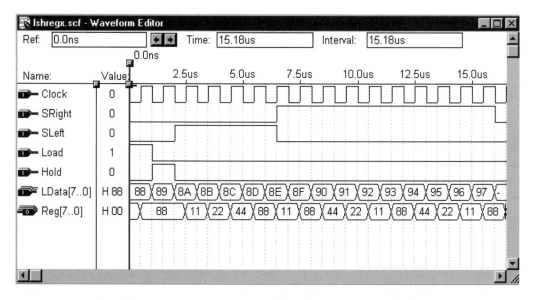

Simulation of Program 3.4: Load/Hold/L-R Circular Shift Register

3.4   AN ALTERNATIVE SOURCE FILE
FOR A LOAD/HOLD/L-R CIRCULAR SHIFT REGISTER

To introduce a new construct of the language, we now show a implementation of the shift register of program 3.4, except that we accomplish the register decision-making with the if-then construct methodology. A comparison of programs 3.4 and 3.5 clearly demonstrates the interpretation to be applied to the if-then language feature. We will not describe the processing of program 3.5 in detail. A comparative examination of the two source files should easily permit the reader to glean the required information.

```
1     Subdesign 'LSHReg'
2     (
3     Clock                                     :Input;
4     LData[7..0]                               :Input;
5     Load, Hold, SRight, SLeft                 :Input;
6     Reg[7..0]                                 :Output;
7     )
8     Variable
9     Reg[7..0]                                 :dff;
10    Begin
11    Reg[].clk = Clock;
12    % ***** Load Logic ***** %
13    If(Load) Then
14         Reg[7..0].d = Ldata[7..0];
15    End If;
16    % ***** Hold Logic ***** %
17    If(Hold) Then
18         Reg[7..0].d = Reg[7..0].q;
19    End If;
20    % ***** Circular Shift Right Logic ***** %
21    if(SRight) Then
22         Reg[6..0].d = Reg[7..1].q;
23         Reg[7].d =Reg[0].q;
24    End If;
25    % ***** Circular Shift Right Logic ***** %
26    if(SLeft) Then
27         Reg[7..1].d = Reg[6..0].q;
28         Reg[0].d =Reg[7].q;
29    End If;
30    End;
```

PROGRAM 3.5   An Alternative Method for Program 3.4

The following simulation confirms that programs 3.4 and 3.5 provide identical functionality. Both programs require that the designer insure that one and only one of the control signals be asserted during any single timing interval. Although we make constant reference to the *programs* involved in the design, we should not lose sight of the fact that we are actually designing hardware.

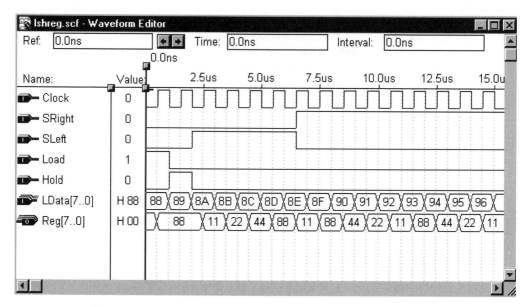

Simulation for Program 3.5: An Alternative Register Configuration

3.5   TRI-STATE CONTROL

It is often desirable to drive a single set of data or control lines (a bus) from more than one signal source. If more than one signal source or driver is active during a single period of time, the resulting bus signal is effectively indeterminate unless special precautions are taken. The solution to this design alternative is the tri-state buffer or tri-state driver. The tri-state buffer has three accessible ports. These ports are accessible by utilizing the fully qualified port name, which is accessed with the corresponding extention or suffix.

Tri-State Buffer Port Definitions

Port	Definition
.in	*input:* accepts the input signal
.out	*output:* provides the buffer output signal
.oe	*output enable:* if a logic 1, out port equals .in port; if a logic 0, .out port provides high impedance

If the outputs of two or more signals are tied to the same bus line through tri-state drivers and one and only one of the .oe port signals is asserted (in other words, in the logic-one state) during any interval, then the selected driver controls the value of the output signal. The following schematic diagram is an example of the use of tri-state drivers in a typical system. The diagram contains two buffers named A_Buffer and B_Buffer, respectively. The output enable control lines (.oe extensions) determine which of the two buffers asserts a signal on the common bus. It is the designer's responsibility to assure that only one of the output enable signals is asserted at any point in time. If multiple control lines are asserted during the same interval, the output is indeterminate. When a single output enable signal is asserted, then the corresponding input signal is placed on the output bus. The selected output signal reflects the state of the corresponding input signal.

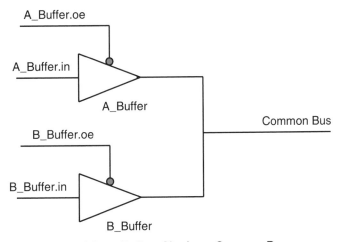

Two Tri-State Buffers Sharing a Common Bus

We introduce the concept through a brief AHDL example. In program 3.6, we employ variable names similar to those used in the tri-state figure diagram above.

```
1    Subdesign 'Tri-1'
2    (
3    Ain[3..0], Bin[3..0]          :Input;
4    Aoe[3..0], Boe[3..0]          :Input;
5    Out[3..0]                     :Output
6    )
7    Variable
8    Abuff[3..0]                   :Tri;
9    BBuff[3..0]                   :Tri;
```

PROGRAM 3.6 An Initial Tri-State Design

```
10    TriNode[3..0]                           :Tri_State_Node;
11    Begin
12    ABuff[].oe = Aoe[];
13    BBuff[].oe = Boe[];
14    ABuff[].in = Ain[];
15    BBuff[].in = Bin[];
16    TriNode[] = ABuff[];
17    TriNode[] = BBuff[];
18    Out[] = TriNode[];
19    End;
```

PROGRAM 3.6   *Continued*

The description for program 3.6 is provided here.

Lines 1–6: This subdesign section declares two four-bit input buses; one four-bit output bus and two four-bit output enable control lines which are inputs to the chip.

Lines 7–10: The variable section of the source file declares two four-bit tri-state buffers and one four-bit internal tri-state node. A tri-state node declaration provides a single node where outputs are to be connected. The control of the signals connected at the node is left to the designer, but the signal sources connected must originate from buffers of type TRI which are capable of tri-state control.

Lines 12–13: The output enable ports for the tri-state buffers are connected to the A and B chip input control buses intended to control the state of the tri-state buffers.

Lines 14–15: The input ports for the tri-state buffers are connected to the chip data input buses.

Lines 16–17: The outputs of the tri-state buffers are connected to a common node. If the control lines to the tri-state buffers are correctly designed (designer responsibility), this node will operate as intended.

Line 18: Although two four-bit input buses drive signals into this node, a single four-bit bus from this node is routed to the output terminals (chip output pins). The correct action of this digital system requires that proper control logic be applied to the tri-state control lines (.oe ports).

Below is a simulation of source code shown in program 3.6. When the Aoe bus contains all logic ones (in other words, Aoe[3..0] = 0xF) and the Boe bus contains all logic zeroes (in other words, Boe = 0x0), the chip output lines reflect the Ain bus content.

When the Aoe bus contains all logic zeroes (in other words, Aoe[3..0] = 0x0) and the Boe bus contains all logic ones (in other words, BoE[3..0] = 0xF), the chip output lines reflect the Bin bus content.

3.6   A TRI-STATE INTERFACE FOR REGISTERS

In the previous example, we routed a pair of chip input signal buses directly to tri-state buffers. This demonstrated the utilization of enable controls and the use of a tri-state node for interconnecting lines directly. The next illustration shows a slightly modified design in

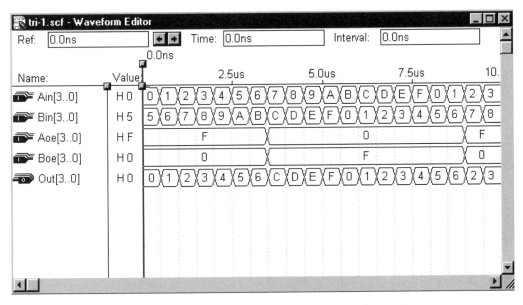

Simulation Results for Program 3.6: Tri-State Control

which the output of two registers are routed to distinct tri-state buffers and the buffer outputs are, in turn, routed to a tri-state node. The node output is then routed to a single-chip output bus which is connected to output pins of the implementation chip. The reader is encouraged to make a block diagram representing the logical design of program 3.7. The source listing for our tri-state register interface is shown below.

```
1     Subdesign 'Tri-2'
2     (
3     Clock                             :Input;
4     Aoe[3..0], Boe[3..0]              :Input;
5     Out[3..0], AReg[3..0], Breg[3..0] :Output
6     )
7     Variable
8     Abuff[3..0],BBuff[3..0]           :Tri;
9     TriNode[3..0]                     :Tri_State_Node;
10    AReg[3..0], BReg[3..0]            :Dff;
11    Begin
12    % ***** connect clocks ***** %
13    AReg[].clk = clock;
14    BReg[].clk = clock;
15    % ***** increment registers ***** %
```

PROGRAM 3.7   A Tri-State Register Pair Interface

```
16    AReg[].d = AReg[].q + 1;
17    BReg[].d = BReg[].q + 2;
18    % ***** connect enable buses ***** %
19    ABuff[].oe=Aoe[];
20    BBuff[].oe=Boe[];
21    % ***** tri-state the registers ***** %
22    ABuff[].in=AReg[].q;
23    BBuff[].in=BReg[].q;
24    % ***** connect buffers to common node ***** %
25    TriNode[]=ABuff[];
26    TriNode[]=BBuff[];
27    % ***** output from common node ***** %
28    Out[]=TriNode[];
29    End;
```

PROGRAM 3.7 *Continued*

Lines 1–6: The subdesign section of the code declares a clock input signal, two output enable buses to control the tri-state buffers, one four-bit output bus (shared by the tri-state-controlled buffers), and output pins for two internal registers.

Lines 7–10: The variable section of the file declares two tri-state buffers, ABuff and BBuff. It also declares one tri-state node to be used as a common interconnect point for the buffers. Finally, the two registers composed of D-type flip-flops are reserved.

Lines 12–14: The clocks are connected to the two registers.

Lines 15–17: The two registers are arranged as up counters using direct language incrementing. The A register counts up by one with each clock pulse. The B register counts up by two with each clock signal.

Lines 18–20: The two input, tri-state enable buses are connected to the tri-state buffers.

Lines 21–23: The register outputs ports are connected to the tri-state buffer input ports.

Lines 24–26: The two tri-state buffer outputs are routed to the same node which they will share through the use of tri-state enable control signals.

Lines 27–28: The tri-state node signals are routed to the chip output pins.

In the simulation that follows, it is clear that the tri-state enable lines control which of the four-bit register values are permitted to drive the chip output pins. Aoe and Boe jointly select the appropriate register. Of course more than two registers may share the same output bus, if desired, as long as the tri-state control logic is managed appropriately.

3.7 RETROSPECTIVE

In this chapter, we have examined the several basic processes involved in developing control logic for digital systems. First we developed a timing generator which defined a sequence of timing pulses and may be utilized to set up a domain in which actions of a digi-

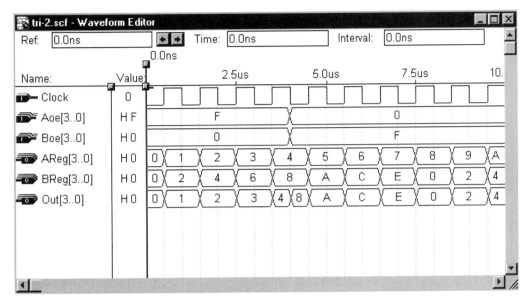

Simulation for Program 3.7: Tri-State Register Pair Interface

tal system are ordered. We then demonstrated a manner in which memories (D flip-flops) could be controlled to any desired state at instants in time defined by the ordered timing pattern previously defined. Applications were then developed that demonstrated the use of timing signals and control signals to manage the content and state of a general shift register. We concluded by illustrating the sharing of common system buses through the utilization of tri-state devices. The tri-state devices are controlled by enabling ports. The timing of the control signals for the tri-state shared resources may obviously be controlled by timing signals which were developed in earlier sections.

CHAPTER 3 EXERCISES

1. A given digital subsystem contains the following components and data paths:
   - Input clock with a period of 15 ns
   - An eight-state timing generator which produces T_0 to T_7
   - A four-bit operation code input named OpCode[3..0]
   - A one-bit new-command input
   - Two four-bit operand inputs, Arg1[3..0] and Arg2[3..0]
   - One output port, Result[7..0]
   - Three eight-bit registers, R1[7..0], R2[7..0] and R3[7..0]
   - A four-bit adder/subtracter
   - A one-bit output error flag, Err
   - You may add registers if your design requires them

Opcode, Arg1, and Arg2 are valid at the chip inputs only during the interval, T_0. A new Opcode is present at the Opcode port only when the new command input bit is true during interval T_0. The subsystem is to read operation codes and operands from the input ports and then perform indicated operations on the given operands. The results of internal operations are to be placed on the output port during T_7. The Err flag must be true whenever the command cannot be executed correctly. It must be false otherwise. All output signals must be valid during T_7 intervals and must remain stable thereafter until the next valid new-command signal. All input signals may vary any time but must only be considered valid during T_0 intervals.

The operation codes include the following:

Hex Opcode	OpCode, Interpretation
0x0	Copy1, (Result $\leftarrow$ Arg1)
0x1	Copy2, (Result $\leftarrow$ Arg2)
0x2	UnMinus1, (Result $\leftarrow -$ Arg1) , 2's complement
0x3	UnMinus2, (Result $\leftarrow -$ Arg2) , 2's complement
0x4	Pow1, (Result $\leftarrow$ (Arg1) $\times 2^n$), $n \equiv$ Arg2
0x5	Pow2, (Result $\leftarrow$ (Arg2) $\times 2^n$), $n \equiv$ Arg1
0x6	Add, (Result $\leftarrow$ Arg1 + Arg2)
0x7	Sub, (Result $\leftarrow$ Arg1 $-$ Arg2)
0x8	Min, (Result $\leftarrow$ min[Arg1, Arg2])
0x9	Max, (Result $\leftarrow$ max[Arg1, Arg2])
0xA	BitInv1,(Result $\leftarrow$ Arg1 with each bit inverted)
0xB	BitInv2,(Result $\leftarrow$ Arg2 with each bit inverted)

Design a subsystem processor which implements the commands described in the table above using HDL. Develop a simulation which verifies each of the commands to be executed.

2. Remove the original timing generator from the subsystem processor defined in (1), above. Given the subsystem processor of exercise 1 above, an additional input pin is to be added. This input pin carries a timing signal which is true during every T_7. The timing input signal is false during the intervals defined by T_0 to T_6. Read the timing pulse into the first stage of a shift register which is eight bits long. Use the register stage outputs to generate T_6 to T_0. Produce a simulation which verifies system operation.

3. Redefine the architecture of the system so that unless an unforeseen error occurs, the error flag will not ever be set.

4. Redesign the counter of program 3.1 using the CASE construction in place of the If-Then as the major control logic process.

5. Modify the hardware design of program 3.4.
   a) Provide "two-place" left and right shifts for each clock period with the corresponding commands SLeft2 and SRight2.

   b) Provide "four-place" left and right shifts for each clock period with the corresponding commands SLeft4 and SRight4.
6. Design a tri-state bus system which is shared by three sources of information.
   a) Model the system design after program 3.6.
   b) Provide a simulation which tests your system design.
7. Make a block diagram of the logic hardware represented by program 3.7.
8. Design a tri-state bus system which is shared by three sources of information.
   a) Model the system design after program 3.7.
   b) Provide a simulation which tests your system design.

CHAPTER 4

AN OVERVIEW
OF COUNTING METHODS

4.1 INTRODUCTION

Chapters 2 and 3 examined twisted ring or Johnson digital counters. We did not perform a concentrated study of the counters, but instead examined them as essentially coincidental to the primary topics of those chapters. The current chapter examines, more closely, the process of counting and the design and implementation of digital counters. The current chapter examines several applications of counters as a context for our studies.

4.2 COMMENTARY ON TWISTED-RING COUNTERS

The twisted-ring counters of the previous chapters are elegant in their simplicity. Without the need for any gates for the formation of combinational Boolean logic functions, the twisted ring generates a cyclic digital sequence. Cyclic sequences have countless (no pun intended) applications in digital systems. An additional advantage of twisted-ring counters is that, since they require no combinational logic gating in the normal sequencing, twisted rings may be operated at relatively high speeds. On the other hand, since the twisted-ring cycle is of length 2n, where n is the number of memory elements, long twisted rings tend to inefficiently use their memory elements. For example a twisted-ring system containing eight flip-flops has cycle length of 16. A binary counter with eight memory elements has a cycle length of 2^n or 256 in this case. To achieve a cycle length of 256 for a twisted ring requires 128 flip-flops, which for many applications would be impractical for reasons of cost, space, silicon area, or any number of other considerations.

Perhaps even a more difficult problem is the large number of illegal states. An eight flip-flop twisted ring contains 256 minus 16 or 250 *illegal* states. If reliable operation must be achieved for a given application, then all of the illegal states may have to be decoded. The decoding is used to recover the counter. The decode states are used to reset the counter into a legal sequence so that it will not remain *beached* until a power reset is accomplished. Obviously, in any given situation, the designer must make the decision about which design alternatives to pursue. The current chapter demonstrates alternatives available to the designer.

4.3   NATURAL BINARY COUNTERS

Natural, binary counters are among the most popular components in any digital system (for obvious reasons). We therefore spend a substantial amount of time demonstrating their design and performance. The next section discusses a design method for binary counters which bridges traditional design methods with the use of HDL implementation.

4.3.1   Manual Truth Table Design for Binary Counters

In this section, we illustrate the design of binary counters using a manual or "paper and pencil" method employing truth tables to establish the fundamental design sequence. Karnaugh maps are subsequently used to reduce the resulting logical forms. After completing the design using this method, the developed equations are mapped into the Altera HDL and a program for use with programmable arrays is developed. We conclude this section with a simulation of the final implementation along with some concluding remarks on cost and performance.

We begin the discussion of binary counters with an example. The truth table of a straight, binary sequence counter is given below. We now present the design of a modulo-16 counter.

Truth Table for a Modulo-16 Counter

	Current State				Next State			
Seq.	Q_3^n	Q_2^n	Q_1^n	Q_0^n	Q_3^{n+1}	Q_2^{n+1}	Q_1^{n+1}	Q_0^{n+1}
0	0	0	0	0	0	0	0	1
1	0	0	0	1	0	0	1	0
2	0	0	1	0	0	0	1	1
3	0	0	1	1	0	1	0	0
4	0	1	0	0	0	1	0	1
5	0	1	0	1	0	1	1	0
6	0	1	1	0	0	1	1	1
7	0	1	1	1	1	0	0	0
8	1	0	0	0	1	0	0	1
9	1	0	0	1	1	0	1	0

	Current State				**Next State**			
Seq.	Q_3^n	Q_2^n	Q_1^n	Q_0^n	Q_3^{n+1}	Q_2^{n+1}	Q_1^{n+1}	Q_0^{n+1}
10	1	0	1	0	1	0	1	1
11	1	0	1	1	1	1	0	0
12	1	1	0	0	1	1	0	1
13	1	1	0	1	1	1	1	0
14	1	1	1	0	1	1	1	1
15	1	1	1	1	0	0	0	0

For simplicity we assume the use of a D-type memory element or D flip-flops as the primary building block of the counter. The combinational logic for the counter utilizes the current state as the input and produces the next state as output. Using D flip-flops, the next state is simply applied to the D-input terminals of the appropriate memory elements. That is, the following equations are applicable using D flip-flops. Other types of flip-flops would obviously employ equations suitable to the particular flip-flop type selected.

$$D_3^n = Q_3^{n+1}$$
$$D_2^n = Q_2^{n+1}$$
$$D_1^n = Q_1^{n+1}$$
$$D_0^n = Q_0^{n+1}$$

The corresponding K-map for the Q_0 member is given by:

K-Map for Q_0

		$Q_3 Q_2$			
		00	01	11	10
	00	1	1	1	1
$Q_1 Q_0$	01				
	11				
	10	1	1	1	1

Writing the logic equation for Q_0 results in

$$Q_0^{n+1} = D_0^n = \overline{Q_0^n} \tag{4.1}$$

Similarly, the map for the value of Q_1 becomes

K-Map for Q_1

	$Q_3 Q_2$			
$Q_1 Q_0$	00	01	11	10
00				
01	1	1	1	1
11				
10	1	1	1	1

Once again, writing the equation directly from the map we obtain

$$Q_1{}^{n+1} = D_1{}^n = Q_1 \oplus Q_0 \tag{4.2}$$

K-Map for Q_3

	$Q_3 Q_2$			
$Q_1 Q_0$	00	01	11	10
00		1	1	
01		1	1	
11	1			1
10		1	1	

From the K-map for Q_3 we obtain

$$Q_2{}^{n+1} = D_2^n = Q_2 \bar{Q}_1 + \bar{Q}_2 Q_1 Q_0 + Q_2 Q_1 \bar{Q}_0 \tag{4.3}$$

And finally the map for Q_4 becomes

K-Map for Q_4

	$Q_3 Q_2$			
$Q_1 Q_0$	00	01	11	10
00			1	1
01			1	1
11		1		1
10			1	1

So that the equation for Q_4 becomes

$$Q_3^{n+1} = D_3^{\;n} = Q_3 \bar{Q}_2 + Q_3 \bar{Q}_1 + Q_3 Q_1 \bar{Q}_0 + \bar{Q}_3 Q_2 Q_1 Q_0 \qquad (4.4)$$

    The four-bit binary counter is shown schematically in the following logic diagram. As indicated in the diagram, logical equations (4.1) through (4.4) are utilized to design the D-control inputs for the memory elements. From a visual inspection of the design equations and the logic diagram, it is clear that the logic required to control the states of the memory elements becomes more complex as we approach the more significant bits of the counter. The control for the least significant bit is merely a wire (or more appropriately, a transmission line). For the next significant bit, the control logic is a single exclusive-Or circuit. The logic for the most significant bit is sufficiently complex that it is somewhat cumbersome to place on the diagram, so it is symbolically represented in the system diagram. Documentation as well as implementation of digital logic is substantially more compact and efficient in a text design file than in the classical diagrammatic format.

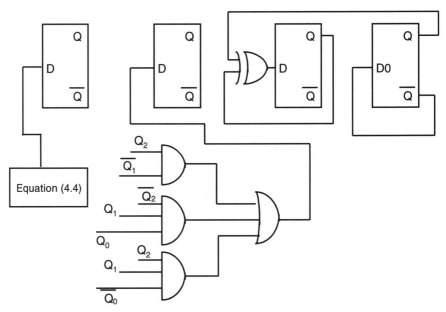

Four-Bit Binary Counter (Modulo 16 Counter)

    A program to implement the four-bit binary counter design is shown below as program 4.1. A description of the program is presented directly following the program listing.

```
1    Subdesign 'BinCnt'
2    (
3    M[3..0]                              :Output;
4    Clock                                :Input;
5    )
6    Variable
7    M[3..0]                              :Dff;

8    Begin
9    M[].clk = Clock;
10   M[0].d = !M[0];
11   M[1].d = M[1] Xor M[0];
12   M[2].d = M[2] & !M[1] #
13                !M[2] & M[1] & M[0] #
14               M[2] & M[1] & !M[0];
15   M[3].d = M[3] & !M[2] #
16               M[3] & !M[1] #
17               M[3] & M[1] & !M[0] #
18               !M[3] & M[2] & M[1] & M[0];
19   End;
```

PROGRAM 4.1   A Modulo-16 Binary Counter

Lines 1–5: These source lines declare the chip I/O signals.

Lines 6–7: These lines reserve (or create instances of) the four required memory elements from "on-chip" memory resources (assuming PLD implementation).

Lines 10–19 directly implement the logic derived from the truth table above.

The simulation below verifies that the counter, designed with program 4.1, performs as expected. The counter provides a count sequence of length sixteen, 0x0 through 0xF.

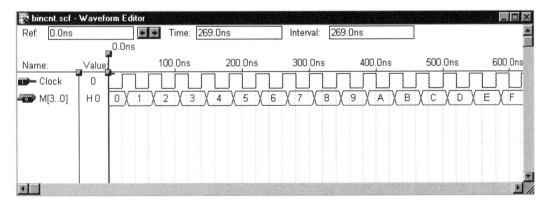

Simulation of Program 4.1: Modulo-16 Binary Counter

Although the functional performance as presented in the simulation of program 4.1 above is correct, two observations concerning the counter are worth noting. First, examining equations (4.1) through (4.3) reveals an interesting trend. The equations become more complex as the equations represent the D-input terms increasingly toward the most significant bit of the implemented system. Here, complexity is measured in the number of product terms and, in turn, the relative complexity of each of the product terms. As the number of product terms increases, increased amounts of programmable chip resources are required. The most obvious impacts include cost, number of parts, and physical size of the completed product. (We have only developed a four-bit counter. The reader might want to verify this design procedure and observe the results for an eight bit counter. We will leave this as an exercise for the reader.) There is in addition, a performance penalty which may be nontrivial in any given application (this matter is always left as a decision for the designer). Recall the process by which the system maintains sequence relationships. The current state of the counter is retained in the memory elements. The current state is then observed by the associated combinational logic, which produces a "vector" which constitutes the next logical system state. This vector, applied to the input terminals of the memory elements, *steers* the system to the next correct state. The system assumes the subsequent state on the rising edge of the system clock. All memory elements essentially acquire their respective new states simultaneously. (Not quite, but this will be a matter for future consideration. For the current time we need not consider finer detail.) At the rising edge of the clock, the memory elements begin to acquire their new states. The time required to reach the new states, including propagation time to the chip output pins, is defined as

$$\text{Clock-to-output time} \equiv T_{CO} \qquad (4.5)$$

After the memory elements have reached their new states, these new state values are applied to the input of the combinatorial logic gates which produce, after an appropriate propagation delay, the estimates for the next sequential states. We define this propagation delay as:

$$\text{Combinatorial propagation delay} \equiv T_{PD} \qquad (4.6)$$

Finally, the values for the next state arrive at the input of the memory elements. These values must be stable for a short period of time prior to the arrival of the clocking edge which will induce registration of these values into the memory. The time required for these values to be present is referred to as the setup time of the memory elements. We define the setup time as

$$\text{Setup time} \equiv T_{Setup} \qquad (4.7)$$

The minimum time required between successive clocking intervals is now given by:

$$T_{Clock} \geq T_{CO} + T_{PD} + T_{Setup} \qquad (4.8)$$

The data sheet for a particular programmable part (for example, Altera 7000 series) may be utilized to estimate worst case values for (4.5) and (4.7). The value corresponding to (4.6) is to some extent dependent upon the design of the combinational logic (in other words, the number of gates, number of logic levels, etc.). The reader is encouraged to obtain a data sheet and compute the minimum clock period using (4.8). A series of simulations may then be used to verify the accuracy of the data sheet values.

4.3.2 HDL Truth Table for Binary Counters

The reader should now be familiar with the basic language features of truth tables. Therefore we proceed directly to an AHDL program which will implement the same counter as that of the previous section by using a truth table directly in the source file. While the truth tables must conform to the syntax expected by the compiler, little difference between the source code truth table and common manual truth table descriptions is evident.

```
1     Subdesign 'BinCnt2'
2     (
3     Mem[3..0]                              :Output;
4     Clock                                 :Input;
5     )
6     Variable
7     Mem[3..0]                              :Dff;
8     Begin
9     Mem[].clk = Clock;
10    Table
11    Mem[3..0] => Mem[3..0].d;
12    H"0"       => H"1";
13    H"1"       => H"2";
14    H"2"       => H"3";
15    H"3"       => H"4";
16    H"4"       => H"5";
17    H"5"       => H"6";
18    H"6"       => H"7";
19    H"7"       => H"8";
20    H"8"       => H"9";
21    H"9"       => H"A";
22    H"A"       => H"B";
23    H"B"       => H"C";
24    H"C"       => H"D";
25    H"D"       => H"E";
26    H"E"       => H"F";
27    H"F"       => H"0";
28    End Table;
29    End;
```

PROGRAM 4.2   An AHDL Table-Driven, Natural Binary Counter

Not only is program 4.2 simpler and more readable than the corresponding program with exactly the same function (program 4.1), but the engineering time spent to create the logical function is greatly reduced. It would seem, with productivity-enhancing tools such as HDL, in this case AHDL, that the cost and time-to-market considerations are greatly in favor of a text-driven design methodology. That is not to say that, in any given circumstance, the designer may not find significant advantages to the other design methodologies. Final design judgment is always the designer's prerogative. Nevertheless, HDL is a powerful method. In addition, with programmable devices, the implementation time is greatly reduced over custom/semi-custom microcircuits and the wiring and associated debug time is greatly reduced over MSI implementations. Assuredly, many advantages of custom and semi-custom VLSI implementations exist, but these advantages accrue at the expense of a great deal of time and money. In each circumstance, a trade-off should be made to arrive at a proper decision as to which circuit technology is appropriate.

4.4 Classical Nonbinary Counters

Although natural binary counters are among the most popular subsystems in any digital system, there is always abundant need of other types of counting methods. For obvious reasons (for example, the decimal system is very popular), decade counters are often sought and present some interesting design alternatives. Left to its own "natural" cycle, a digital counter will generate a cycle length of 2^n, where n is the number of memory stages. This is another way of saying that a natural binary counter counts modulo $2^n - 1$. On the other hand, counters which count modulo 9_{10} provide a variation on natural binary counters. We next examine some decade counters by example.

4.4.1 A Low-Performance Decade Counter

Given the discussion above, we can proceed directly to the design process of the decade counter. First we select the number of memory elements. Since the system must count to nine (in other words, zero through nine yields ten counts), we need at least four flip-flops. The counter design will require a sequential count (0x0 through 0x9). The counter will be steered from the 0x9 state into the 0x0 state to obtain the required ten count. We first demonstrate a method of design which is often used in either low-performance systems or low-speed systems where its inferior performance may not present a problem. In fact, the design is sufficiently "poor" that it may not perform correctly at all, but in most cases it will simply work "poorly" or "adequately" depending upon personal definitions of such descriptions. Program 4.3 which implements a *not-recommended-for-use* technique demonstrates the implementation. The method shown here is selected primarily because it frequently appears in various forums and sources. It may, additionally, assist the reader in avoiding this design method in practice.

```
1     Subdesign 'Decade'
2     (
3     Mem[3..0], Nine            :Output;
```

PROGRAM 4.3 A Low-Performance Decade Counter

```
4    Clock                          :Input;
5    )
6    Variable
7    Mem[3..0]                      :Dff;
8    Begin
9    Mem[].clk = clock;
10   Mem[].d = Mem[] + 1;
11   Nine = Mem[3] & Mem[0];
12   Mem[].clrn = !Nine;
13   End;
```

PROGRAM 4.3 *Continued*

We now proceed directly to the detailed program description.

Lines 1–5: These source lines declare the familiar chip I/O signals.

Lines 6–7: The source declarations reserve single-bit memories (flip-flops) from the programmable chip.

Line 10: This single source line implements the entire binary count sequence. The compiler's implicit binary addition capability is invoked by this statement.

Line 11: Here the "nine" state (0x9) of the counter is decoded so that it may subsequently be utilized to "short-cycle" the count sequence and therefore achieve a decade count sequence.

Line 12: The 0x9 decode signal is used here to generate the active low, asynchronous clear signal. Asynchronous implies that the resetting action is not coincident with the system clock.

It is perhaps most straightforward to explain the shortcomings of this design methodology by showing its simulation.

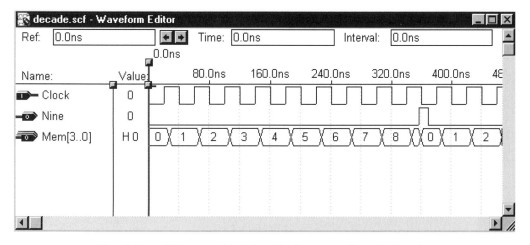

Simulation of Program 4.3: A Low-Performance Decade Counter

Typical reasons for the use of counters in digital systems include (a) determining a timing interval both accurately and with repeatable precision; and (b) establishing a set of evenly spaced and dependable timing pulses which will subsequently be employed to establish a *sequence domain* into which the details of a machine's operation will subsequently be placed. Two observations are readily apparent from the simulation diagram. First, the tenth-time interval (interval number nine) is not equal to the interval for all other sequence members. Therefore, this system may not be relied upon in the temporal sense. For each unit produced, the interval may well differ. Since interval nine cannot be depended upon, then neither can the overall interval (sequence zero through nine). Second, the recover time of the devices to reestablish synchronous operation is not necessarily determined very precisely and devices are often relatively slow to recover from the effects of an asynchronous action. The results manifest in problems readily observed from the simulation. Not only is interval number nine excessively short, but the slow recovery time from asynchronous control has also abbreviated interval zero. Finally, an additional problem which is not obvious from the simulation is that since the reset pulse from the decoder is not of any guaranteed duration, the memory elements of the system may not reset at the same instant. The reset thresholds of the various devices involved may be slightly different. If this occurs, the system may reset to either state 1_{10} or to state 8_{10}. The system is then clearly flawed and does not perform the intended function. A more insidious version of this latter problem occurs when the counter works (although marginally) when it is first constructed. Then later as the circuit ages and/or undergoes environmental changes (for example, temperature), the error manifests intermittently in the fielded application. This type of problem is very difficult to find in applications and can usually be found only through analysis of the design. It is best to avoid the design problem altogether.

4.4.2   An Improved Decade Counter

The error-prone counting method of the previous section may be correctly implemented with a design employing synchronous methods. The counter which we now examine is intended to demonstrate one correct method of designing and implementing the counter that was implemented improperly in the previous section. The improved counter will produce evenly spaced timing intervals and equally spaced dependable pulses which can reliably be used for timing purposes. The system will operate uniformly over the specified temperature range of the programmable parts used for the implementation. All important events are keyed to the clock and the digital system is referred to as a synchronous, digital system. The asynchronous inputs may be utilized in such a design along with power startup, reset signals, or with a power transient signal but not for "at speed" operations.

```
1     Subdesign 'Decade1'
2     (
3     Mem[3..0], Eight        :Output;
```

PROGRAM 4.4   An Improved Decade Counter

```
4     Clock                        :Input;
5     )
6     Variable
7     Mem[3..0]                    :Dff;
8     Eight                        :Dff;
9     Begin
10    Mem[].clk = clock;
11    Eight.clk = Clock;
12    Mem[].d   =    (!Eight) & (Mem[] + 1);
13    Eight.d =      Mem[3] & !Mem[2] & !Mem[1] & !Mem[0];
14    End;
```

PROGRAM 4.4 *Continued*

The description of program 4.4 is as follows.

Lines 1–5: These source lines incorporate the declaration of chip I/O signals.

Lines 6–8: This section constitutes the instantiation of four flip-flops as an array (Mem[3..0]) and a single flip-flop named Eight.

Line 12: This source line is a variation of the set-or-hold control format. This control process permits the decade counter to count normally (in binary) as long as the Eight flip-flop generates a false output. However, all of the D-inputs of the array memory elements are synchronously set to zero when the Eight memory is set.

Line 13: The decode of the eight state of the counter sets a flip-flop which will be true for one clock period (in other words, guaranteed to be true for one clock period). This generated detection of the eight state synchronously and reliably resets the counter thereby setting a reliable, repeatable decade characteristic.

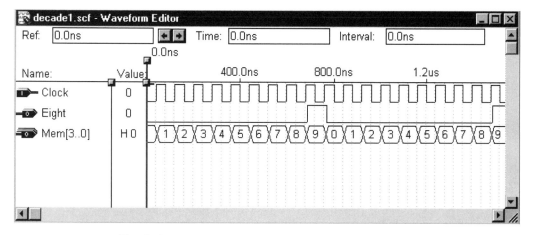

Simulation of Program 4.4: An Improved Decade Counter

The simulation that follows clearly shows the result of synchronous action in the control of the counter memory elements. Notice that the decode of the D input (not shown in the simulation diagram) must have occurred during the number the $Mem[3..0] = 0x8$ interval of the system. This action, in turn, sets the D-memory logic signal, Eight, at the beginning of count "nine." Then, "eight," in turn, synchronously resets the counter out of the binary sequence, hence establishing the decade sequence.

4.4.3 A Duodecade Counter

To emphasize the point that the process used to produce the improved decade counter above is suitable for producing a reliable and well-behaved counter of any modulus, we now apply the same principle to a modulo-eleven counter which we refer to as a duodecade counter. The source code is shown below as program 4.5.

```
1     Subdesign 'DuoDec'
2     (
3     Mem[3..0], Ten          :Output;
4     Clock                   :Input;
5     )
6     Variable
7     Mem[3..0]               :Dff;
8     Ten                     :Dff;

9     Begin
10    Mem[].clk = clock;
11    Ten.clk = Clock;
12    Mem[].d =      (!Ten) & (Mem[] + 1);
13    Ten.d =        Mem[3] & !Mem[2] & Mem[1] & !Mem[0];
14    End;
```

PROGRAM 4.5   A Well-Behaved Duodecade Counter

We will not present a detailed line-by-line description of the program since the structural design method of program 4.5 is virtually identical to that of program 4.4. When reviewing the program simply recall that the D input of the Ten flip-flop is decoded one bit-time early (in other words, at bit time ten), which is a value of 0xA. Then the Ten flip-flop is actually set at bit-time eleven (0xB), which dislodges the counter from its natural binary sequence and produces the reliable, modulo-eleven sequence. The synchronous processing assures that the timing intervals are all identical. If the counter is used to control the sequence of, say, signal or data processing, then the processing may proceed with a uniform minimum resolution if the designer so desires. The simulation of program 4.5 is presented without further comment.

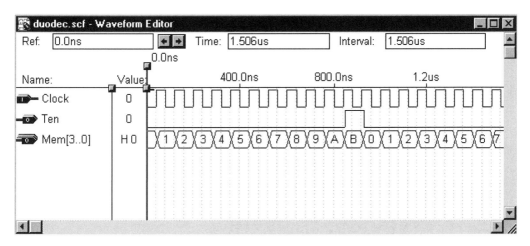

Simulation of Program 4.5: A Reliable Duodecade Counter

4.5 POLYNOMIAL COUNTERS

One of the problems with natural binary counters is the relative complexity growth of the combinational logic terms required as the count sequence length increases. Recall from our previous discussion that the combinational logic terms become more complex toward the most significant bit of the counter. A class of counters which overcomes this problem (albeit, not without consequences) is referred to variously as (a) polynomial counters, (b) pseudo-random counters, (c) m-sequence generators, or (d) maximal length sequence generators. The mathematical basis for these counters will not be covered in the current text. Although an interesting undertaking, pursuit of this theory would unnecessarily divert us from our primary tasks of designing digital logic and implementing digital systems.

Assume that a designer requires a counter which is permitted to be nonbinary and, in addition, need not be of cycle length 2^n, where n is the number of memory elements in the counter implementation. Certainly, of the counting techniques studied thus far, a twisted ring comes to mind. However, one problem with a twisted ring is that it contains a large number of illegal states (in other words, states which are not members of the primary sequence generated). In addition, the twisted ring generates a sequence length of 2n, which is reasonably inefficient in its use of memory requirements, especially for moderate-to-large numbers of states. The next section introduces a method of counting which (a) will produce a sequence length of $2^n - 1$, and (b) does not require increasingly complex gating structures as the sequence length grows. The only state outside the range of the primary (not a member of the maximal length generated sequence) is zero (each memory element of the counter is reset). Program 4.6 illustrates a three-bit counter with the prescribed characteristic.

4.5.1   A Three-Bit Polynomial Counter

We begin, as usual, with an illustration that provides a concrete basis for further discussion. A three-bit *polynomial* counter is shown below. Notice the resemblance of the "poly" counter to the twisted-ring counter. Simplicity in the combinational portion of the counter is one of the characteristics often sought in digital systems. Both the twisted ring and the polynomial counters exibit this feature.

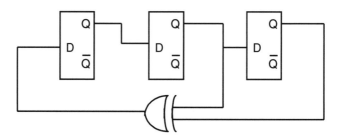

Three-Bit Polynomial Counter

In program 4.6, a three-bit polynomial counter is presented as an illustration of the process of designing any counter of this class. Particularly, observe that source statement 14 or an equivalent will be required in any implementation. This statement serves to prevent the system from being beached at the zero count (which, incidentally, is the sole illegal state of this counter class). Statements 11 and 12 form the essence of the normal operation of the counter.

```
1     Subdesign 'poly3'
2     (
3     M[2..0]                        :Output;
4     Clock                          :Input;
5     )
6     Variable
7     M[2..0]                        :Dff;
8     Begin
9     M[].clk = Clock;
10    if(M[2..0] != H"0") Then
11            M[1..0].d = M[2..1];
12            M[2].d = M[1] Xor M[0];
13    else
14            M[0].d =Vcc;
15    end if;
16    End;
```

PROGRAM 4.6   A Three-Bit Poly Counter

A discussion of the implementation of program 4.6 follows directly.

Lines 1–5: Three chip output signals and one chip input signal are declared in the subdesign section of the source file.

Lines 6–7: The three required memory elements configured as D flip-flops are re-served from the available chip resources.

Lines 10–15: In line 10, the contents of the register are examined for the presence of a zero value (0x0). If the register flip-flops are not all reset, then the counter is permitted to count in its normal, nonbinary sequence. The normal count sequence is accomplished by configuring the memory elements as a right-shift register, with feedback. Lines 11 and 12 provide the right-shift and feedback functions, respectively. If each and every memory element of the register is discovered to be reset (the only *invalid* state) then the register is coerced into a *valid* state by source line 14.

The simulation shown below reveals the overall performance of the system. The counting sequence gives some indication for the description *pseudo-random* given to the signal generator. The nature of the count sequence, while deterministic, contains elements of a random sequence. In fact, in some applications the pseudo-random signals produced by this class of circuit are directly utilized particularly for their random nature. These applications are beyond the scope of the current discussion and here we use the circuits as a means of developing relatively simple counting techniques.

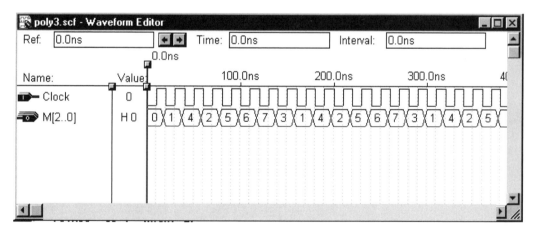

Simulation of Program 4.6: A Three-Bit "Poly" Counter

4.5.2 "Poly" Counters with Sequence Lengths 3 through 65,535

As stated above, the counters of the polynomial class generate sequences of length $2^n - 1$. Thus far, only a single counter of the polynomial class has been demonstrated. The table presented on the next page may be employed in designing two-bit counters (with sequence length $2^2 - 1 = 3$) through sixteen-bit counters (with sequence length $2^{16} - 1 = 65,535$). In the table below, the first column indicates the number of stages (number of memory elements) in the implementation. Column two indicates the stages which must be exclusive Or'ed to form a feedback signal. For example in two-, three-, and four-stage counters, the outputs of the zero stage (in other words, lowest order stage or least significant bit) and first stage (second-to-least significant bit) are exclusive Or'ed. The output of the exclusive Or gate always provides feedback to the input of the most significant stage. The final column indicates the length of the generated sequence.

Number of Stages	Xor Stages	Sequence Length
2	1, 0	3
3	1, 0	7
4	1, 0	15
5	2, 0	31
6	1, 0	63
7	1, 0	127
8	4, 3, 2, 0	255
9	4, 0	511
10	3, 0	1,023
11	2, 0	2,047
12	6, 4, 1, 0	4,095
13	4, 3, 1, 0	8,191
14	10, 6, 1, 0	16,383
15	1, 0	32,767
16	12, 3, 1, 0	65,535

The feedback from the exclusive-Or combinational gates is always routed to the input of the most significant bit. In most cases, a single two-input exclusive-Or gate is used. In a few cases, the outputs of four stages must be exclusive-Or'ed to achieve the desired result. This emphasizes another feature of the current method. There are a limited number of feedback connections and associated routing paths which must be made. This minimizes the resource utilization and layout geometry problems associated with feedback routing. This is a particularly important factor when such counters are employed utilizing either electrically programmable logic devices (EPLDs), gate-array implementation, mask programmable array implementation (MPLDs), or custom logic circuits.

For convenience in interpreting the current discussion, we now show an eight-bit pseudo-random counter design, along with a corresponding simulation of the first few members of the count sequence.

```
1    Subdesign 'poly8'
2    (
3    M[7..0]                :Output;
4    Clock                  :Input;
5    )
```

PROGRAM 4.7   An Eight-Bit "Poly" Counter

```
6     Variable
7     M[7..0]                        :Dff;

8     Begin
9     M[].clk = Clock;
10    if(M[7..0] != H"0") Then
11            M[6..0].d = M[7..1];
12            M[7].d = M[4] Xor M[3] Xor m[2] Xor m[0];
13    else
14            M[0].d =Vcc;
15    end if;
16    End;
```

PROGRAM 4.7   *Continued*

The simulation shown below was performed directly from the netlist of program 4.7. Clearly it is not possible to show the entire sequence of 255 member states in the current setting. Since the program is relatively short and the design process is straightforward, the reader is encouraged to produce a source code listing and verify the performance by examining the entire count sequence.

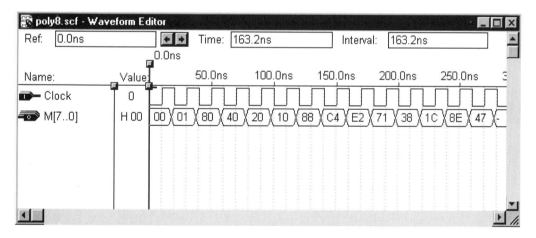

Simulation of Program 4.7: An Eight-Bit "Poly" Counter

4.5.3   Autocorrelation and Maximal Length Sequences

The polynomial counters are often referred to as maximal length sequence generators. The reason they are so-named is that for a given register length (say n stages), the generators produce a maximal length sequence (in other words, sequence length = $2^n - 1$ for a register of n stages). That is, no pseudo-random sequence of greater length may be generated with a generator of length n. Pseudo-random serial sequences are produced if the outputs are taken from the least significant stage (in other words, stage 0) of the register. For example, if a generator of length three is taken (see program 4.5 above), then the sequence of states for the counter are demonstrated in the table below.

Maximal Length Code with n = 3

Ordinal Sequence	Binary State	Hex State
0	001	0×1
1	100	0×4
2	010	0×2
3	101	0×5
4	110	0×6
5	111	0×7
6	011	0×3
7	001 (repeat)	0×1 (repeat)

The serial PN (pseudo-random) code derived from the three-bit generator above is

1,0,0,1,0,1,1 ....

The seven-bit serial pattern above continuously repeats as long as the generator continues to operate.

Maximal length codes have interesting autocorrelation properties. Assume that we have two such generators which are in-phase. By in-phase, we mean that the generators are initialized to the same values and that they are operated by the same clock so that they generate identical patterns. We refer to the PN (pseudo-noise) code as

$$x(k), k = 0, 1, 2 .... \qquad (4.9)$$

So that for the sequence of length seven above we have

$$
\begin{aligned}
x(0) &= 1 \\
x(1) &= 0 \\
x(2) &= 0 \\
x(3) &= 1 \\
x(4) &= 0 \qquad (4.10) \\
x(5) &= 1 \\
x(6) &= 1
\end{aligned}
$$

End of first period
$$
\begin{aligned}
x(7) &= 1 \\
x(8) &= 0
\end{aligned}
$$
etc.

In general and in most realistic application situations, $x(k)$ may be considered to be a function of infinite duration. Therefore we define the autocorrelation at shift m as $R_{xx}(m)$ where:

$$R_{xx}(m) = \sum_{k=0}^{2^n-2} x(k)x(k+m) \qquad \infty < m < \infty \qquad (4.11)$$

It should be noted here that most authors (for example, Rabiner and Gold, 1978, p. 401)[1] define the autocorrelation function as

$$R_{xx}(m) = \frac{1}{n} \sum_{k=0}^{2^n-2} x(k)x(k+m)$$

but the multiplier term, $1/n$, provides no additional value in the current context and so we have omitted it.

The product term inside the summation of (4.11) is defined as follows. If the values of $x(k)$ and $x(k+m)$ are the same, we define the product, $x(k)\,x(k+m)$, to be $+1$. If the values of $x(k)$ and $x(k+m)$ differ, then we assign the product, $x(k)\,x(k+m)$, a value of -1.

We now examine the values of the autocorrelation function for the three-bit maximal length sequence generator. If $m = 0$, we simply get

$x(k) = 1, 0, 0, 1, 0, 1, 1, 1, 0, 0, 1, 0, 1, 1, 1, 0, 0, 1, 0, 1, 1$ .....
$x(k+0) = 1, 0, 0, 1, 0, 1, 1, 1, 0, 0, 1, 0, 1, 1, 1, 0, 0, 1, 0, 1, 1$ (4.12)
$R_{xx}(0) = 1+1+1+1+1+1+1 = 7$

For $m = 1$, we see that

$x(k) = 1, 0, 0, 1, 0, 1, 1, 1, 0, 0, 1, 0, 1, 1, 1, 0, 0, 1, 0, 1, 1$ .....
$x(k+1) = 0, 0, 1, 0, 1, 1, 1, 0, 0, 1, 0, 1, 1, 1, 0, 0, 1, 0, 1, 1$ (4.13)
$R_{xx}(1) = -1+1-1-1-1+1+1 = -1$

For $m = 2$

$x(k) = 1, 0, 0, 1, 0, 1, 1, 1, 0, 0, 1, 0, 1, 1, 1, 0, 0, 1, 0, 1, 1$ .....
$x(k+2) = 0, 1, 0, 1, 1, 1, 0, 0, 1, 0, 1, 1, 1, 0, 0, 1, 0, 1, 1$ (4.14)
$R_{xx}(2) = -1-1+1+1-1+1-1 = -1$

For $m = 3$

$x(k) = 1, 0, 0, 1, 0, 1, 1, 1, 0, 0, 1, 0, 1, 1, 1, 0, 0, 1, 0, 1, 1$ .....
$x(k+3) = 1, 0, 1, 1, 1, 0, 0, 1, 0, 1, 1, 1, 0, 0, 1, 0, 1, 1$ (4.15)
$R_{xx}(3) = +1+1-1+1-1-1-1 = -1$

For $m = 4$

$x(k) = 1, 0, 0, 1, 0, 1, 1, 1, 0, 0, 1, 0, 1, 1, 1, 0, 0, 1, 0, 1, 1$ .....
$x(k+4) = 0, 1, 1, 1, 0, 0, 1, 0, 1, 1, 1, 0, 0, 1, 0, 1, 1$ (4.16)
$R_{xx}(4) = -1-1-1+1+1-1+1 = -1$

For $m = 5$

$$x(k) = 1, 0, 0, 1, 0, 1, 1, 1, 0, 0, 1, 0, 1, 1, 1, 0, 0, 1, 0, 1, 1 \ldots.$$
$$x(k+5) = 1, 1, 1, 0, 0, 1, 0, 1, 1, 1, 0, 0, 1, 0, 1, 1 \qquad (4.17)$$
$$R_{xx}(5) = +1-1-1-1-1+1+1-1 = -1$$

For $m = 6$

$$x(k) = 1, 0, 0, 1, 0, 1, 1, 1, 0, 0, 1, 0, 1, 1, 1, 0, 0, 1, 0, 1, 1 \ldots.$$
$$x(k+6) = 1, 1, 0, 0, 1, 0, 1, 1, 1, 0, 0, 1, 0, 1, 1 \qquad (4.18)$$
$$R_{xx}(6) = +1-1+1-1-1-1-1+1 = -1$$

For $m = 7$

$$x(k) = 1, 0, 0, 1, 0, 1, 1, 1, 0, 0, 1, 0, 1, 1, 1, 0, 0, 1, 0, 1, 1 \ldots. \qquad (4.19)$$
$$x(k+7) = 1, 0, 0, 1, 0, 1, 1, 1, 0, 0, 1, 0, 1, 1$$
$$R_{xx}(7) = +1+1+1+1+1+1+1 = +7$$

It is clear from inspection of the calculations above that the autocorrelation of the maximal length sequence:

1. Is an even function of the shift (delay) factor, m;
2. Is a periodic function of the shift variable m;
3. Is relatively sharply peaked in the vicinity of $m = 0$.
4. Exhibits a peak at $R_{xx}(0)$. The peak value is $2^n - 1$,
5. Obtains a value of -1 for discrete shifts of $m = 1, 2, ..., 2^n - 2$.

We have not proven anything here, but merely illustrated the primary characteristics of the autocorrelation function of maximal length sequences by utilizing an example. Nevertheless we state without proof that the properties illustrated above are typical and useful characteristics of PN sequences.

Because the properties of the function $R_{xx}(m)$ are so distinctive, they are surprisingly useful in communication and navigation systems. In communications systems, they are used to synchronize transmitter and receiver systems.

In navigation systems, a reference generator is placed in a known location (or locus, such as a satellite orbit). A second generator is located with a traveler. The two generators are initialized with identical state vectors and furthermore kept in identical states by precision clock sources (for example, atomic/cesium clocks). If the traveler receives the sequence from the reference, then the difference between the clock "phases" of the reference and the traveler sequences must be produced solely by propagation delay between the reference and the traveler. If the characteristics of the propagation path are known, the location of the traveler relative to the reference may be inferred. Since the "absolute" location of the reference is known, the absolute location of the traveler may be inferred. Although the discussion here is greatly simplified, this navigation method is the essence of the modern, satellite-based global positioning system (GPS).

Below, a simplified application example incorporating maximal length codes is presented. For the current illustration, we provide two five-bit maximal length code generators. The two generators will be referred to as PolyA and PolyB respectively. In the illustration presented below, we permit the two generators to run concurrently. Since the registers have relatively few stages (in actual practice, very long registers are often used), the total sequence length in this illustration is small (in other words, n = 5, sequence length = $2^n - 1 = 31$ in this case).

As the two generators run at the selected 100-ns clock rate, we calculate a set of running autocorrelation functions. We name these autocorrelation functions for the source file as follows.

$$
\begin{aligned}
R_{xx}(0) &= \text{correl0} \\
R_{xx}(1) &= \text{correl1} \\
R_{xx}(2) &= \text{correl2} \\
R_{xx}(3) &= \text{correl3} \\
R_{xx}(4) &= \text{correl4}
\end{aligned}
\qquad (4\text{--}20)
$$

The autocorrelation function values are computed (in hardware) by using (4.11) and utilizing phase-shifted values in the respective register stages of the generator. To facilitate the discussion, the source file is presented directly below.

```
1    Subdesign 'correl2'
2    % design of a correlator operating
3    with two five bit maximal length
4    sequence generators %
5    (
6    clock                 : Input;
7    Init                  : Input;
8    polyA[4..0]           : Output;
9    polyB[4..0]           : Output;
10   correl0[5..0]         : Output;
11   correl1[5..0]         : Output;
12   correl2[5..0]         : Output;
13   correl3[5..0]         : Output;
14   correl4[5..0]         : Output;
15   Count[4..0]           : Output;
16   )
17   Variable
18   PolyA[4..0]           :dff;
19   PolyB[4..0]           :dff;
20   correl0[5..0]         :dff;
21   correl1[5..0]         :dff;
```

PROGRAM 4.8   Autocorrelation of a Five-Bit PN-Sequence

```
22   correl2[5..0]        :dff;
23   correl3[5..0]        :dff;
24   correl4[5..0]        :dff;
25   Count[4..0]          :dff;

26   Begin
27   %***** initializations *****%
28   PolyA[4..1].clrn = Init;
29   PolyA[0].prn = Init;
30   PolyB[4..1].clrn = Init;
31   PolyB[0].prn = Init;
31   correl0[5..0].clrn = Init;
32   correl1[5..0].clrn = Init;
33   correl2[5..0].clrn = Init;
34   correl3[5..0].clrn = Init;
35   correl4[5..0].clrn = Init;
36   Count[4..0].clrn = Init;
37   %***** clocking *****%
38   PolyA[].clk = clock;
39   PolyB[].clk = clock;
40   correl0[5..0].clk = clock;
41   correl1[5..0].clk = clock;
42   correl2[5..0].clk = clock;
43   correl3[5..0].clk = clock;
44   correl4[5..0].clk = clock;
45   Count[4..0].clk = clock;
46   %***** first PN generator *****%
47   PolyA[3..0].d = PolyA[4..1].q;
48   if(PolyA[] == H"0") then
49           PolyA[0].d = Vcc;
50   else
51           PolyA[3..0].d = PolyA[4..1].q;
52           PolyA[4].d = PolyA[0].q Xor PolyA[2].q;
53   end if;
54   %***** second PN generator *****%
55   if(PolyB[] == H"0") then
56           PolyB[0].d = Vcc;
57   else
58           PolyB[3..0].d = PolyB[4..1].q;
59           PolyB[4].d = PolyB[0].q Xor PolyB[2].q;
60   end if;
61   %***** Rxx(0) *****%
62   if(PolyA[0] == PolyB[0]) then
63           correl0[5..0].d = correl0[5..0] + 1;
64   else
65           correl0[5..0].d = correl0[5..0]-1;
```

PROGRAM 4.8   *Continued*

```
66    End if;
67    %***** Rxx(1) *****%
68    if(PolyA[1] == PolyB[0]) then
69            correl1[5..0].d = correl1[5..0] + 1;
70    else
71            correl1[5..0].d = correl1[5..0]-1;
72    End if;
73    %***** Rxx(2) *****%
74    if(PolyA[2] == PolyB[0]) then
75            correl2[5..0].d = correl2[5..0] + 1;
76    else
77            correl2[5..0].d = correl2[5..0]-1;
78    End if;
79    %***** Rxx(3) *****%
80    if(PolyA[3] == PolyB[0]) then
81            correl3[5..0].d = correl3[5..0] + 1;
82    else
83            correl3[5..0].d = correl3[5..0]-1;
84    End if;
85    %***** Rxx(4) *****%
86    if(PolyA[4] == PolyB[0]) then
87            correl4[5..0].d = correl4[5..0] + 1;
88    else
89            correl4[5..0].d = correl4[5..0]-1;
90    End if;
91    %***** sequential counter *****%
92    %***** to keep track of ordinal *****%
93    %***** position of p-n sequence *****%
94    Count[] = Count[] + 1;
95    End;
```

PROGRAM 4.8 *Continued*

The details of the program 4.8 source file are now presented.

Lines 1–16 constitute the subdesign section of the program file and are used to declare all of the chip I/O signals. In the current case, we declare the system input clock, the ordinal sequence output, and count the outputs of the two m-sequence generators, PolyA and PolyB, respectively. In addition, we declare output signals for the five specific accumulated values of the autocorrelation function. The correlation values are maintained in registers under the array names of correl0[] through correl4[].

Lines 17–25 constitute the variable section of the source file in which the memory assets of the chip are allocated. Memory resources are allocated for the sequence generators, correlation memories, and the ordinal reference counter.

Lines 27–36 provide the initializations for the various memory structures. The two sequence generators must be initialized into legal sequence members of the maximal length sequence generators. The ordinal counter is initialized to zero as is each of the starting correlation values. The initializations are accomplished with the asynchronous preset and clear signals routed to the D-type flip-flops which are the essential building blocks of the various subsystems.

Lines 37–45 are used to provide the structural connections of the clock signals to the various synchronous processing blocks of the system

Lines 46–53 provide the logical design of the first of two maximal length sequence generators.

Lines 54–60 provide the logical design of the second of the two maximal length sequence generators.

Lines 61–66 calculate the running autocorrelation, $R_{xx}(0)$. The final, correct value of the autocorrelation function is valid only during the interval when the ordinal value, Count, equals 0x1F.

Lines 67–72 calculate the running autocorrelation, $R_{xx}(1)$. The final, correct value of the autocorrelation function is valid only during the interval when Count equals 0x1F.

Lines 73–78 calculate the running autocorrelation, $R_{xx}(2)$. The final, correct value of the autocorrelation function is valid only during the interval when Count equals 0x1F.

Lines 79–84 calculate the running autocorrelation, $R_{xx}(3)$. The final, correct value of the autocorrelation function is valid only during the interval when Count equals 0x1F.

Lines 85–90 calculate the running autocorrelation, $R_{xx}(4)$. The final, correct value of the autocorrelation function is valid only during the interval when Count equals 0x1F.

In the simulation shown below, we see that during the intervals just prior to the interval in which the autocorrelation functions are valid, the value of $R_{xx}(0)$ is systematically approaching 0x1F, as expected. The final value of $R_{xx}(0) = $ 0x1F is achieved when the complete autocorrelation function is calculated (see the time interval in which the ordinal sequence, Count, has reached 0x1F). The other values which are shown (in other words, $R_{xx}(1)$through $R_{xx}(4)$) are "hunting" about the correct value of -1_{10} (in other words, 0x3F) in the closing time periods of the calculation. In the timing interval shown, the values continue to "hunt" in the range 0x3B to 0x03, (-5_{10} through $+3_{10}$). The final values of $R_{xx}(m)$ for $m \neq 0$ reach their final values of $-1_{10} = $ 0x3F when the ordinal counter has reached its final value of 0x1F.

More interesting studies may be usefully conducted on the current topic. However, for the current time, we leave this subject to continue to pursue our primary topics. The reader is referred to the problems at the end of the chapter for additional considerations on this matter.

4.5.3.1   A Simplified Encryption/Decryption System   This section slightly regresses from our main theme of counting methods and the associated number sequences that are generated. Here we demonstrate, in a simplified illustration, one introductory method of a communications encoding-decoding methodology. The current example assumes a digital data message is being transmitted in a typical NRZ (non-return-to-zero)

Name:	Value:	2.75us			3.0us			3.25us			3.5u
clock	1										
Init	1										
polyA[4..0]	H 10	1D	0E	17	0B	15	0A	05	02	01	10	08
polyB[4..0]	H 10	1D	0E	17	0B	15	0A	05	02	01	10	08
correl0[5..0]	H 01	17	18	19	1A	1B	1C	1D	1E	1F	20	21
correl1[5..0]	H 3F	03	02	01	02	03	02	01	00	3F	3E	3F
correl2[5..0]	H 3F	3B	3C	3B	3C	3B	3C	3D	3E	3F	3E	3F
correl3[5..0]	H 3F	01	02	01	00	01	00	3F	3E	3F	3E	3F
correl4[5..0]	H 3F	3B	3C	3D	3E	3D	3E	3F	3E	3F	3E	3D
Count[4..0]	H 01	17	18	19	1A	1B	1C	1D	1E	1F	00	01

Simulation of Program 4.8: Autocorrelation of a Five-Bit PN Sequence

format. For illustrative purposes, we assume that transmission of the raw data is inappropriate. Therefore, the sender will *cover* the clear message with a code generated from a PN sequence generator. The cover, in this simplified example, is to be provided with a three-bit m-sequence generator which generates a seven-bit long PN sequence. The PN sequence is selected, again for simplicity, to have a rate four times that of the clear NRZ data. In actual practice, this multiple might be selected in an entirely different range. The NRZ sequence to be transmitted is generated by mixing the seven-bit PN sequence with the clear, NRZ data patterns. The mixing is produced by exclusive-Oring of the NRZ PN sequence with the NRZ information sequence. In the simulation shown, the clear message is named Msg and the seven-bit PN sequence generated from the three-bit polynomial generator is named Poly0. The reader may readily verify that the sequence to be transmitted, CryptMsg in this case, has been generated by the process

$$CryptMsg = Msg \oplus Poly0.$$

The simulation below is for a simulated transmitter. From a simple inspection of the simulation, it is not apparent that the clear message, Msg, is contained within the encoded message, CryptMsg. Clearly the process of covering the clear message improves as the PN sequence becomes longer and/or the ratio of the PN-generator-clock-to-clear-message-clock increases.

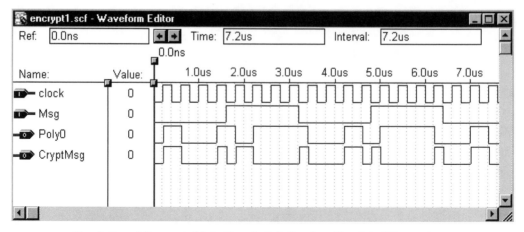

Simulation of Program 4.8.1: Signals Existing in a Simulated Transmitter

The receiver, which is designed to decode or de-encrypt the message above, must be capable of generating a PN code identical to that used to cover the clear signal in the transmitter. To further simplify our current discussion, we assume that the receiver, perhaps at some significant propagation distance from the transmitter, has been able to synchronize its locally generated PN sequence to that of the transmitter. That is, the transmitter and receiver PN sequences are *in-phase*. Given that the receiver and transmitter PN sequences are synchronized, the clear message may easily be recovered from the received sequence, CryptMsg.

An HDL file, program 4.8.1, is given below which contains simulated transmitter and receiver code to provide a simulation. The source file contains no code which synchronizes the two PN generators.

```
1     Subdesign 'Encrypt1'
2     (
3     clock                           :Input;
4     Msg                             :Input;
5     CryptMsg                        :Output;
6     Poly[2..0]                      :Output;
7     DecodeMsg                       :Output;
8     )
9     Variable
10    Poly[2..0]                      :Dff;
11    Begin
12    % ** connect clocks ** %
13    Poly[].clk = clock;
14    % ** generate poly code ** %
15    if(Poly[] == H"0") then
16          Poly[0].d = Vcc;
17    else
```

PROGRAM 4.8.1   A Communications Coder/Decoder

```
18              Poly[1..0].d = Poly[2..1].q;
19              Poly[2].d = Poly[1] XOR Poly[0];
20     end if;
21     % ** encrypt message ** %
22     CryptMsg = Poly[0] XOR Msg;
23     % ** "de-encrypt" message ** %
24     DecodeMsg = CryptMsg XOR Poly[0];
25     End;
```

PROGRAM 4.8.1 *Continued*

In HDL program 4.8.1, the processing is accomplished as follows.

Lines 1–8 provide the declarations of chip I/O signals.

Lines 9–10 declare the three flip-flops that are to be allocated for the PN sequence generator.

Lines 14–20 create the seven-bit PN sequence generator.

Line 22 generates the encoded NRZ sequence to be transmitted by mixing the transmitted clear message with the transmitter-generated PN sequence.

Line 24 decodes the original transmitter message from the encoded, received message by mixing the locally generated receiver PN sequence with the received, encoded sequence. In the current source file, there is only one PN sequence which, for obvious reasons we use for both the transmitter and receiver PN sequence. In actual applications, there are two generated sequences which require pre-synchronization prior to any data transmission-reception processing.

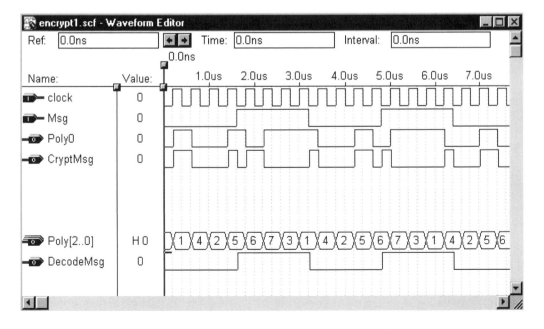

Simulation of Program 4.8.1: A Communications Encoder/Decoder

In the simulation of program 4.8.1, it is apparent that the transmitted message (Msg) and the received message after decoding (DecodeMsg) are identical. The reader is referred to the source code of program 4.8.1 for detailed processing descriptions.

4.5.4   Decoding Selected Vectors from a "Poly" Counter

A matter of some annoyance when using polynomial counters is that, since the sequence generated is pseudo-random, it can be quite inconvenient to find the particular decode value associated with a given sequence number. This may be "worked-out" by hand for a relatively small sequence counter, but for longer counters (for example, say a ten-bit counter or longer), this is a matter of significant annoyance. An HDL program may be developed which employs an ordinal counter and a selected polynomial counter which execute in synchronism. The corresponding values yield the appropriate decode values for the polynomial counter.

4.6   AN UP-DOWN COUNTER USING CONDITIONAL TABLES

The earlier study of counting methods and HDL is now resumed to demonstrate the use of truth tables which are conditioned upon a given logical signal. In methods of classical design, it is not unusual to require that a counter or other device have a conditional behavior depending upon a selected set of control signals. To demonstrate this control process using the "table" command of the Altera hardware description language we now present an up-down counter using the table command. The program is given below as program 4.9. The operation of the system depends solely upon the input control line named UpDn. If the signal UpDn is in the logic-1 state, then the counter counts up. If the control signal UpDn is in the logic-0 state then the counter counts down.

```
1     % ***** An UpDown Counter Using Conditional ***** %
2     % ***** Truth Tables ***** %
3     Subdesign 'updown'
4     (
5     FF1, FF0                    :Output;
6     Clock,UpDn                  :Input;
7     )
8     Variable
9     FF1, FF0                    :Dff;
10    Begin
11         FF1.clk = Clock;
12         FF0.clk = Clock;
13         if(UpDn) Then
```

PROGRAM 4.9   An Up-Down Counter Using Conditional Tables

```
14                      Table
15                      FF1, FF0 => FF1.d, FF0.d;
16                      0,       0  =>      0,          1;
17                      0,       1  =>      1,          0;
18                      1,       0  =>      1,          1;
19                      1,       1  =>      0,          0;
20                      End Table;
21          end if;
22          if(!UpDn) Then
23                      Table
24                      FF1, FF0 => FF1.d, FF0.d;
25                      0,       0  =>      1,          1;
26                      1,       1  =>      1,          0;
27                      1,       0  =>      0,          1;
28                      0,       1  =>      0,          0;
29                      End Table;
30          end if;
31   End;
```

PROGRAM 4.9   *Continued*

It would be relatively straightforward to add additional control lines and consequently add additional counting modes. For example if a hold count mode were to be desired, an additional control line could be added. The control of the counting state machine could then be described by the following truth table.

Possible Control Modes

Control Lines, C_1C_2	Counter Mode
00	hold
01	down
10	up
11	don't care

Clearly, adding additional control lines would add additional modes. This method of designing controlled digital systems is also clearly not limited to counters but could easily be extended to other systems. For the current time, we leave the extension of the conditional table counter to the reader. A simulation of the table-driven counter's behavior (program 4.9) is shown below.

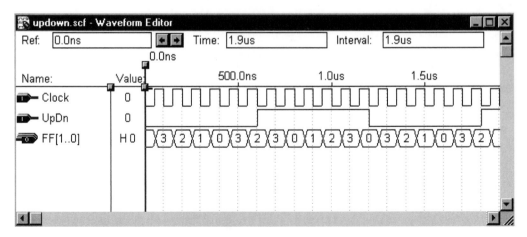

Simulation of Program 4.9: An Up-Down Counter Using Tables

Clearly the system behavior matches the behavior indicated in the source file. The system changes state on the rising edge of the clock and the direction of change is dictated by the state of the single-input control signal.

4.7 A RIPPLE COUNTER

Inevitably, sooner or later, a designer will need a simple, inexpensive ripple counter. While the ripple counter as they say, "isn't pretty," it is by comparison inexpensive (in terms of parts required), reliable, and easily developed. In a low-speed application, for the purposes of implementing dividing chains with large divisors, it is often a worthy subsystem to be employed. While typically not employed in high-speed applications, depending upon physical implementation, it can be a surprisingly good performer. The name "ripple" comes from the fact that the lowest-order stage is typically clocked by the system clock. The lowest-order stage, in turn, clocks the next higher-order stage. Subsequently, each stage clocks the next higher-order stage. Consequently, the counter "ripples" from the current state to the next state.

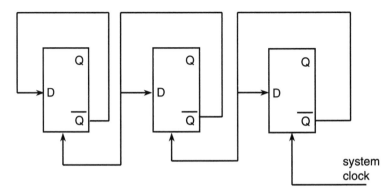

A Three-Bit Ripple Counter

From the diagram above and the brief description of the ripple counter, it is a direct process to deduce its behavior. We now present the HDL source code which may be used to implement the three-bit ripple counter in the figure. We have added a decoder which is by no means new to the reader at this point. However, the decoder provides a vehicle by which to visit a topic which has merely been touched upon so far. The decoder will be discussed shortly. For the present, we simply provide the source listing for the ripple counter.

```
1     Subdesign 'ripple3'
2     (
3     clock                   :Input;
4     ripp[2..0]              :Output;
5     Init                    :Input;
6     zero, one, two          :Output;
7     three, four, five       :Output;
8     six, seven              :Output;
9     )

10    Variable
11    ripp[2..0]              :dff;

12    Begin
13    ripp[].clrn = Init;
14    % ***** %
15    ripp[0].clk = clock;
16    ripp[0].d = !ripp[0];
17    % *****%
18    ripp[1].clk = !ripp[0];
19    ripp[1].d = !ripp[1];
20    % ***** %
21    ripp[2].clk = !ripp[1];
22    ripp[2].d = !ripp[2];
23    % ***** the decoder ***** %
24    zero = !ripp[2] & !ripp[1] & !ripp[0];
25    One = !ripp[2] & !ripp[1] & ripp[0];
26    two = !ripp[2] & ripp[1] & !ripp[0];
27    three = !ripp[2] & ripp[1] & ripp[0];
28    four = ripp[2] & !ripp[1] & !ripp[0];
29    five = ripp[2] & !ripp[1] & ripp[0];
30    six = ripp[2] & ripp[1] & !ripp[0];
31    seven = ripp[2] & ripp[1] & ripp[0];
32    End;
```

PROGRAM 4.10 Three-Bit Ripple Counter

The ripple counter details from program 4.10 are given below.

Lines 1–9 provide the chip I/O signal declarations. Each of the declared signals in this section will occupy a chip I/O pin.

Lines 10–11 declare the three flip-flops to be used for the ripple counter. These flip-flops are allocated from the resources available if a programmable logic device is utilized.

Line 13 provides the initialization signal routing which is connected to the asynchronous clear signal of the allocated flip-flops.

Lines 15 and 16 provide the clocking and control logic for the lowest-order bit of the counter.

Lines 18 and 19 provide the clocking and control logic for the second most significant bit of the counter.

Lines 21 and 22 provide the clocking and control logic for the most significant bit.

Lines 24–31 create the decoder logic for the counter states.

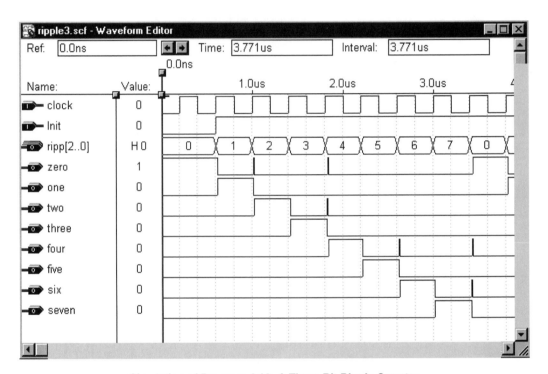

Simulation of Program 4.10: A Three-Bit Ripple Counter

In the simulation of program 4.10, the system performs largely as expected and is similar in function to several of the counters presented earlier, including the full decoder logic. Therefore the primary functional performance will not be elaborated upon further. However, the reader may clearly observe that there are six "glitches" clearly visible in the section of the simulation record shown in the figure. The left-most glitch in the zero decode line occurs at or near the 1-μsec simulated time-grid marker. This glitch occurs at the boundary of the 0x1 state to 0x2 state transition of the counter. Since the least significant bit of the counter is clocked first, the least significant bit of the counter transitions to a zero. Therefore the decoder output transitions, momentarily, to the logic-zero state.

However, the transition of the least significant bit triggers the transition of the next most significant bit which, in turn, brings the counter to the logic-two state. Therefore the "zero" decode output resets and the decoder "two" output transitions to the logic-one state. Glitches in this illustration arise from nonsynchronous operation of the flip-flop memory devices. Similar transient responses of this type may also arise even when the memory devices are operated synchronously. The causes in such circumstances arise when the propagation delays through various combinational logic paths differ thereby causing the transient responses in the logical outputs.

The simplest circuit, which demonstrates static hazard is described below. The Boolean function, $x \cdot \bar{x}$ identically equals zero. However, in the circuit implementation shown, the circuit will occasionally produce a logic-one output as shown in the signal timing diagram. This problem is caused by the non-zero inverter delay.

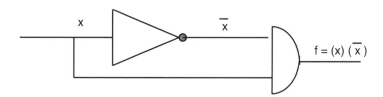

A Simple Logic Circuit Exhibiting a Static Hazard

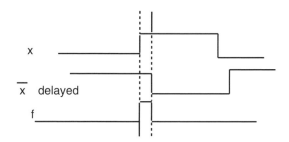

Static Hazard Response in the *Function f = x · x̄*

In the execution of the ripple counter, whenever the transition between consecutive states requires more than one stage of the memory associated to change, a *glitch* in the decoder output occurs. Of course this problem is exacerbated by the fact that the counter stages *ripple* into their new, respective states. However, when only a single flip-flop transition is required between adjacent states, the output is glitch free.

4.8   GRAY-CODE COUNTERS

The section on ripple counters highlights the problem of static hazards and non-synchronous operation. Nevertheless, ripple counters are not the only counters which demonstrate the static hazard characteristic. In any counting system, the flip-flops making up the counter may not switch at identical speeds. Additionally, the combinational logic interconnecting the flip-flops may exhibit differing propagation times. As a result, glitches may occur in the decoded state outputs of the counter. Such glitch outputs are typical of those shown in the simulation of the ripple counter. Even some synchronous counters exhibit glitches in their decode outputs.

In most applications of synchronous digital logic, such glitches are of no particular concern. Since the digital signals are switching states at the beginning of the clocking period and are not sampled again until the end of the clocking period, the outputs have sufficient time to settle before sampling takes place. In some systems, however, glitches of the type discussed present an intolerable problem. In such applications, the problem is often solved by the use of a gray-code counter. Since the gray code is designed such that only one bit of the code may change at a single instant, glitches may be avoided. A three-bit gray-code sequence is shown in the table below.

Three-Bit Gray Code

Sequence	Gray Code
0	000
1	001
2	011
3	010
4	110
5	111
6	101
7	100
8	000

A gray-code counter will generally produce clean, glitch-free output signals. We now present the source code for a gray-code counter with a full decoder.

```
1    % Gray Code Counter %
2    Subdesign 'gray'
3    (
4    Clock              : Input;
5    G[2..0]            : Output;
6    zero, one          : Output;
7    three, two         : Output;
```

PROGRAM 4.11   A Gray-Code Counter

```
8    six, seven            : Output;
9    five, four            : Output;
10   )
11   Variable
12   G[2..0]               :Dff;
13   % ***** %
14   Begin
15   G[2..0].clk = clock;
16   CASE G[2..0] IS
17        WHEN H"0" =>
18            G[0].d = Vcc;
19            G[1].d = Gnd;
20            G[2].d = Gnd;
21        WHEN H"1" =>
22            G[0].d = Vcc;
23            G[1].d = Vcc;
24            G[2].d = Gnd;
25        WHEN H"3" =>
26            G[0].d = Gnd;
27            G[1].d = Vcc;
28            G[2].d = Gnd;
29        WHEN H"2" =>
30            G[0].d = Gnd;
31            G[1].d = Vcc;
32            G[2].d = Vcc;
33        WHEN H"6" =>
34            G[0].d = Vcc;
35            G[1].d = Vcc;
36            G[2].d = Vcc;
37        WHEN H"7" =>
38            G[0].d = Vcc;
39            G[1].d = Gnd;
40            G[2].d = Vcc;
41        WHEN H"5" =>
42            G[0].d = Gnd;
43            G[1].d = Gnd;
44            G[2].d = Vcc;
45        WHEN H"4" =>
46            G[0].d = Gnd;
47            G[1].d = Gnd;
48            G[2].d = Gnd;
49   END CASE;
50   % ***** %
51   zero = !G[2] & !G[1] & !G[0];
52   one = !G[2] & !G[1] & G[0];
53   three = !G[2] & G[1] & G[0];
```

PROGRAM 4.11 *Continued*

```
54   two = !G[2] & G[1] & !G[0];
55   six = G[2] & G[1] & !G[0];
56   seven = G[2] & G[1] & G[0];
57   five = G[2] & !G[1] & G[0];
58   four = G[2] & !G[1] & !G[0];
59   End;
```

PROGRAM 4.11 *Continued*

Lines 1 through 10 define the subdesign section of the source file. These source lines define the chip I/O signals.

Lines 11 and 12 declare the memory resources required for the gray-code counting system.

Lines 14 through 49 create the control logic design of the gray-code sequence. The particular language construction used is the CASE construct.

Lines 51 through 58 develop the decode logic from the gray-code sequence. Many other possibilities might have been employed and are left as exercises for the reader. Such possibilities include (1) HDL table methods, (2) truth tables and (3) K-map designs. The resulting logic equations may then be implemented in the source file.

In the following simulation, only one of the flip-flops of the gray-code counter change state at any one instant. The decoder therefore displays a glitch-free output.

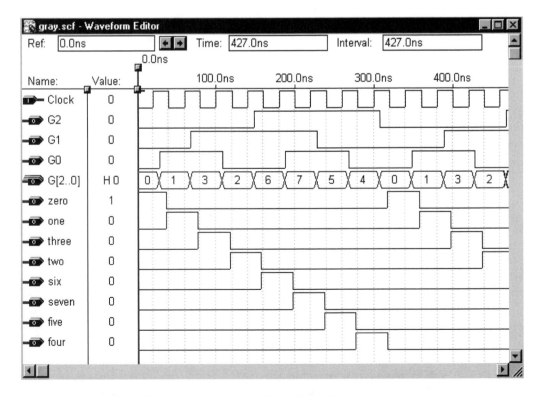

Simulation of Program 4.11: A Gray-Code Counter with Decoder

4.9   RETROSPECTIVE

In this chapter, we have studied the behavior and performance of a number of classical counters which are relatively commonplace in digital system design and implementation. We have also studied some of the characteristics of some less usual but increasingly common counting methods, given the expanding applications of large-scale integrated circuits. Along with the behavior and performance characteristics, we have examined some straightforward but useful applications. We have seen through applications that it is relatively simple to use the power of HDL and programmable arrays to achieve counters with clock rates in the hundreds of megahertz. Last, but certainly not least, we have explored the use of a variety of HDL methods in the implementation of this fundamental digital subsystem.

CHAPTER 4 EXERCISES

1. Design a modulo-15 counter similar to the counter of program 4.1, but using J-K flip-flops instead of D flip-flops.
   a) Develop the system using truth tables and K-maps. Develop the logic equations from the K-map entries. Implement the counter in a manner similar to program 4.1, employing the developed logic equations in the HDL program. Recall that the instantiation statement employing a J-K memory element is (analogous to line 7 of program 4.1):

   ```
   M[3..0]        :JKFF;
   ```

   For convenience, the truth table of a J-K flip-flop is repeated here

   J-K Flip-Flop Table

J	K	Q^n	Q^{n+1}
0	0	0	0
0	0	1	1
0	1	0	0
0	1	1	0
1	0	0	1
1	0	1	1
1	1	0	1
1	1	1	0

   b) Create a system simulation, verifying the counting sequence and consequently the developed logic equations.
2. Design a six-bit polynomial counter.
   a) Write an HDL program which will implement a six-bit polynomial counter.
   b) Create a simulation which verifies the operation of the counter.
3. Design a second six-bit polynomial counter

a) Write an HDL program for a second polynomial counter within the same source file as the HDL program designed in (2) above. The second counter is enabled for counting only when the first counter is in its maximum count state.

b) Create a simulation which verifies the operation of the counting pair.

c) Design a decoder which decodes (i) the middle count of the counter (in other words, exactly half of the sequence length), (ii) the sixtieth count of the sequence.

4. Design a polynomial counter which has a sequence length of 1,023.

a) Write a source file which represents the desired counter.

b) Create a simulation to verify the system performance.

c) Design a decoder which decodes (i) the middle count of the counter (in other words, exactly half of the sequence length), (ii) the 200th count of the sequence.

d) Modify the counter to "start-over" (generate a new cycle) after the 850th member of the sequence has occupied the state for one clock period.

5. Design an all digital one-shot timer which times exactly 100 clock pulses (the output is to be a logic-one for exactly 100 clock pulses).

a) Write a source program which will implement a one-shot timer function. Whenever a start-pulse occurs, the timer is to be started. The start pulse is to be valid for one clock interval. At the beginning of the interval, a flip-flop is to be set and the flip-flop output is to be used as the one-shot time representation.

6. Modify the one-shot timer above such that a user loads a count between 0 and 100 into a control register. The value in the control register, in turn, determines the duration of the one-shot pulse. The user control register must be prepared to accept a new value at any clock time, on demand. The user demand count is valid in the same clock period whenever a new input control line named data_valid is true.

7. The polynomial counters covered in section 4.5 are also referred to as maximal length sequence generators.

a) Design and simulate a five-bit maximal length sequence generator (say, PolyA[4..0]).

b) Design a second maximal length generator (PolyB[4..0]) and develop a set of simulations which include the calculation for the autocorrelation function between the two sequence generators.

c) Perform sufficient simulations to permit the estimation of: $R_{xx}(0)$, $R_{xx}(-1)$, $R_{xx}(1)$, $R_{xx}(-2)$, $R_{xx}(2)$, $R_{xx}(-3)$, $R_{xx}(3)$, $R_{xx}(4)$, $R_{xx}(-4)$.

8. A maximal length sequence generator consisting of eleven stages, say Poly[10..0], requires only one two-input exclusive-Or gate. This gate takes inputs from the Poly[0] and Poly[2]

a) Design a PN generator consisting of eleven stages. The generator will develop a sequence of length $2^n - 1 = 2,047$. To ease the problem of tracking the m-sequence generator for simulation purposes, design an ordinal, binary counter to run along side the m-sequence generator. Develop a simulation to assure that the m-sequence generator is executing properly.

b) Design a finite state machine which gathers statistical information concerning the m-sequence generator. The fsm is to detect all runs of zeroes and all runs of ones.

At the completion of the $2^n - 1$ generation intervals, the fsm is to contain the number and size of runs as follows.

Run Variable	Run Size	Number of Runs
Logic 0	1	xxx
	2	yyy
	3	zzz
	4	www
	......	....
Logic 1	1	x'x'x'
	2	y'y'y'
	3	z'z'z'
	4	w'w'w'
	.....	....

The number of runs is to be generated by the fsm.

9. Consider the ripple counter of this chapter. For each point in the simulation where a state transition occurs:

   a) If there is a glitch, explain why the glitch occurs.

10. Consider the gray code counter designed in this chapter.

   a) Can flip-flop and/or gate delays be adjusted to generate glitches?

   b) Name two applications where glitches may not be tolerated.

REFERENCE

1. L. R. Rabner & B. Gold (1978). *Theory and Applications of Digital Signal Processing*. Englewood Cliffs, NJ: Prentice Hall.

CHAPTER 5

A SIMPLIFIED UART/PC COM PORT RECEIVER

5.1 INTRODUCTION

The study, in the previous chapters, of the essential principles and design methodologies establishes the theoretical principles and tools with which systems applications are created. While some applications have been examined in previous chapters, we undertake a somewhat more significant application in this chapter. In this chapter, we undertake the process and design of a relatively complete hardware receiver, which is capable of receiving serial digital signals. When completed, this receiver may readily be tested, in any environment that has a personal computer (PC). The processor must be programmed with software that transmits information through a serial port. The design topic incorporated in this chapter is an example of a realistic design that might be within a modern organization. We begin the process by reviewing the structure of a standard serial digital signal which is generated when software "writes" to a serial port of a modern PC.

5.2 SIGNAL DEFINITION

COM port signals are defined as serial signals conforming to specifications as described below.

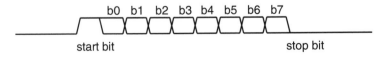

Serial Data Signal Format

As shown in the figure, the serial signal format of the COM port (as implemented in the PC) is specified such that the binary signal states are +12.5 V and −12.5 V. The *rest state* of the digital signal is at −12.5 V. That is, any time when data is not being transmitted, the signal will be in the −12.5 V state. Each data "word" consists of ten bits. The bit lengths are determined by the bit rates to be transmitted. For example, if the bit rate is 9600 b/sec, the bit duration is 1/9600 = 104.17 µsec. If the bit rate is 14,400 b/sec, the bit duration is 69.444 µsec. A synopsis of some of the more common standard bit rates are shown in the following table.

Some Standard Bit Rates

Bit Rate	Bit Duration
1200 b/sec	833.33 µs
2400 b/sec	416.67 µs
4800 b/sec	208.33 µs
9600 b/sec	104.17 µs
14,400 b/sec	69.444 µs
28,800 b/sec	34.722 µs

5.2.1   RECEIVER ARCHITECTURE

Shown below is a simplified architecture which is based upon receiving a serial digital signal. In such a digital data stream, independent characters may be separated by a single bit time but may, on the other hand, be separated by arbitrarily large periods of time. The architecture, as might be expected, is driven largely by the signal structure of the digital signals which must be detected. A block diagram of the receiver is shown.

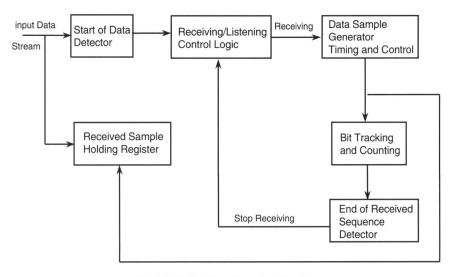

Serial Digital Receiver Architecture

Each new transmitted word begins with a start bit, which is a defined as a +12.5 V level. The start bit remains at this level for one-bit time. This single leading bit is known as the start bit and its sole purpose is the designation of the beginning of a serial character. The next seven bits (b_0 through b_6) are the ASCII data bits and are transmitted low order bit first. In the format selected for the PC, the bits are transmitted as a −12.5 V for a logic-one and a +12.5 V for a logic-zero. The ASCII (American Standard Code for Information Interchange) characters for any of the $2^7 = 127$ legal characters may be found in standard tables of ASCII characters. The eighth "data" bit is actually a parity bit. In most systems, the parity bit may be set to (a) even parity, (b) odd parity, (c) always one parity, or (d) always zero parity. We now proceed directly to the design considerations for a desired serial receiver.

5.3   CREATING THE CORRECT INTERFACE VOLTAGE RANGE

As stated previously, the voltage range of the serial information interface signal is ± 12.5 V. The programmable chips that we will select for the implementation of the current receiver are capable of *nominal* voltages of: (1) +5 V for a "true" signal and (2) 0 V for a "false" signal. The chips are *not* capable of handling the ± 12.5 V which are produced by the computer. We therefore undertake the design of a passive voltage-level converter circuit which will produce the required signal range from the range available. We could have selected an active circuit type for the desired converter but the added complexity is not called for here, so we proceed with the passive circuit design.

When the computer logic signal is +12.5 V we desire that the chip(s) that form the receiver are presented with +5 V. We therefore form a voltage divider with resistors R_1 and R_2 which create the correct voltage with the relationship

$$\frac{R_2}{R_1 + R_2} \, 12.5 = 5 \tag{5.1}$$

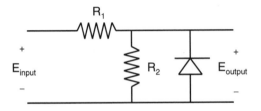

Passive Level Converter ±12 V to +5, 0 V

From (5.1) we find that

$$R_1 = 1.5 \, R_2 \qquad\qquad (5.2)$$

If we select $R_2 = 1,000 \, \Omega$, then $R_2 = 1,500 \, \Omega$, we then arrive at a final design as shown in the previous figure.

The voltage divider formed by R_1 and R_2 creates the 5-V nominal value when the input is 12.5 V. The diode clamps the output voltage to 0-V (actually closer to −.7) when the input voltage is −12.5 V. If the implementation chip is to be of the 5-V circuits, the circuit shown, or a similar circuit to control the voltage to the chip, is required. If the intended circuit is to be implemented on a 3.3-V chip, assure that the calculations illustrated here are modified appropriately to produce a +3.3-V true level and 0-V false level. If any question exists concerning the voltages of the serial port transmitter to be utilized, appropriate measurements should be made to assure compatibility between the generated signals at the computer port and the selected programmable chip.

5.4 ASYNCHRONOUS SIGNAL DETECTION

In the design of the signaling structure for the serial data, consideration has been given to the process of synchronization. Bits within a word are spaced evenly at the inverse of the bit rate (for example, see the standard bit rate table above). However, the transmitter has the freedom to send words contiguously (essentially no space between adjacent transmissions) or to space successive transmissions at any interval. The start bit is defined so that there will be at least one transition of the data line, in a defined direction, which indicates the onset of an information word. The data line transition, from a 0-V state to a +5-V state indicates the onset of the information transmission. It is up to the receiver to detect such a transition. The best possible resolution for the detection of an edge is within one clock time of the system clock. In the logic diagram shown below, the circuit will detect every leading edge in a serial digital data stream. The output gate will produce a single pulse which represents the leading edge of the start bit. The single pulse will be sustained for a single clock time of the system clock. Based upon the selections made below, this single pulse will have a duration of slightly more than 289 ns.

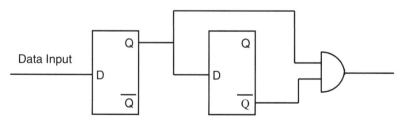

Start Bit/Leading Edge Detector

For the purposes of the current illustration, we now select 3.456 MHz as the frequency of the system clock (period = 289.35 ns). Here, a frequency is selected for the purpose of being explicit in the design process. If the reader intends to implement the receiver, in all probability, a different clock rate will be utilized. Again for specificity, one of the standard data rates is selected. We select 28,800 b/sec as the RS232 data transmission rate. If we name the serial input data line to the receiver as DataIn, the equations representing a leading edge detection (there may be many others) are provided within the source file PosEdge, shown below.

```
1     Subdesign 'posedge'
2     (
3     Clock, DataIn                    :Input;
4     PosEdge                          :Output;
5     )
6     Variable
7     DataPlus[1..0]                   :Dff;
8     Begin
9     DataPlus[1..0].clk = Clock;
10    DataPlus[1].d = DataIn;
11    DataPlus[0].d = DataPlus[1].q;
12    PosEdge = DataPlus[1] & !DataPlus[0];
13    End;
```

PROGRAM 5.1   Positive Edge Detector, PosEdge

Lines 1–5: The subdesign section of the source file provides I/O signal declarations. The input data line, DataIn, and the clock are declared as input variables of the chip on which the circuit will be implemented. The signal PosEdge (for positive edge), which indicates that a positive going transition has been detected in the data line, is declared as an output signal of the chip.

Lines 6–7: The variable section of the source file declares or reserves two D-type flip-flops from the available, programmable chip resources.

Lines 8–13: The body of the implementation is contained between begin and end statements.

Line 9: The system clock is structurally connected to the clock terminals of the two declared memory elements.

Lines 10–11: The data input line, DataIn, is routed through the two-bit shift register which is composed of DataPlus[1] and DataPlus[0], two reserved D-type memory elements.

Line 12: The logical output of the two memories are combined to form a single digital output which indicates that an edge has occurred.

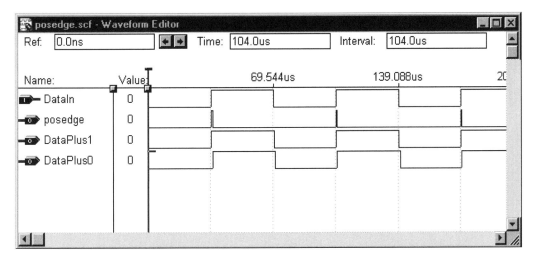

Simulation of Program 5.1: Positive Edge Detector

The simulation of program 5.1 clearly indicates that the positive edge detector produces a one clock-time duration pulse indicating that a positive going transition of the input data line has occurred. The bit period of the data is shown as 34.772 μsec. The edge detection pulses, posedge, are 289.35 ns in duration (dependent upon the system clock period). The clock trace has been eliminated from the simulation because the disparity in timing between the clock (289.35 ns) and the digital data waveform (34.77 μsec) renders the clock waveform as a mere blur on the current simulation figure displayed. The reader may want to perform a simulation, include the clock display and provide a *zoom-in* display which will verify clock timing and edge-detection resolution.

If the signal-to-noise ratio is sufficiently high, we may assume that the vast majority of edge detections will be for valid data transitions. We therefore do not plan on an error-detection process for "erroneous starts" in the current design. In practice, such error correction is often utilized to provide suitable performance in low signal-to-noise situations. This function could easily be added and is left as an exercise for the reader.

For the present, the detection of positive data edges is complete. Once the onset of received transmissions is detected, the receiver must initiate the process of receiving the transmitted data word. To allow the processing of the receiving data to continue, we require an internal receiver signal which controls the receiver processing function. In the next section, we generate the required signal.

5.5 SAMPLING THE STREAM

The internal circuitry of the receiver must persist in the processing for as long as the serial data stream is expected to continue. In the present illustration, given that the serial input data signal has started (in other words, the start bit has been detected), then processing must continue for the sequence of ten serial bits. Of course the receiving process should be abandoned if the decision is made that the start of transmission was erroneous in some sense, but for the current time, we disregard this possibility and continue with the design of the error-free processing.

5.5.1 Persistence in Processing

Assuming that the start bit is genuine and the serial data is streaming into the receiver, samples must be generated and the received data bits must be placed into registers. We first generate a signal which indicates that the receiver is in active receive mode. For convenience, this signal is named Receiving. To generate the signal Receiving, we employ a flip-flop with the set-or-hold control form developed in the chapter on control logic. In the Altera HDL, the set-or-hold control equation takes the form

$$\text{Receiving.d} = PosEdge \; \# \; \text{Receiving.q} \; \& \; Stop\text{Receiving} \qquad (5.3)$$

Equation (5.3) may be expressed in the logical circuit representation shown below.

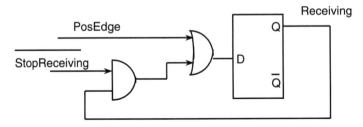

Circuit Implementation of Equation 5.3

The Q output of the circuit is utilized to maintain the active receiving state of the receiver. When the designated output is true, the receiver is maintained in active receiving mode. If the designated output is false, the receiver is placed into listening mode.

In (5.3) the variable $Stop$Receiving is a place holder for the variable that will be required and consequently generated when the decision is made concerning the end of the reception cycle. For the present, we know that the presence of the signal $PosEdge$ indicates that reception has commenced. Therefore, we use this $PosEdge$ term to initiate the process of reception, and we indicate this concurrently by setting the variable Receiving. The intent here is that whenever the signal Receiving is in the logical-one state, then the receiver is actively receiving information and clocking data into the receive buffers.

Whenever the signal Re*ceiving* is in the logical-zero state, then the receiver is in the waiting state. Equation (5.3) reveals that whenever the signal Re*ceiving* has been set (by the *PosEdge* signal), it will remain set by virtue of hold-type internal feedback until the signal, *Stop*Re*ceiving*, becomes true. Directly below is presented the source file for the Altera HDL that performs the desired functions.

```
1      Subdesign 'posedge'
2      (
3      Clock, DataIn                              :Input;
4      StopReceiving                             :Input;
5      PosEdge                                   :Output;
6      DataPlus[1..0]                            :Output;
7      Receiving                                 :Output;
8      )
9      Variable
10     DataPlus[1..0]                            :Dff;
11     Receiving                                 :Dff;
12     Begin
13     % ***** connect the clocks ***** %
14     DataPlus[1..0].clk = Clock;
15     Receiving.clk = Clock;

16     % ***** Connect data Input ***** %
17     DataPlus[1].d = DataIn;

18     % ***** Perform Edge Detection ***** %
19     DataPlus[0].d = DataPlus[1].q;
20     PosEdge = DataPlus[1] & !DataPlus[0];

21     % ***** set receiving control signal ***** %
22     Receiving.d = PosEdge # Receiving.q &
23                          !StopReceiving;
24     End;
```

PROGRAM 5.2   Establishing Active Receive Mode

We now describe the functions performed by the program 5.2. The content of program 5.2 will become a fundamental part of the design of an overall COM port receiver. It should be studied for its basic properties and for any insights which it may provide when the entire receiver source file is presented.

Lines 1–8: These lines, belonging to the subdesign section of the program declare I/O signals to be used by the system implementation chip(s). In the current example, many more signals than necessary are declared as I/O signals. This is done for simplicity of testing. If the current design is implemented, these signals will appear at the chip output so that actual performance may be confirmed using an oscilloscope or logic analyzer. In a practical design case, the number of I/O pins used can be minimized by declaring some of these signals as internal *nodes* so that they do not consume valuable I/O resources.

Lines 9–11: The variable section declares the two memory elements, Data-Plus[1..0], which are fundamental components of the edge-detection process. This is identical to the code of program 5.1. In addition, the memory element, Receiving, is declared to reserve a flip-flop for the purposes of managing *persistence* in the receiving process.

Line 17: The data input signal is connected to the edge-detector memories.

Lines 18–20: The digital logic contained in this section performs the edge-detection process.

Lines 22–23: This source code uses a set-or-hold control equation to set the persistence control signal. In the present example, we use the signal StopReceiving as an external input. However, in the final design of the receiver circuitry, it will be necessary to derive an internal control signal equation with which to replace this external signal. The external, StopReceiving signal is merely being used as an intermediate test signal with which to facilitate intermediate simulations and results.

The simulation results of program 5.2 are shown below. The dataIn signal is input to the chip and the on-chip processing generates the PosEdge and, in turn, the Receiving signal. The StopReceiving signal has been used to demonstrate its effect upon the Receiving flip-flop signal. Lines 22–23 in program 5.2 control the persistence signal, Receiving, with a set-or-hold control equation as shown in the source code. Of course in the final design, after the Receiving signal has been driven false, the next positive edge transition of the data line will regenerate the PosEdge signal which, in turn, will regenerate the Receiving signal and the process will repeat for each received character. It should be clear from the discussion that the reception and recovery of digital data at the receiver proceeds a single character at a time (actually a single bit at a time).

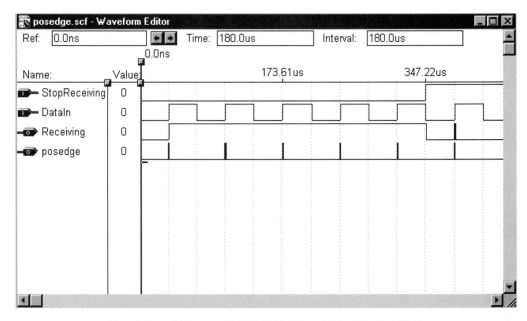

Simulation of Program 5.2: Establishing Active Receive Mode

5.5.2   Receiver Design

After completing the process of creating a signal that will permit the continuous reception of information within a contiguous steam of data bits, the design of sampling and storing received information may be undertaken. We therefore proceed to the process of sampling and registering the data. Recall that the system clock is 3.456 MHz and the data rate of the serial COM port information is 28,800 b/sec. The ratio of the system clock frequency to the data rate is given by

$$\frac{System\ Clocks}{Data\ Bits} = \frac{3.456 \times 10^6}{2.88 \times 10^4} = 120 \qquad (5.4)$$

The question of what constitutes an optimal location on which to sample the serial data bits is now a consideration. Of course in a noisy environment, we may choose to sample each of the bits at several, selected temporal locations and use the information to generate a single estimate. As a result of the multiple sampling per bit, the signal quality may be estimated and consequently a decision process put into place. For the current illustration, we merely decide to detect the received information at the center of each bit and make the assumption (not a particularly poor decision) that this estimate of the respective data stream bit value is suitable for use. Since the sampling is at the bit center, we require an interval of time equal to 60 system clock ticks to arrive at the center of the received start bit. Subsequent data samples must be taken at intervals spaced by 120 clock ticks.

5.5.3   Overview of Receiver Design Requirements

A description of the processes that must be conducted for the serial reception of seven-bit characters, plus a parity bit, framed with start and stop bits will now be given. This is the same data format given in the figure at the beginning of section 5.1, Signal Definition. Clearly, a large number of alternative design techniques and methodologies will accomplish this design objective. The one selected here is simply a method which will convey the fundamental digital system design and implementation principles in a straightforward manner.

Consider that the receive data line has been at rest for sufficient time to allow the receiver to acquire the waiting state. Recall that the meaning of at rest is that the receive data signal line has been at −12.5 V (modified to nominally 0 V by the passive-level converter circuit provided earlier). The beginning of data transmission is initiated by the data signal line transition from −12.5 to +12.5 V (modified to nominally + 5.0 V by the passive-level converter circuit). The data signal is routed to a positive-edge detector circuit which operates precisely as described in section 5.2 and for which source code is provided in program 5.1. The positive edge detector "sees" the positive going transition and produces a pulse of duration equal to the period of the system clock (in this illustration, 289.35 ns). This positive going, leading edge of the data signal is assumed to be the beginning of a start bit. The start bit is nominally of the same duration as any other bits in the data stream. Bits in the data stream are of duration 34.722 μsec in the current illustration, which corresponds to 28,800 b/sec. Given that the detection described is the beginning of the start bit, this bit will be followed by nine other valid bits (data bits b_0 to b_6, a parity bit, and a stop bit). Although multiple stop bits are possible in some systems, they are easily handled and we will not consider them further here.

The fact that the onset of communications has been detected must be remembered by the receiver. A flip-flop signal named Receiving will be assigned the memory responsibility. The output of the edge detector is routed to a one-bit memory (D-type flip-flop), which is controlled with a set-or-hold type control equation. The output emanating from this memory element is named Receiving.

Once the Receiving signal is set, the receiver knows that it must systematically maintain a portrayal of the important characteristics of the waveform. The temporal location of the edges and centers of the bits certainly qualify for attention. Therefore, a counter is started (initialized to zero) and allowed to count, at the system clock rate (3.456 MHz in this case) to locate the center of the first bit (start bit). The counter must increment its way to a content of $34.772 \times 10^{-6}/289.35 \times 0^{-9} = 120$ to indicate the trailing edge of the start bit or to 60 to indicate the middle (center) of the start bit. This counter is clearly a nonbinary counter, so the reader may choose to review alternative methods of performing this function (presented earlier). If the value of 0x3C is decoded from the counter state, ostensibly the decoder output will indicate the center of the bit. However, it must be remembered that one clock time will be taken to perform a positive-edge detection and one more clock time will be required to prepare the Receiving signal. Therefore, these accrued clock times, and any others utilized in alternate methodologies, must be accounted for in the final decode value. By counting the correct number of pulses, we can easily track the "edges and "centers" of the receive data bit time intervals.

Once the correct "center" decode value is found and utilized at the output of the subsystem which is tracking the significant points of interest, this "center" pulse may be used to sample the received data stream. The center is a reasonable point if only one sample is selected since it tends to avoid the effects of noise disturbances, amplitude distortion, and phase distortion which tend to "randomly" move the edges of the bits from their otherwise idealized positions in the incoming data stream. An additional consideration in sampling is the unavoidable variation (however small) in the system clock frequencies between the transmitter clock and the receiver clock. Typically for crystal clocks, the frequencies may be maintained within 100 ppm. If the initial sample (for example, start bit sample) is made at the precise center of the start bit, then any difference between receiver-system clock frequency and transmitter clock frequency will cause the center sample to "walk away" from the idealized center for successive bits. This "walking" will accrue additional sample-time error throughout the ten bits of each transmitted word. When a new word arrives the receiver re-synchronizes at the leading edge of the stop-bit-to-start-bit transition. Sampling as close to the center of the bit as possible minimizes the risk that sampling "walk-off" will create errors for the latter bits in each received word.

Sampling the data stream, in the current context, implies the process of reading the value of each bit and storing that bit value into a receive-data-register. Once the active receive mode has been entered by the receiver, data samples must be generated and stored as representations of the transmitted data. Assurance that valid words have been received must be ascertained. This usually involves counting bits and testing for some form of parity. Recall that once a start bit is recognized, only a single received word may be anticipated. The receiver must read the transmitted information for the single word and then reenter the so-called waiting or listening mode until the onset of another word is detected. The receiver must, therefore, count the received bits and when it decides that the transmitted word has been read and stored it must generate a StopReceiving signal which may also be interpreted as an enter-waiting-mode signal.

5.5.4 Receiver Logic Design

The digital design details for the receiver are presented in this section. As with previous examples, the substance of the design detail is contained in AHDL source code. The source code for the receiver is given below as program 5.3. Many of the subsystem designs covered in previous examples are included as fundamental subsystems of the current receiver design. The complete design is included to provide an illustration of the application of principles provided earlier. In addition, the receiver design assists by providing an example of pragmatic design considerations being satisfied by fundamental design techniques. Without additional discussion, we present the source code for the RS232/COM Port receiver written in AHDL.

```
1     Subdesign 'Rcvr1'
2     % ***** Clock frequency is 3.456 MHz ***** %
3     % ***** clock period is 289.35 ns ***** %
4     % ***** data rate is 28,800 bps ***** %
5     % ***** DataIn period is 34.72 us ***** %
6     (
7     clock, DataIn                              :Input;
8     PosEdge                                    :Output;
9     DataDelay[1..0]                            :Output;
10    SampleCount[5..0], BitEdge                 :Output;
11    InRegister[7..0]                           :Output;
12    SampleCountReset                           :Output;
13    Receiving, BitCounter[3..0]                :Output;
14    StopReceiving                              :Output;
15    BitClock                                   :Output;
16    )

17    Variable
18    DataDelay[1..0]                            :Dff;
19    Receiving                                  :Dff;
20    InRegister[7..0]                           :Dff;
21    SampleCount[5..0]                          :Dff;
22    SampleCountReset                           :Dff;
23    BitCounter[3..0]                           :Dff;
24    BitClock                                   :Dff;
25    StopReceiving                              :Dff;

26    Begin
27    % ***** Connect Clocks ***** %
```

PROGRAM 5.3 A Serial Data, COM Port Receiver

```
28    DataDelay[1..0].clk = Clock;
29    SampleCount[].clk = Clock;
30    InRegister[].clk = BitClock;
31    SampleCountReset.clk = Clock;
32    Receiving.clk = Clock;
33    StopReceiving.clk = Clock;
34    BitCounter[].clk = BitClock;
35    BitClock.clk = BitEdge;

36    % ***** Connect Input Data Line ***** %
37    DataDelay[1].d = DataIn;
38    InRegister[7].d = DataIn;
39    InRegister[6..0].d = InRegister[7..1].q;

40    % ***** Perform Edge Detection ***** %
41    DataDelay[0].d = DataDelay[1].q;
42    PosEdge = DataDelay[1] & !DataDelay[0];

43    % ***** Set the receiving signal ***** %
44    Receiving.d = PosEdge # Receiving.q &
45                        !StopReceiving;

46    % ***** Generate BitEdge Pulses ***** %
47    if (Receiving) Then
48            SampleCount[].d = (SampleCount[].q + 1) &
49                          !SampleCountReset;
50                  Case SampleCount[] IS
51                      WHEN H"3A" =>
52                          BitEdge = Vcc;
53                          SampleCountReset.d = Vcc;
54                      WHEN OTHERS =>
55                          BitEdge = Gnd;
56                          SampleCountReset.d = Gnd;
57                  End Case;
58    end if;

59    % ***** centers and edges ***** %
60    BitClock.d = !BitClock.q;
61    BitClock.clrn = Receiving;

62    % ***** increment bit counter ***** %
63    BitCounter[].d = BitCounter[] +1;
64    BitCounter[].clrn = Receiving;

65    % ***** set end of data word ***** %
66    if(BitCounter[] == H"9") Then
67            StopReceiving.d = Vcc;
68    else
69            StopReceiving.d = Gnd;
70    end if;

71    End;
```

PROGRAM 5.3 *Continued*

5.5.4.1 Definition of Receiver Variables A list of the significant logical variable names for the receiver is given below. These definitions may clarify some of the digital system design and implementation contained in program 5.3.

BitClock. This internally generated clock is used by the receiver to sample serial data bits as they stream into the receiver on the input data line.

BitCounter. This counting circuit is a nonbinary counter which keeps track of the number of bits sampled. This tally is updated as the bit samples are stored in the input data register.

BitEdge. A variable indicating the presence of either the edge or the center of an idealized received data bit.

DataIn. The receive data signal line which carries serial data into the receiver input terminal.

DataDelay. This two-bit serial register produces the signals DataIn[n], DataIn [n − 1], where n is the nth sample of the DataIn signal.

InRegister. This is an eight-bit input data register into which received data samples are stored.

PosEdge. A signal generated by the receiver which indicates that a positive going data signal transition (positive edge) has been detected on the incoming data stream.

Receiving. This signal is established by the receiver and is in the Boolean true state whenever the receiver is in the active receiving mode.

SampleCount. This variable represents a five-bit counter which estimates the temporal centers and edges of idealized bit times.

StopReceiving. This signal is generated by the receiver when the receiver decides that all of the bits in a given transmitted word have been received and properly stored. It removes the receiver from the active receive mode and places the receiver into the waiting state.

SampleCountReset. This signal is generated by the receiver each time the receiver has estimated either an ideal bit-time-edge or a bit-time-center. It resets the estimator so that it can begin the estimation of the next temporal critical point.

5.5.4.2 Receiver Hardware Description *Lines 2–5:* These lines contain comments concerning some of the basic design parameters of the receiver.

Lines 6–16: The input and output signals which essentially define the receiver as an entity are declared here. These signals are defined in some detail above (see Definition of Receiver Variables).

Lines 17–25: The variable section of the receiver source file declares the resources required from the available logic cells on the implementation chip. In this case, the entire receiver fits into a single Altera 7032 chip with less than 75% resource utilization. The number of pins required also fits into the 7032 EPLD. This includes the excessive I/O pins declared by the design of program 5.3. Recall all key signals were desired (but not required) as outputs simply to support hardware testing.

Lines 36–39: The input data signal is connected to the input data register (line 39) and the register used to determine InData[n] and InData[n − 1].

Lines 40–42: A positive edge detector is formed by these source lines. A positive pulse is produced whenever the Boolean term InData[n] is true and InData[n − 1] is false.

Lines 43–45: The positive-edge-detection pulse is remembered by establishing the Receiving signal through the implementation of a set-or-hold control equation.

Lines 46–58: Signals are generated here to estimate the temporal centers and edges of all bits beginning with the ideal sampling point of the start bit.

Lines 59–61: An internal clocking signal with which to obtain samples of the input data is generated. The use of the asynchronous clear is acceptable in this application since there are approximately sixty system clock pulses between the release of the asynchronous clear signal and the first required synchronous action of the desired clocking signal.

Lines 62–64: The clocking signal generated in lines 59–61 will clock this counter whenever data bits have been sampled and stored. The use of the asynchronous clear is utilized on the same basis as in source lines 59–61.

Lines 65–70: The completion of reception for the current data word is signaled. The signal StopReceiving is generated to coerce the receiver into a waiting state.

5.5.4.3 Simulation of the RS232 Receiver

A simulation of the receiver is shown below. The data pattern used for testing is the so-called dotting pattern (alternating ones and zeroes). The input data register (InRegister[7..0] in the simulation figure) is initialized to 0x00. When the first data bit sample enters (low-order bit into the high-order register position), the register content becomes 0x80. The table below shows the samples of the data signal line "walking" into the receive data input register. For convenience, the information is shown in binary, hexadecimal, and symbolic form. The data arrives, least significant bit first, preceded by the start bit. The register is initialized to zero (eight zero bits).

Data Entering Receiver Input Register, LSB First, Dotting Pattern

Receive Data Signal	High Order Byte	Low Order Byte	Value in register
Signal Line	*InRegister[7..4]*	*InRegister[3..0]*	*high →low order*
0101 | 0101	0000 (0x0)	0000 (0x0)	initialize = 0x00
1010 | 1010	1000 (0x8)	0000 (0x0)	start bit = s
0101 | 0101	0100 (0x4)	0000 (0x0)	$b_0 s$
1010 | 1010	1010 (0xA)	0000 (0x0)	$b_1 b_0 s$
0101 | 0101	0101 (0x5)	0000 (0x0)	$b_2 b_1 b_0 s$
1010 | 1010	1010 (0xA)	1000 (0x8)	$b_3 b_2 b_0 s$
0101 | 0101	0101 (0x5)	0100 (0x4)	$b_4 b_3 b_2 b_1 b_0 s$
1010 | 1010	1010 (0xA)	1010 (0xA)	$b_5 b_4 b_3 b_2 b_1 b_0 s$
0101 | 0101	0101 (0x5)	0101 (0x5)	$b_6 b_5 b_4 b_3 b_2 b_1 b_0 s$
1010 | 1010	1010 (0xA)	1010 (0xA)	$b_7 b_6 b_5 b_4 b_3 b_2 b_1 b_0 s$

Examining the table and comparing the information with the InRegister[7..0] contained in the simulation results given below demonstrates that the data signal appears to be sampled correctly and stored in the register. The reader may want to try various combinations of data patterns to assure that the data is indeed sampled correctly for a reasonable and representative set of test data.

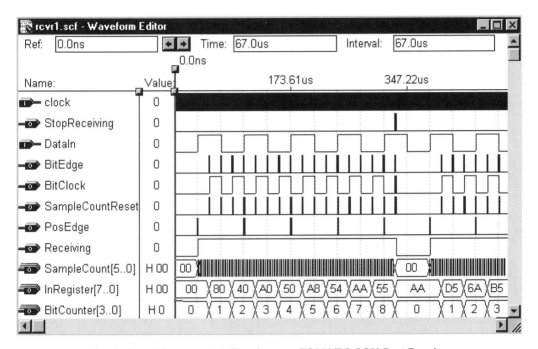

Simulation of Program 5.3: Receiver, an RS232/PC COM Port Receiver

From the simulation, it is apparent that the positive-edge detector signal finds the leading edge of the start bit and immediately (within one clock time) initiates the Receiving signal. The Receiving signal is responsible for maintaining continuous receiver operation throughout the single serial word detection process. Subsequent positive-edge detections may be shut off during the reception of a single character, but this is not required here. The Receiving signal next initiates BitEdge which creates demarcations of the principle points of interest on the bit stream. BitClock then samples the incoming signal and places them into the register, InRegister. The simulation demonstrates that the receiver essentially works as designed. After the last bit from the current data word is sampled and the sample is clocked into the input register, the StopReceiving signal is generated and the receiver returns to the waiting state. The very next positive data transition, which is processed by the receiver generates the positive edge signal. The receiver is then forced out of the waiting state and re-enters the active receiving state.

5.6   RETROSPECTIVE

We have utilized the design principles and methods developed in earlier chapters to design and simulate a first-order COM port receiver. The entire design has been accomplished in Altera HDL. This design may be implemented in a 7032 programmable array (or another of the reader's choice) and tested.

CHAPTER 5 EXERCISES

1. Below is an architecture diagram of the serial, digital receiver designed in this chapter.

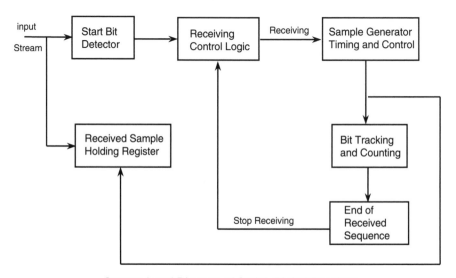

System-Level Diagram of Serial, Digital Receiver

The receiver is designed for 28,800 b/sec and utilizes a 3.456 MHz crystal clock.
  a) Redesign the receiver utilizing the same clock, but modify the system for operation at 14,400 b/sec. Create a set of simulation sequences which verify the correctness of your design.
  b) Redesign the system for operation at 9,600 b/sec and a 3.456 MHz clock. Create a simulation which verifies the correctness of your design.
  c) Combine the original design with the solution to (a) such that a single input control line will select operation at either 28,800 b/sec or 14,400 b/sec.
  d) Combine the original solution with the solutions to (a) and (b) such that a pair of control lines select operation at 28,800 b/sec, 14,400 b/sec, or 9,600 b/sec.
  e) Another standard crystal oscillator frequency is 3.686 MHz. Redesign the solution in part (d) above if system crystal clock operates at 3.686 MHz.

2. The receiver system developed in this chapter utilizes a single sample, optimally placed, for each received bit. In the interest of improved error performance, two or three samples of each bit may often be used in digital receivers.

   a) Redesign the receiver to use three samples, symmetrically placed approximately within the interior one-third of each bit. Select the value of the bit by a majority voting method and place this sample in the received data register.

   b) Create a simulation which verifies the majority voting algorithm sampling process. If the majority voting algorithm fails to properly certify the start bit, the receiver must be taken out of the "active-receiving" mode. It must be placed into "waiting" or "listening" mode.

3. Modify the receiver design by replacing the D-type receiving flip-flop with a J-K type receiving flip-flop. Compile the design and simulate the performance to assure that the design works properly.

4. Design an m-sequence generator with sequence length 511. The system clock is to be divided by sixteen with a ripple counter. The system clock ÷ 16 is to serve as the clock for the m-sequence generator.

   a) Create a source file for the required m-sequence generator. A PN-serial bit stream is to be taken from the low-order bit of the generator.

   b) Create a simulation which verifies the proper operation of the generator.

   c) Create a positive-edge detector which detects each positive edge of the resulting PN bit stream and produces a positive, one (system)-clock pulse duration.

   d) Create an edge detector which produces a pulse of one system clock-time duration for every edge (positive-going and negative-going) of the PN stream produced by the generator.

5. Given the receiver design of program 5.3

   a) Change the BitCounter design from a binary counter to a polynomial counter

   b) Change the SampleCounter design from a binary counter to a polynomial counter

6. Modify the receiver program of this chapter to add an eight-byte register file.

   a) The eight-byte register file is to be used to store consecutively received transmission characters. Write consecutive characters to the eight-byte buffer after they have been received and before the next character begins to fill the received data register from the DataIn line. Use a parallel load operation to fill the eight-byte register.

   b) Repeat part (a), but use a serial load operation for loading the eight-byte buffer.

   c) When the eight-byte buffer is full, raise a signal named interrupt. The interrupt signal is to remain high until it is reset by an external input (external to the chip under design here). The external input goes high asserting that the interrupt request has been serviced by a processor which is external to the receiver module.

7. Using standard 7400 series logic modules and/or CMOS 4000 series logic modules:

   a) Estimate the number of such MSI parts which would be required to implement the VHDL receiver designed in this chapter.

   b) Assuming 14 pins per MSI part, calculate the number of device pins which must be interconnected to achieve the receiver function.

 c) Estimate the number of pins which must be externally connected using the VHDL implementation.

 d) Exclude the I/O pins utilized simply to make testing more convenient and which would be eliminated in a production design using programmable logic.

 e) Discuss the advantages and disadvantages of the programmable logic implementation when compared with the MSI implementation.

8. Design a simple parity generator for the receiver:

 a) Design a system of Boolean logic which sets a flip-flop if the number of one-bits contained in the data bits of the serial stream is even (the sum of bits 1 through 9 is 0, modulo 2). Do not include the start and stop bits in the computation. The flip-flop is to remain set for approximately one-bit time (at the incoming data rate).

 b) Design a system of Boolean logic which sets a flip-flop if the number of one-bits contained in the data bits of the serial stream is odd (the sum of bits 1 through 8 is 1, modulo 2). Do not include the start and stop bits in the computation. The flip-flop is to remain set for approximately one-bit time (at the incoming data rate).

9. Utilize the parity circuits developed in (8) above to signal parity error when necessary. The transmitter corresponding to the receiver assures that the sum of bits 1 through 8 is even. If one of the bits is inadvertently inverted (yielding an odd sum) an error is to be indicated. Otherwise, no error is to be indicated.

 a) Design a complete even-parity check circuit, and integrate it with the receiver and the circuits developed in (8) above.

 b) Design a complete odd-parity check circuit, and integrate it with the receiver and the circuits developed in (8) above.

 Hint: Try two different designs. The first design employs a state machine to generate the sum of 1's modulo 2. The second design employs a parallel design using exclusive Or gates.

CHAPTER 6

APPLICATION OF 7400-SERIES LIBRARY FUNCTIONS

6.1 INTRODUCTION

Application programmers applying any software programming languages (e.g., C, Pascal, Ada, FORTRAN) typically utilize standard library functions that are part of the development environment. Libraries are typically delivered with the core compiler as part and parcel of an integral development system. HDLs, in general, contain similar types of structures. Many experienced logic designers are eminently familiar with the use of 7400-series commercial MSI (medium-scale integrated circuit) digital logic parts (and their 5400-series military counterparts). These classical 7400/5400 parts have provided many years of powerful capability in the design community. For those designers already familiar with the myriad of capabilities provided by these time-honored MSI systems, there is no need to surrender the utility of the accrued experience and knowledge. Permitting and even facilitating the use of standard 7400/5400 functions in programmable systems clearly enhances advanced digital design capabilities. Beginning designers may also readily avail themselves of the tremendous wealth of capability in the 7400/5400 logic families with relatively simple procedures as will be demonstrated. The Altera system, as well as other systems, typically is delivered with a broad set of traditional MSI 7400 logic functions, available in library form. These libraries of functional part descriptions are readily available to the designer implementing digital systems through HDL design methods. The designer need only instantiate the built-in digital function in a manner similar to the instantiations provided in earlier chapters for user-defined digital functions. The process will be introduced through the use of source-code illustrations, in a manner consistent with the practical source code of earlier chapters. It is the primary purpose of this chapter to introduce means by which the designer may access the functions available in MSI libraries. We will concurrently demonstrate some of the quintessential functionality encased in these digital design libraries. We now proceed directly to a set of illustrations.

6.2   A 74176-STYLE PRESETTABLE DECADE COUNTER

The 74176 presettable decade counter is a popular MSI function which has been used for many years. A description of the operation of this counter follows. The counter, as shown in the figure, has four input data lines. Specifically, these line are designated A, B, C, and D.

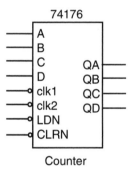

74176 Decade Counter

The corresponding four output lines are QA, QB, QC, and QD, respectively. There are two clock signals, whose functions are described as needed, and finally there are active low preset and clear control lines.

The tables on the next page indicate that if the clear control line (CLRN) is low and the load (LDN) control signal is high, then all of the flip-flops in the 74176 are cleared. Similarly, if the CLRN is high and the LDN is low, then the input data signals are transferred directly to the flip-flop contents. Note that if both of the asynchronous control lines are maintained high, then the 74176 is permitted to count on the appropriate clock transitions.

Asynchronous Control for 74176 Decade Counter

		Inputs							Outputs		
clrn	*ldn*	*clk*	*D*	*C*	*B*	*A*	*QD*	*QC*	*QB*	*QA*
L	H	X	x	x	x	x	L	L	L	L
H	L	X	d	c	b	a	d	c	b	a
L	L	X	x	x	x	x	N/A			
H	H				"Count"					

In summary, the table above indicates that:

- When the active low clear signal, CLRN, is low and LDN is high, the four Boolean output values, Q_D, Q_C, Q_B, and Q_A are driven low.
- When the active low-load signal LDN is low and CLRN is high, the output signals, Q_D, Q_C, Q_B, and Q_A are driven to the corresponding values of the inputs.
- When the CLRN and LDN signals are both high, the counter is permitted to proceed in its normal synchronous counting sequence.

The normal, synchronous counting sequence is shown in the table that follows.

Characteristics of a 74176 Counter

	Decade Counting, Connect QA to CLK2			
Count	Q_D	Q_C	Q_B	Q_A
0	L	L	L	L
1	L	L	L	H
2	L	L	H	L
3	L	L	H	H
4	L	H	L	L
5	L	H	L	H
6	L	H	H	L
7	L	H	H	H
8	H	L	L	L
9	H	L	L	H

The 74176 counter may also be used in a biquinary count mode, but we will disregard that alternative for expediency in illustration. We employ the information in the tables above to create a source file for implementation. The source file of interest is listed below as program 6.1.

```
1    % 74176: A Loadable DecadeCounter %
2    FUNCTION 74176 (clrn, ldn, clk1, clk2, d, c, b, a)
3    RETURNS (qd, qc, qb, qa);
4    Subdesign 'Demo176'
5    (
6    Loadbar, ClearBar, Clock              :Input;
7    In[3..0]                              :Input;
8    Q[3..0]                               :Output;
9    )
10   Variable
11   Count                                 :74176;
12   Begin
13   % ***** Connect Ext. Inputs to 74176 ***** %
14   Count.(clk1) = Clock;
15   Count.clk2 = Count.qa;
16   Count.clrn = ClearBar;
17   Count.ldn = Loadbar;
18   Count.clk2 = Gnd;
19   Count.(d,c,b,a) = In[3..0];
20   % ***** Connect Ext. Outputs to 74176 ***** %
21   Q[3..0] = Count.(qd, qc, qb, qa);
22   End;
```

PROGRAM 6.1   A 74176 Decade Counter

A brief description of program 6.1, which incorporates the 74176 decade counter macrofunction from Altera, will now be presented.

Lines 2–3: These lines are required to include the 74176 macrofunction into the current source file. This is in contrast to the syntax of the . . . [include "filename.inc"] . . . approach discussed in earlier chapters. While the semantics of including a file are quite different from the semantics of incorporating a 7400-library function, the results are essentially the same. In the 7400-type function definition, the arguments provided in parentheses directly following the required "function 74176" macro declaration are all predefined input signals to the macrofunction. These signals must be provided as source signals by the enclosing program source code. The arguments provided after the Returns statement are all signals which are outputs of the referenced macrofunction. These *returns* signals are accessible to the enclosing source file.

Lines 4–9: The subdesign section declares the chip I/O signals. Line 6 declares an active low-load signal (LoadBar), an active low-clear signal (ClearBar), and the system clock. Line 7 declares a four-bit wide data input bus (in other words, input to the implementation chip). Line 8 declares a four-bit wide output bus.

Lines 10–11: The variable section of the source file instantiates (line 11) a single decade counter of type 74176 which will be referred to by the name Count in the HDL source code.

Lines 13–19: These lines connect the designated chip input lines to the corresponding input lines on the instantiated decade counter. The decade counter, Count, has inherited the 74176 macro function I/O terminals. Therefore, the port Count.clk1 is connected to the chip input signal, Clock in line 14. Similarly, external lines LoadBar and ClearBar are connected to the corresponding decade counter terminals Count.ldn and Count.clrn in lines 16–17. Only line 15 in this grouping does not quite meet the designation of routing chip input signals. Line 15 actually wraps an output to an input signal within the instantiated counter. This is required to coerce the 74176 to count in a decade mode (re: standard 74176 data sheet). Line 19 demonstrates that groupings of signals (buses) may be routed with single commands as long as ordinal representations are maintained.

Line 21: The group of four Count[] array output signals [in other words, the count output bus consisting of Count.(qd,qc,qb,qa)] are routed to the chip output pins with a single command.

A simulation of the 74176 counter is shown below. The data input lines, as well as the asynchronous load and clear-control lines, have not been asserted. Therefore, the decade counter counts in its normal, decade mode. From program 6.1 it is obvious that the 74176-counter library macrofunction has provided all of the digital design detail for this device. The essential program logic simply instantiates the counter and then routes the proper data and control lines to the I/O pins on the implementation chip.

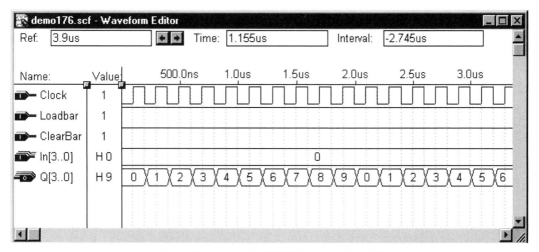

Simulation of Program 6.1: 74176 Decade Count Mode

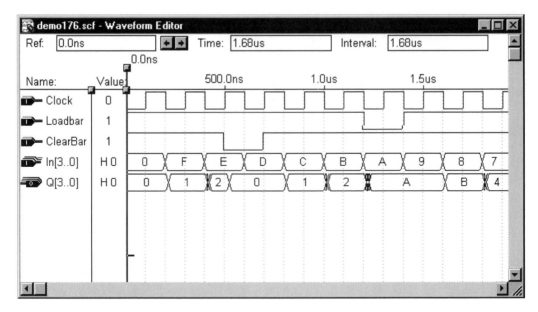

Simulation of Program 6.1 with Load and Clear Incorporated

Above, a second simulation is provided for the same program (program 6.1). In this second simulation, input data lines have been used and the asynchronous load and clear lines have been asserted to elaborate on the completeness of the emulation of the MSI macrofunction component. The reader is encouraged to examine the simulation in some detail. Exercises at the end of this chapter provide further guidance in the development of implementation practice using similar control lines.

6.3   A 74181 ARITHMETIC LOGIC UNIT (ALU) MACROFUNCTION

Often, a logic synthesis process may desire the advantages of a well-established and well-defined combinational logic function such as the 74181 four-bit ALU. In this section, we explore the utilization of this very useful 7400-series macrofunction. The function prototype for this MSI equivalent macrofunction is:

```
function 74181 (s[3..0], m, cn, a3n, a2n, a1n, a0n, b3n, b2n,
  b1n, b0n)
returns (gn, pn, f3n, f2n, f1n, f0n, aeqb, cn4);
```

74181

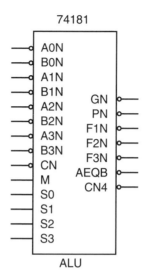

A 74181 Arithmetic and Logic Unit (ALU)

The 74181 macrofunction duplicates both the active-high and active-low functional performance of the corresponding 74181/54181 TTL or corresponding CMOS part. The 74181 I/O consists of two four-bit input signal buses. If the M (mode) control line is maintained high, the system produces a set of logical functions that are responsive to the selection bus signals, s[3..0]. If the mode control line is held low, then the ALU produces a set of arithmetic function as determined by the selection lines. The four-bit bus, F[3..0], produces the output signals which are either logic or arithmetic functions as described above. The AEQB line indicates either equality or inequality of the two four-bit input buses.

The 74181 will operate in either active-high mode or active-low mode. Only the active-high truth tables for this combinational logic function will be utilized and they are provided below. Active low data definitions are sometimes useful but will not be discussed further in the current context. For the active high mode, the subject ALU provides function input lines S_3 through S_0 which are employed to select from either sixteen arithmetic functions or sixteen logic functions depending upon the state of the mode control signal, M. The ALU as implemented in program 6.2 fits onto an Altera 7032 programmable ELPD and utilizes half of the available 32 logic cells (the last three digits of the part number indicate the number of logic cells available on a 7000-series Altera component). Since 7032, (32 cells) 7064 (64 cells), and 70128 (128 cells) components are readily available, it is clear that the current 74181 implementation easily fits into the available 7000-series logic cells. This fact indicates the large amounts of computational power and logic available to those knowledgeable in modern digital automation methods and advanced programmable logic methods.

Functional Truth Table for Active-High Signals, 74181 Macrofunction

Selection $S_3S_2S_1S_0$	Logic Functions	$\overline{C}_n = H$ (No Carry)	$\overline{C}_n = L$ (With Carry)
	M = H	*M = L; Arithmetic Operations*	
LLLL	F = /A	F = A	F = A plus 1
LLLH	F = /(A + B)	F = A + B	F = (A + B) plus 1
LLHL	F = (/A)B	F = A + /B	F = (A + /B) plus 1
LLHH	F = 0	F = minus 1 (2s Comp)	F = ZERO
LHLL	F = /(AB)	F = A plus A(/B)	F = A plus A(/B) plus 1
LHLH	F = /B	F = (A + B) plus A(/B)	F = (A + B) plus A(/B) plus 1
LHHL	F = A $ B	F = A minus B minus 1	F = A minus B
LHHH	F = A(/B)	F = A(/B) minus 1	F = A(/B)
HLLL	F = /A + B	F = A plus AB	F = A plus AB plus 1
HLLH	F = /(A $ B)	F = A plus B	F = A plus B plus 1
HLHL	F = B	F = (A + /B) plus AB	F = (A + /B) plus AB plus 1
HLHH	F = AB	F = AB minus 1	F = AB
HHLL	F = 1	F = A plus A*	F = A plus A plus 1
HHLH	F = A + /B	F = (A + B) plus A	F = (A + B) plus A plus 1
HHHL	F = A + B	F = (A + /B) plus A	F = (A + /B) plus A plus 1
HHHH	F = A	F = A minus 1	F = A

*Each bit is shifted to the next more significant position

We now present a program which instantiates the 74181 macrofunction and routes the most prominent signals to the I/O pins of the implementation chip. Program 6.2 below illustrates the use of the 74181 macrofunction available from the Altera macrofunction library.

```
1    function 74181 (s[3..0], m, cn, a3n, a2n, a1n, a0n, b3n,
        b2n, b1n, b0n)
2    returns (gn, pn, f3n, f2n, f1n, f0n, aeqb, cn4);
3    Subdesign 'Demo181'
```

PROGRAM 6.2   A 74181 Macrofunction Implementation

```
4    (
5    s[3..0]                                    :Input;
6    A[3..0], B[3..0]                           :Input;
7    m, Cn                                      :Input;
8    f[3..0], C4                                :Output;
9    )
10   Variable
11   ALU4                                       :74181;
12   Begin
13   ALU4.(s[3..0])=s[3..0];
14   ALU4.(a3n,a2n,a1n,a0n)=A[3..0];
15   ALU4.(b3n,b2n,b1n,b0n)=B[3..0];
16   ALU4.cn=cn;
17   ALU4.m=m;
18   f[3..0]=ALU4.(f3n,f2n,f1n,f0n);
19   c4=ALU4.cn4;
20   End;
```

PROGRAM 6.2   *Continued*

Lines 1–2: These required lines of the source code provide for the availability of the 74181 ALU macrofunction as a template in the current source file.

Lines 3–9: The subdesign section of the source code declares the chip I/O signals which will eventually consume I/O pins of the implementation chip. Line 5 provides the selected function for the ALU. Line 6 provides the input pins for the two four-bit operands. Line 7 implements the mode control and carry input connections. Line 8 furnishes the pins for the function which is the result of ALU processing.

Lines 10–11: The variable section of this source file contains only a single processing command (line 11) which instantiates one 74181 four-bit ALU. This user-defined variable is declared with the object name ALU4.

Lines 13–15: These lines route the selected function command and the input data buses from the input pins to the corresponding terminals of the instantiated object, ALU4.

Lines 16–17: These source lines route the mode control signal and carry signals to the ALU object.

Lines 18–19: The two source lines furnish the connection of the results of computation from the instantiated 74181 macrofunction to the pins of the chip.

Simulations of program 6.2 have been conducted and are shown in the following figures. The large number of possibilities for input variable combinations precludes showing a complete set of input combinations of the input signals. A representative number of cases is presented to provide insight into the utilization of the ALU and the available functionality.

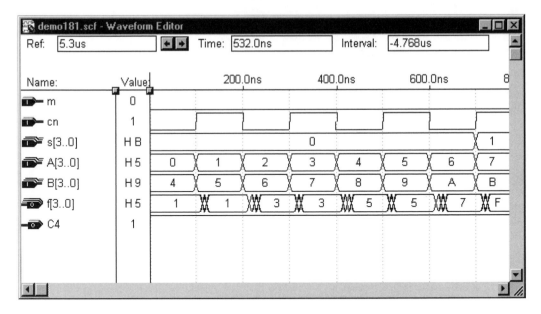

Simulation 1 of Program 6.2: A 74181 ALU Macrofunction

In simulation 1 above, the array variable, s[3..0] select lines, are maintained at 0x0 for first 700 ns. The carry input line is toggled and the mode input line remains at logic zero. Control input, m, is maintained at a logic-zero condition which yields the arithmetic functions of the ALU as contrasted to the logical functions that are produced if the control input, m, is set to a logic-one condition. The processing is summarized in the following table. Since the select lines of the 74181 are maintained at all zeroes, the output of the ALU will be either equal to the operand, A, or will be equal to the operand A plus one. Note that with the selected value of control input the second operand, B, is ignored by the ALU. The B operand is utilized in the simulation merely to verify the operation including the fact that the B operand is indeed neglected by the current simulation. The table is intended to assist in the interpretation of the source code and corresponding simulation. Note the approximate 25 ns delay.

Table to Assist in Reading Simulation 1 of Program 6.2

Time Interval	Result of ALU Processing	Conditions
0–100 μsec	A[3..0] + 1 = 1	s[3..0] = 0, m = 0, carry-in
100–200 μsec	A[3..0] = 1	s[3..0] = 0, m = 0, no carry-in
200–300 μsec	A[3..0] + 1 = 3	s[3..0] = 0, m = 0, carry-in
300–400 μsec	A[3..0] = 3	s[3..0] = 0, m= 0, no carry-in

A second simulation provides some additional insight into the simulation process and the performance of the 74181 macrofunction.

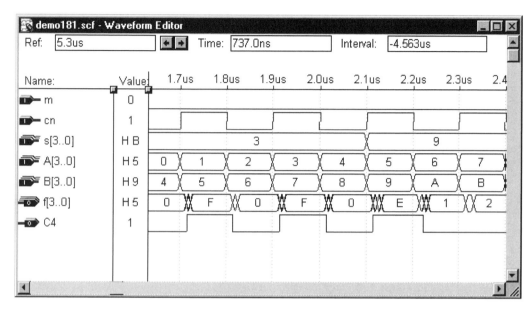

Simulation 2 of Program 6.2: A 74181 ALU Macrofunction

From the logic table of the 74181 ALU presented earlier, it is clear that when the ALU select lines are set to 0x3, the ALU produces 0xF if the control input, m, is maintained at a logic-zero condition and the active-low carry input is held at a logical one. However, when the active-low carry input is set to a logical zero, then the ALU produces an output of 0xF. For the latter several hundred nanoseconds of the simulation, the control input lines are modified to the 0x9 condition, where the sum of the two operands are produced, with or without carry-out depending on the appropriate action for the particular case. The table below may assist in interpreting the results of processing.

Table to Assist in Reading Simulation 2 of Program 6.2

Time Interval	Result of ALU Processing	Input Conditions
1.6–1.7 μsec	0x0	s[3..0] = 0x3, m =0 , carry-in
1.7–1.8 μsec	0xF	s[3..0] = 0x3, m = 0, no carry-in
1.8–1.9 μsec	0x0	s[3..0] = 0x, m = 0, carry-in
1.9–2.0 μsec	0xF	s[3..0] = 0x3, m = 0, no carry-in
2.1–2.2 μsec	A[3..0] + B [3..0] = 0xE, no carry-out	
	(0x05 + 0x09 = 0xE), no carry-out	s[3..0] = 0x9, m = 0, no carry-in
2.2– 2.3 μsec	A[3..0] + B[3..0] = 0xA	
	(0x06 + 0xA = 0x1), carry out	s[3..0] = 0x9, m = 0, carry-in

6.4   A 74176 COUNTER/7445 DECODER TIMING GENERATOR

This section presents a timing generator similar to those developed in earlier chapters. The reader may readily compare the design methodologies associated with creating instances of 7400-series standard-function logical modules and the methodologies associated with producing the essentially equivalent functions directly in the designer's source code. Of course the speed performance of such functional replicas is representative of the implementing PLD (or other implementing device) and not the original TTL or CMOS logical part from which the functional performance is derived. This illustration implicitly elaborates on the flexibility associated with text logic design methods and programmable logic implementation. The flexibility and productivity associated with these design methods plays an important role in the current, expansive development of the computer and digital industry. The timing generator below (program 6.3) consists of a 74176 logic function counter combined with a 7445 logic function decoder. Instances of the two hardware objects are generated and appropriately interconnected. It is clear from the source listing that the 74176 counter function requires the following inputs.

```
clrn   Active low clear signal
ldn    Active low load signal
clk1   Primary clock used for clocking the device
clk2   Second clock (not used here) for bi-quinary operation
d      Input to flip-flop d
c      Input to flip-flop c
b      Input to flip-flop b
a      Input to flip-flop a
```
Input Signals for 74176 Instance

The output signals for the 74176 follow.

```
qd     Output of flip-flop d
qc     Output of flip-flop c
qb     Output of flip-flop b
qa     Output of flip-flop a
```
Output Signals for 74176 Instance

Similarly, the input signal for the 7445 are given as follows.

```
d      Input argument for the high order decoder stage
c      Input argument for the 2² decoder stage
b      Input argument for the 2¹ decoder stage
a      Decoder argument for the low order decoder stage
```
Input Signals for 7445 Instance

Finally we arrive at the 7445 decoded output signals which are the ten mutually exclusive signals from the decoder which indicate the value of the state of the input vector of the decoder. These signals are known respectively as: o0n, o1n, o2n, o3n, o4n, o5n, o6n, o7n, o8n, and o9n. We now present program 6.3 which implements the counter and decoder combination.

```
1    % ***** 74176: Decade Counter ***** %
2    FUNCTION 74176 (clrn, ldn, clk1, clk2, d, c, b, a)
3    RETURNS (qd, qc, qb, qa);
4    % ***** 7445 Decoder ***** %
5    FUNCTION 7445 (d, c, b, a)
6    RETURNS (o0n, o1n, o2n, o3n, o4n, o5n, o6n, o7n, o8n,
     o9n);

6    Subdesign 'timer176'
7    (
8    Loadbar, ClearBar, Clock         :Input;
9    In[3..0]                         :Input;
10   Q[3..0]                          :Output;
11   Numb[9..0]                       :Output;
12   )

13   Variable
14   Count                            :74176;
15   decode                           :7445 ;

16   Begin
17   % ***** Connect Ext. Inputs to 74176 ***** %
18   Count.(clk1) = Clock;
19   Count.clk2 = Count.qa;
20   Count.clrn = ClearBar;
21   Count.ldn = Loadbar;
22   Count.clk2 = Gnd;
23   Count.(d,c,b,a) = In[3..0];

24   % ***** Connect Ext. Outputs to 74176 ***** %
25   Q[3..0] = Count.(qd, qc, qb,qa);

26   % ***** Route counter to decoder ***** %
27   decode.(d,c,b,a) = count.(qd,qc,qb,qa);
28   Numb[9..0] = decode.(o0n, o1n, o2n, o3n, o4n, o5n, o6n,
     o7n, o8n, o9n);
29   End;
```

PROGRAM 6.3 A 74176/7445 Timing Generator

Lines 1–6 of the source file (program 6.2) declare the two key functions to be utilized in the current design. The 74176 counter function and 7445 decoder function are the macrofunctions used in the current implementation.

Lines 6–12 make up the subdesign section and, as such, are used to declare the I/O signal lines.

Lines 13–15 instantiate a 74176 decade counter named count and a 7445 decoder named decode.

Lines 16–25 are used to route the input signals directly from the pins of the implementing chip to the objects which were instantiated in lines 13 through 15.

Line 27 routes the signals from the output of the instantiated counter to the input of the decoder.

Line 28 routes the output of the decoder circuit to the output pins on the implementing chip.

The simulation that follows is accomplished directly as a result of program 6.3 and demonstrates the operation of the system. The simulation reveals that the system performs as desired. The simulator provided with the Altera Max+PlusII system is sufficiently detailed that glitches during state transitions, probably due to static hazards in the 7400 logic emulations or due to 74176 counter emulation ripple delays. Explaining the specific glitches is left as an exercise.

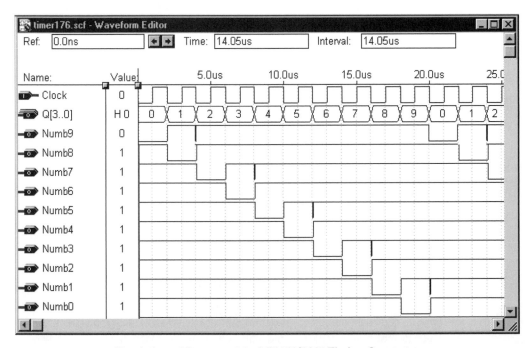

Simulation of Program 6.3: A 74176/7445 Timing Generator

6.5 A 74276 LIBRARY REGISTER MACROFUNCTION

In this section, we discuss and utilize a 7400 register-chip emulation which, in turn, utilizes a series of J-K-type flip-flops.

6.5.1 Introduction

This section continues the examination the 7400 series macrofunctions by examining the 74276 macrofunction, which is a J-K-type register. The register, as shown below, contains four flip-flops, each with J and K_n input signal ports. As indicated in the 74276 data sheet information, the J input is an active-high signal while the K_n signal is active low.

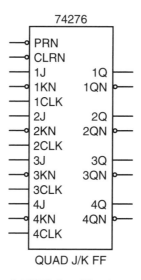

A 74276 Quad Register

The flip-flops of the 74276 are separately clocked, but have common inputs for active low clear (clrn) and active low preset (prn). The truth table is shown below and indicates that the four flip-flops contained are negative-edge triggered. Note that the K_n input to each register is an active-low input signal so that although the register is of a J-K type, the inversion on the K side must be taken into consideration. The first two rows of the table indicate that the active low clear and active low preset signals are asynchronous. The third row indicates that the user may not assert the clrn and prn signals simultaneously (without invoking an indeterminate output). The remaining rows indicate that the registers are negative-edge triggered. Comparing row four with a normal J-K element, recall that in a normal J-K flip-flop, the J = 0, K = 0 retains the previous state. Comparing row five to the table below recall that a normal J-K flip-flop, the J = 1, K = 0 would set the flip-flop. Similarly the traditional J-K flip-flop for the next two rows yields: J = 0,

K = 1 results in a reset and J = 1, K = 1 results in a toggle. To simplify the comparisons, a truth table for a conventional, negative-edge triggered, J-K flip-flop is shown below.

Truth Table for Conventional J-K Flip-Flop

Input					Output	
clrn	prn	J	K	clk	Q	Qn
L	H	X	X	X	L	H
H	L	X	X	X	H	L
L	L	X	X	X	N/A	N/A
H	H	L	L	$\downarrow$	Q_0	Q_{n0}
H	H	H	L	$\downarrow$	H	L
H	H	L	H	$\downarrow$	L	H
H	H	H	H	$\downarrow$	not Q_0	not Q_{n0}

Truth Table for 74276 Macrofunction

Input					Output	
clrn	prn	J	Kn	clk	Q	Qn
L	H	X	X	X	L	H
H	L	X	X	X	H	L
L	L	X	X	X	N/A	N/A
H	H	L	H	$\downarrow$	Q_0	Q_{n0}
H	H	H	H	$\downarrow$	H	L
H	H	L	L	$\downarrow$	L	H
H	H	H	L	$\downarrow$	not Q_0	not Q_{n0}

6.5.2 Using the 74276 in a Text-Design File

This illustration structurally connects all of the contained flip-flops but utilizes only one of the devices for the purposes of illustrating behavior (each of the flip-flops is identical). Program 6.4 below is a source file used to examine and demonstrate the behavior of the typical register flip-flop of this series. The source file also serves as another illustration of the means for utilizing the 7400-series library. The source file is presented below.

```
1    FUNCTION 74276 (prn, clrn, 1j, 1kn, 1clk, 2j, 2kn,
2    2clk, 3j, 3kn, 3clk, 4j, 4kn, 4clk)
3    RETURNS (1q, 1qn, 2q, 2qn, 3q, 3qn, 4q, 4qn);
4    Subdesign 'jkreg'
5    (
6    clock                                        :Input;
```

PROGRAM 6.4 A 74276 Series J-K Register Macrofunction

```
 7    InJ, InKn                                          : Input;
 8    Out[4..1]                                          : Output;
 9    )
10    Variable
11    QFF1                                              :74276;
12    Begin
13    % ***** clock setup ***** %
14    qff1.1clk = clock;
15    qff1.2clk = clock;
16    qff1.3clk = clock;
17    qff1.4clk = clock;
18    % ***** j and k input ***** %
19    qff1.1j = InJ;
20    qff1.1kn = InKn;
21    qff1.2j = InJ;
22    qff1.2kn = InKn;
23    qff1.3j = InJ;
24    qff1.3kn = InKn;
25    qff1.4j = InJ;
26    qff1.4kn = InKn;
27    % ***** flip-flop outputs ***** %
28    Out[4] = qff1.4q;
29    Out[3] = qff1.3q;
30    Out[2] = qff1.2q;
31    Out[1] = qff1.1q;
32    End;
```

PROGRAM 6.4   *Continued*

Lines 1–3: These lines define the function which represents the 74276 register. The input signals are listed in the parentheses in the function declaration and the returned values (outputs of the register macrofunction) are declared in the *returns* statement.

Lines 4–9: The subdesign section declares the I/O signals. In this case we need only two input signals since we are demonstrating the function of a single flip-flop. In normal design practice these flip-flop input signals would be supplied from on-chip processing circuitry or chip input as demonstrated here.

Lines 10–11: The variable section of the source file is used to create an instance of the 74276 register. The single instance is named Qff1.

Lines 13–17 of the body of the source file connect the system clock to each of the register clock inputs.

Lines 18–26 connect the input signals to each of the registers. All four sets of inputs are connected (redundantly in this case) to permit compilation without errors. Only one flip-flop output is used in the following demonstration however.

Lines 27–31 simply connect the four flip-flop outputs to the corresponding output pins on the implementation chip.

6.5.3 Simulation

In the simulation below, one flip-flop of the register set is exercised to demonstrate the performance of the source code which creates and utilizes an instance of the 74276. The truth tables given above provides a convenient means of interpreting the simulation results.

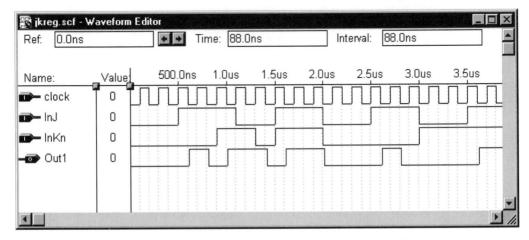

Simulation of Program 6.4: A 74276 Register Macrofunction

6.6 AN INTEGRATED APPLICATION OF 7400-SERIES CIRCUITS

In this section, an integrated application, consisting of multiple 7400 logic functions is examined. The illustration also implements a hierarchical demonstration of 7400 functional components utilized in conjunction with *built-in* instantiated components (for example, D-type flip-flops).

6.6.1 Introduction

The instantiated 7400-series macrofunctions may be used interactively with instances of other built-in component types such as flip-flops, memory elements, and other components. We now demonstrate a hierarchical manner in which 7400 library functions and text-design files may be employed in a design environment. Program 6.3, defined and utilized earlier in this chapter, utilized the 7400 macrofunctions, 74176, which is a decade counter with preset input and a single 7445. These two functions were employed in combination to provide a demonstration-timing generator. In program 6.3, a single instance of each 7400 macrofunction was created and then structurally interconnected to provide the requisite function. In the current example, we desire a timing generator to be used to control a flip-flop which is created as an instance of a built-in D-type flip-flop. However, in the current illustration, we prefer not to repeat any of the instance declarations for the 74176 counter function or for the 7445 decoder function. In addition, we prefer not to repeat any of the activities associated with the creation of the original timing generator. Therefore, we choose to compile program 6.3 into a header file. The header file then defines a template from which objects may be created or instantiated. We then include the associated header file into the current program, allowing the current program to create instances of the object.

6.6.2 Text-Design File

Below, we present program 6.5 which includes a timing generator and a single D-type flip-flop which is to be controlled within the generator discrete-time structure. The text-design file in this example incorporates the following features.

- Inclusion of timer176.inc, which provides an object of type timer176.
- Timer176, in turn, incorporates instances of the 74176 macrofunction and the 7445 macrofunction.
- An instance of type timer176 is created and named Timer.
- The instance Timer inherits the ports of the object timer176, namely: (1) clock, (2) loadbar, (3) clearbar, (4) in[3..0] and Numb[9..0].

We now present program 6.5 which provides the hierarchical demonstration.

```
1     include "timer176.inc";
2     Subdesign '74cont'
3     (
4     clock                              :Input;
5     TimeNum[9..0]                      :Output;
6     FF1                               :Output;
7     )
8     Variable
9     Timer                             :timer176;
10    FF1                               :Dff;
11    Begin
12    % ***** timer setup ***** %
13    Timer.clock = clock;
```

PROGRAM 6.5   Application of 7400 Macrofunctions

```
14    Timer.loadbar = Vcc;
15    Timer.clearbar = Vcc;
16    Timer.in[3..0] = Gnd;
17    TimeNum[9..0] = Timer.Numb[9..0];
18    % ***** flip-flop equations ***** %
19    FF1.clk = clock;
20    FF1.d = !TimeNum1 # !TimeNum5 # FF1.q & TimeNum3 &
      TimeNum8;
21    End;
```

PROGRAM 6.5   *Continued*

The details associated with program 6.5 are given below.

Line 1: This line incorporates the results of previous processing and supplies a template for creating objects of type timer176 in the current program.

Lines 2–6: The subdesign section declares all of the I/O signals. Clock and the array TimeNum[9..0] are inputs which will be provided to instances of the flip-flop under test. FF1 is the output associated with the internally declared flip-flop, which is to be controlled.

Lines 8–10: The variable section is reserved for variable instantiation or reservation. Line 9 declares an instance of the user-defined timer176 object named Timer. Line 10 declares an instance of the built-in, D-type flip-flop.

Lines 13–17 provide structural connections to the Timer instance of the object of type timer176. Line 19 provides connection from the system clock pin to the built-in Dff named FF1. Line 20 provides the control logic equation for FF1, where the input control lines are all internally generated signals emanating from the Timer instance.

6.6.3   Simulation

In the simulation below, the control logic implementation may be verified directly from waveforms presented. Readers wanting to review the logical structure of the control-logic equation in line 20 may want to review the section on control-logic equations in Chapter 3.

Certainly, as stated above, the system performs as intended. Nevertheless, the appearance of glitches in the decoder output lines is one point of the simulation which easily draws attention. The causes of the glitch-type defects are left as an exercise for the reader.

6.7   RETROSPECTIVE

In this chapter, we covered examples of the use of 7400 standard-logic macrofunctions. The macrofunctions employed in this chapter are a mere sampling of the 7400 standard-logic functions available to the designer from the available libraries. The library functions employed were selected from the Altera 7400 macrofunction library. Most capable systems contain a comparable sampling of 7400 functionality.

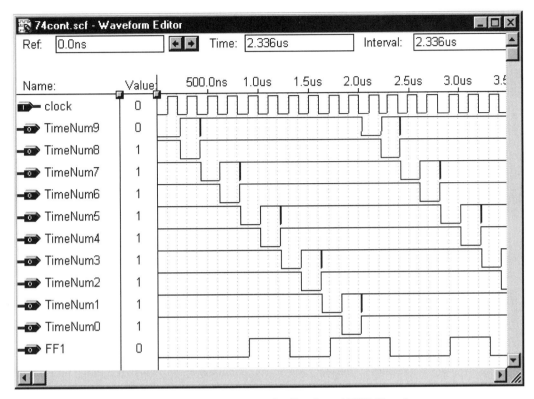

Simulation of Program 6.5: Application of 7400 Circuits

Although only a sampling of the available functions is included in this chapter, the methodology employed is virtually identical for the inclusion of virtually all 7400 library functions into AHDL source files. Later, it will be shown that semantics of inclusion of 7400 macrofunctions into VHDL source files differs substantially from the current semantics. However, the essential purpose and results are identical. In this sense, this chapter has demonstrated the generalized use of the 7400 library functions. For additional assistance, the reader is referred to any handbook of standard logic which contains descriptions of the 7400/5400 standard circuit functions. In addition, the help files of the Altera system contain a full complement of circuit functions.

The examples included in this chapter do no not exhaustively cover the various semantic means for incorporating the 7400 library macrofunctions. Other semantic approaches exist that the reader may or may not view to be of equal convenience in the inclusion of standard logic functionality. However, the final result of the inclusion of 7400 library functions will be identical. The reader is referred to the documentation of any system-specific implementation for alternative means.

CHAPTER 6 EXERCISES

1. Examine the truth table for the 7475 four-bit bi-stable latch shown below.

7475 Truth Table

D	C	Q	$\overline{Q^n}$
L	H	L	H
H	H	H	L
X	L	Q_o	$\overline{Q}_o$

The truth table essentially indicates that the latch responds to the D input as long as the clock, C, is high. Otherwise, the latch ignores the D input and retains the Q^n/Q^n state.

a) Incorporate the latch into an HDL source file. Instantiate the latch function in an object named Latch1. Study the performance of the latch and verify its behavior through simulation.

b) Verify the 7475 truth table through simulation.

2. Describe the essential differences between a flip-flop and a latch. Enumerate some applications suitable for the incorporation of a latch.

3. The 74283 logic device is a four-bit full adder with fast carry. The function prototype of the 74283 is shown directly below.

```
FUNCTION 74283 (a[4..1], b[4..1], cin)
RETURNS (cout, sum[4..1]);
```

a) Instantiate the fast-carry adder and study its performance.

b) Compare the speed performance to the adder developed in Chapter 1.

4. The 74180 is a nine-bit parity generator/checker. The 74180 truth table is shown below.

Function Table for Nine-Bit Parity Circuit

Inputs			Outputs	
Sum of 8 Input 1's	*Even*	*Odd*	*Even*	*Odd*
Even	H	L	H	L
Odd	H	L	L	H
Even	L	H	L	H
Odd	L	H	H	L
X	H	H	L	L
X	L	L	H	H

The 74180 logic circuit operates as follows. If the eight inputs (usually labeled A through H) sum to an even integer and the Even and Odd input lines are H and L respectively, then the Even and Odd outputs are also H and L respectively. This combination could indicate a "good check" on even parity (see row 1 in the table above). On the other hand, if the A through H input lines are odd and the Even and Odd input lines are H and L, respectively, this could be used to indicate an "error" for even parity (see row 2 of the table). Similarly the third and fourth rows could be used to indicate "good parity check" and "parity error" on odd parity, respectively.

Examine the performance of the 74180 part by using a source file and incorporating the parity checker/generator into the source file by proper instantiation. Then create a simulation to study the performance of the circuit. The function prototype for the parity circuit is shown directly below.

```
FUNCTION 74180 (a, b, c, d, e, f, g, h, evni, oddi)
RETURNS (evns, odds);
```

5. Incorporate the 74180 circuit into the receiver logic of Chapter 5. Modify the receiver to examine parity at the completion of each received data character (ten-bit word containing a seven-bit ASCII data character, one-bit parity, and properly framed by start and stop bits). Create a simulation in which the receiver input contains combinations of correct and incorrect parity for both even and odd parity.
   a) Create a simulation test case for "good" even parity.
   b) Create a simulation test case for "bad" even parity.
   c) Create a simulation test case for "good" odd parity.
   d) Create a simulation test case for "bad" odd parity.

6. Discuss the simulation associated with source file, program 6.5.
   a) What are possible causes of the glitches in the decode lines?
   b) Why are certain decode lines completely devoid of glitches?
   c) Compare the program 5 performance to the performance of the ripple counter of Chapter 4.
   d) Speculate on the implementation of the 74176.
   e) Verify your speculation of the mechanization of the 74176 by examining the data sheets in a 7400-series TTL data book and/or a 4000-series CMOS data book.

7. Examine the simulation of program 6.4. Explain the transition of the output signal just after the 2.0 μs time marker.

STATE MACHINES IN AHDL

7.1 INTRODUCTION

Design processes, in general, may be approached in many differing ways and often result in contrasting solutions. In this chapter, we demonstrate a well-known approach to the design of sequential machines utilizing the *state-machine* approach. This approach may be utilized without any specific formalisms in the HDL structure. However, here we also introduce the AHDL constructs that facilitate the implementation of state machines. State machines form a useful and often powerful approach to design problems. A state machine is a popular description of what is often referred to as finite state machine (fsm). In a sense, we have already covered the essence of state machines in previous chapters. The counters covered in previous chapters qualify as state machines. However we did not consider any formal descriptions of the fsm in the previous context. Digital counting systems qualify as state machines in the sense that the counters "know" their current state (After all, the state is contained in the counter's own memory). Knowing its own state, the digital counter makes an internal decision concerning the next state that it will assume. In many of the counters designed earlier, no external-control input existed. Combinational logic, designed as an integral part of the counting system, accepted the present state as an input vector directly from the system's own memory elements (flip-flops). The counting system's combinational logic generated a distinct vector which, in turn, determined the succeeding state that the counter would assume. The counter assumes the next state when the clock transitions. The structure for many of the counters of preceding sections is shown on the next page.

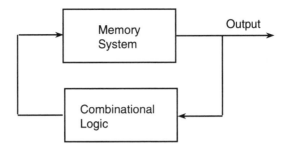

Structure of Some Counting Systems

In this counting system, the feedback and output signals are in the form of vectors (in other words, multiple signal lines, specified as a logical group), with no external input signal. By contrast, the counting system shown below contains a single input signal which determines the count sequence.

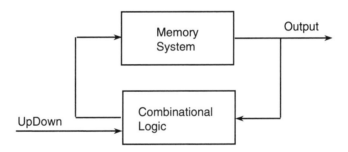

Structure of an Up-Down Counting System

While both of the counting systems shown above qualify as state machines, clearly the one containing external input signals is the more general. The name state machine is another description for what is more commonly referred to as a sequential circuit. The up-down counter contains an external input in addition to the system clock signal. However the output is a function of the present state only. The input signal serves to assist in determining the next state. In this sense, the input signal serves to eventually determine the output. In this chapter, we will consider the topic of state machines in a slightly more formalized manner.

7.2 THE MOORE MODEL OF A STATE MACHINE

A Moore machine is defined as a state machine or sequential circuit in which the output of the system is a function of the present state of the system only. That is, although the digital system may contain input signals, the output of the system does not utilize the input signals in determining the system output. We introduce this section with a simple illustration in the use of state-machine constructions available from the Altera HDL.

7.2.1 A Simple Moore Machine

In this first example we do not fully utilize the concept of state machine, but instead repeat the design of a binary counter utilizing state machine constructions of AHDL. We show (below) a simple state diagram representing the processing accomplished by a sequential machine. The counter steps from state-to-state, depending entirely upon its current state for steering information. The steering signals guide the machine into the next state. In this example, the machine is initialized into the zero state and steps forward at each rising edge of the clocking signal. Classically, the state machine actions are portrayed in a diagram such as that shown below. The diagram serves two purposes. First, it provides a graphical picture which assists in the design and implementation of the machine. Secondly, it provides documentation which is useful during debug, maintenance actions, or subsequent updates which might be required during the deployment of the implemented system.

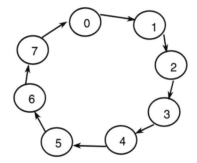

State Diagram, Three-Bit Counter

We now present the source code file of a three-bit counting state machine.

```
1      Subdesign 'Machine1'
2      (
3      Clock                                  :Input;
4      Q2, Q1, Q0                             :Output;
5      )
6      Variable
7      StateMach1: Machine of Bits (Q2, Q1, Q0)
8                      with States    (s0 = 0,
9                                      s1 = 1,
```

PROGRAM 7.1   A Simple State Machine

```
10                                      s2 = 2,
11                                      s3 = 3,
12                                      s4 = 4,
13                                      s5 = 5,
14                                      s6 = 6,
15                                      s7 = 7);
16    Begin
17    StateMach1.clk = Clock;
18    CASE StateMach1 IS
19         WHEN s0 =>
20              StateMach1=s1;
21         WHEN s1 =>
22              StateMach1=s2;
23         WHEN s2 =>
24              StateMach1=s3;
25         WHEN s3 =>
26              StateMach1=s4;
27         WHEN s4 =>
28              StateMach1=s5;
29         WHEN s5=>
30              StateMach1=s6;
31         WHEN s6=>
32              StateMach1=s7;
33         WHEN s7=>
34              StateMach1=s0;
35    END CASE;
36    End;
```

PROGRAM 7.1   *Continued*

A detailed explanation of the content of program 7.1 follows.

Lines 1–5: These initial lines declare the existence of I/O signals which will eventually consume I/O resources of the final implementation chip. In this example, the output is a function of the present state of the system (in other words, Q2, Q1, and Q0 are memory states of the machine and are routed directly to the output of the system). The machine therefore qualifies under our previous definition as a Moore machine.

Lines 6–15: The variable section of the source file declares resources to be used from the implementation chip. In the current example, a state machine is declared in line 7 and lines 8 through 15 define the states which the sequential machine may assume. In the current illustration, the name given to the clocked sequential circuit is StateMach1 (state machine one). AHDL supplies the special purpose language constructs shown here to declare and define the state machine.

Line 17: Since the state machine is a clocked sequential circuit, the system clock must be connected to circuit. The structural connection of the clock signal is accomplished in this line.

Lines 18–35: The body of the source file controls the processing of the state machine. The CASE statement used here forces the state machine into a cyclic pattern.

The simulation of program 7.1 given below verifies the system performance. The states of the machine are conveniently defined the numerical order, s0 through s7, in ordinal correspondence with the binary representation of Q2 through Q0. The verification of the system is accomplished by straightforward inspection of the simulation results.

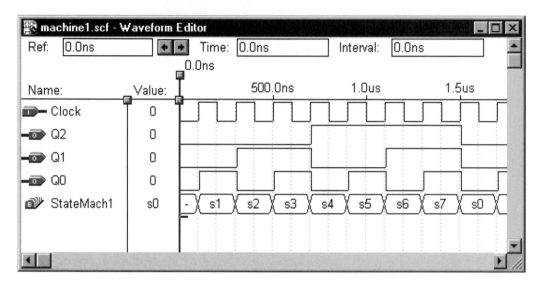

Simulation of Program 7.1: A Simple AHDL State Machine

7.2.2 A Moore Machine Sequence Detector

In this section, a system which falls into the category of an fsm and performs the function of a sequence detector is presented. The system starts in the zero state. The fsm is designed to examine a serial input data stream for the existence of binary sequence 1,0,1. If the system discovers the desired pattern in the serial input data string, it so indicates by virtue of raising an output line named Signal. Then the detector resets itself and continues to look for the desired pattern again. We begin by designing the detection system as a Moore machine. We will later revisit this same fsm detector, designed in the form of a Mealy machine.

```
1      Subdesign 'Machine2'
2      % ***** Search for the sequence "101" ***** %
3      (
4      Clock                                  :Input;
5      Data                                   :Input;
6      Q1, Q0                                 :Output;
7      Signal                                 :Output;
8      )
```

PROGRAM 7.2   A Moore Machine Sequence Detector

```
9     Variable
10    StateMach2: Machine of Bits (Q1, Q0)
11                       with States    (s0 =0,
12                                        s1 = 1,
13                                        s2 = 2,
14                                        s3 = 3);
15    PreSignal                         :Node;

16    Begin
17    StateMach2.clk = Clock;
18                    Signal = Dff(PreSignal, Clock, Vcc,
                      Vcc);
19    CASE StateMach2 IS
20        WHEN s0 =>
21            if (Data = = Vcc) Then
22                    StateMach2=s1;
23            End If;
24        WHEN s1 =>
25            if (Data = = Gnd) Then
26                    StateMach2=s2;
27            else
28                    StateMach2=s1;
29            End If;
30        WHEN s2 =>
31            if (Data = = Vcc) Then
32                    StateMach2=s2;
33                    PreSignal=Vcc;
34            else
35                    StateMach2 = s0;
36            End if;
37        WHEN s3 =>
39                    StateMach2=s0;
40    END CASE;
41    End;
```

PROGRAM 7.2   *Continued*

Program 7.2 contains a source program design consisting of a Moore fsm which will provide the sequence detection. The details are presented below.

Lines 1–8: The subdesign section provides the declaration of I/O signals as usual. The output bits defining the Moore machine are contained, as expected in the output declarations.

Lines 9–15: The variable section of the source file contains all of the resource declarations. An fsm with four defined states is declared in this section of the code. In addition a signal named PreSignal is declared as an internal node of the system. The signal named PreSignal detects the desired sequence as soon as it appears, unrestricted by clocking boundaries. In the body of the source file, this asynchronous detection is resynchronized with the system clock by the use of a D-type flip-flop. This resynchronization is accomplished in a manner much as was accomplished to create equal segment intervals in the design of nonbinary counters (see decade and duodecade counters in earlier chapters).

Lines 16–41: The body of the source file contained between begin-end statement pairs contains the primary logic of the fsm. In the current design, this logic is implemented primarily as a CASE construction which steers the state machine into the proper state. In classical design approaches, a state diagram or state table is normally required to facilitate the design process. Using the text design approach, a state table is essentially contained in the source file and in a sense the design of the system tends to be self-documenting, although care certainly needs to be taken to assure that adequate documentation is provided since no design methodology is completely self-documenting. This is especially so in digital system designs which tend to be large and complex. The CASE statement employed in the current design is straightforward. State 3 is an unreachable state by logical means and can only be arrived at by noise or some other system disturbance. Some special attention is perhaps due for statement number 18. This line provides an implicit declaration of a D-type flip-flop along with signal assignments for each of the Boolean variables. Sometimes an implicit declaration of this type is called an in-line reference. The subject code from program 7.2 is:

$$\text{Signal} = \text{Dff(PreSignal, Clock, Vcc, Vcc)} \tag{7.1}$$

The syntactical format for this implicit declaration is:

$$\text{dff.q} = \text{Dff(dff.d, dff.clk, dff.clrn, dff.prn)} \tag{7.2}$$

In this command, the resynchronization of the unsynchronized signal, PreSignal, is accomplished. The synchronized signal produced by this processing is named Signal.

The simulation of the sequence-detecting fsm is shown directly below.

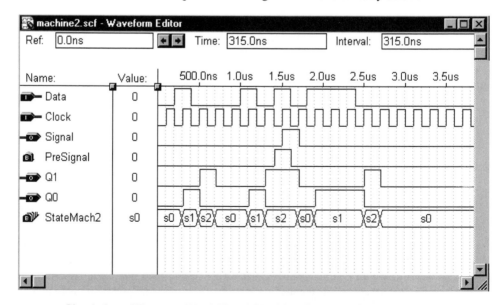

Simulation of Program 7.2: A Moore-Machine Sequence Detector

The simulation verifies that the system starts in the s0 state. After detecting the first one-bit, the system progresses to the s1 state. The following chart may assist in interpreting the simulation. All serial-bit stream detections occur on the rising edge of the system clock.

Table of State Transitions, Moore Sequential Detector

Time Tick	StateMach1	Comment
100 ns	s0	Initial state is s0. Detection of '0' yields s0.
300 ns	s1	s1 + '1' → s1
500 ns	s2	s1 + '0' → s2
700 ns	s0	s2 + '0' → s0
900 ns	s0	s0 + '0' → s0
1.1 μs	s1	s0 + '1' → s1
1.3 μs	s2	s1 + '0' → s2
1.5 μs	s2	s2 + '1' → s2 and output detection signal
1.7 μs	s0	s2 + '0' → s0 and withdraw detection signal

7.3 THE MEALY MODEL OF A STATE MACHINE

A Mealy machine is defined as a state machine in which the output of the system is a function of the input signal(s) and the present state of the system. That is, the system output will change whenever either the current state of the system changes, the input changes, or both the state of the system and the input change. In contrast, recall that the Moore machine output does not change when the input signal(s) changes.

7.3.1 A Mealy-Machine Sequence Detector

In this section, the design of a sequence detector which searches for the serial sequence 101 in an infinitely long serial-bit stream is undertaken. This system is virtually identical to the sequence detector implemented earlier with a single exception. The current system accomplishes the detection with the use of a Mealy machine, while the earlier fsm utilized the Moore-machine design concept. Directly below, the source file of the Mealy-machine sequence detector is presented.

```
1    Subdesign 'Machine3'
2    % ***** Search for the sequence "101" ***** %
3    (
4    Clock                                    :Input;
5    Data                                     :Input;
6    Q1, Q0                                   :Output;
```

PROGRAM 7.3   A Mealy-Machine Sequence Detector

```
7    Signal                                       :Output;
8    )

9    Variable
10   StateMach2: Machine of Bits (Q1, Q0)
11                  with States    (s0 =0,
12                                  s1 = 1,
13                                  s2 = 2,
14                                  s3 = 3);
15
16   Begin
17   StateMach2.clk = Clock;
18   CASE StateMach2 IS
19        WHEN s0 =>
20             if (Data == Vcc) Then
21                    StateMach2=s1;
22             End If;
23        WHEN s1 =>
24             if (Data == Gnd) Then
25                    StateMach2=s2;
26             else
27                    StateMach2=s1;
28             End If;
29        WHEN s2 =>
30             if (Data == Vcc) Then
31                    StateMach2=s2;
32                    Signal=Vcc;
33             else
34                    StateMach2 = s0;
35             End if;
36        WHEN s3 =>
37                    StateMach2=s0;
38        END CASE;
39   End;
```

PROGRAM 7.3 *Continued*

Program 7.3 is almost identical, in most of its structure, to program 7.2. By examining the differences, we focus on the essential differences between Mealy machines and Moore machines. In program 7.2, we discussed the need for synchronization of the output signal. No such synchronization takes place in program 7.3 and, therefore, the output value, Signal, changes value, when appropriate, as the input data line changes state. Examination of the WHEN s2 clauses of both program 7.2 and program 7.3 reveals the essential differences. The reader is encouraged to study and simulate variations on these two programs to obtain a feel for the primary differences in the Mealy- and Moore-machine design approaches.

In the simulation of program 7.3 shown below, the temporal region between 1.0 and 1.6 μsec of simulated time is worthy of particular notice. In this region, whenever the system is in state s2, the output, Signal, follows the input data line as would be expected for a Mealy-machine design.

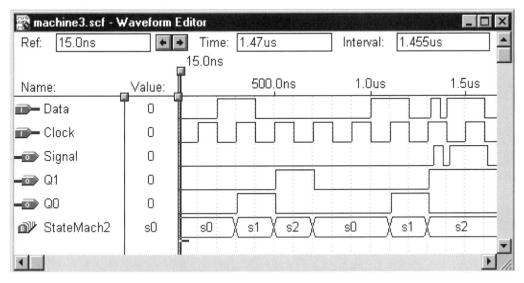

Simulation of Program 7.3: A Mealy-Machine Sequence Detector

For the purpose of emphasizing the points made contrasting Mealy and Moore finite state machines, an additional simulation of program 7.2 is also shown.

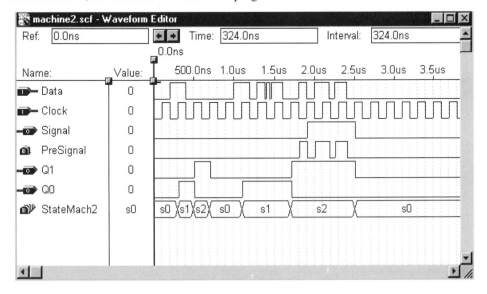

A Second Simulation of Program 7.2: A Moore-Machine Sequence Detector

In this case, since the machine in question is a Moore machine, even though the data line goes through a substantial number of transitions while the state machine is in state s2 (see the region between 1.3 µsec and 1.5 µsec), the output line, Signal, does not move until the rising transition of the system clock signal. This result is produced by the synchronization step discussed at some length above. In a sense, the set of simulations presented above emphasize the essential differences between synchronous and asynchronous machines.

7.4 AN FSM STATISTICAL MONITOR FOR MAXIMAL LENGTH SEQUENCE GENERATORS

In this section, a state machine which monitors a maximal length sequence generator is developed.

7.4.1 INTRODUCTION

In chapter 4, maximal length sequence generators were briefly examined as a means of designing counters and generating pseudo-random digital data patterns. It was shown, by example, that the maximal length sequences created by the maximal length sequence generators exhibit interesting autocorrelation functions. The autocorrelation function for a maximal length sequence of length $M = 2^n - 1$, where n is the number of flip-flops in the generator is:

$$R_{xx}(m) = \sum_{k=0}^{2^n - 2} x(k)x(k + m) \quad \infty < m < \infty$$

Therefore

$R_{xx}(0) = M = 2^n - 1$, where $2^n - 1$ is the length of the sequence
$R_{xx}(m) = -1$, for m ≠ 0

In this section, we examine a state machine which may be used to verify, by measurement, the autocorrelation function of the maximal length sequences utilizing a digital system. Certainly, the autocorrelation functions might well be estimated with an off-line software program or a closed-form equation. However, in practice, there is no substitute for a monitor which determines exactly what is occurring instead of what a designer intended should occur. The illustration presented here also provides an additional opportunity to examine the utility of state-machine design in the context of an application.

7.4.2 State-Machine Description

Consider a maximal length sequence generator which creates a PN sequence of length 2,047. This implies that we require a generator length of eleven stages. In the current context, the generator is expected to supply a binary sequence, which is pseudo-random in nature. The sequence might be used to supply a data sequence for testing a communication facility or a navigation transmitter and receiver. Much longer sequences are often used in actual practice. The measurement system might even be a part of the deployed system and not merely a component of a testing system. It is decided that it is important to determine specific parameters of the PN sequence being generated. Such parameters might include: (1) the number of ones and the number of zeroes in a transmitted sequence, (2) the probability that isolated ones and zeroes are in the data stream, (3) the probability that the sequence of length 2,047 contains subsequences containing runs of ones and zeroes of any specific length. As an illustration we therefore undertake the design of state-machine monitor, which determines the number of runs of exactly four ones and exactly four zeroes in a PN sequence of length 2,047.

The basic principle behind the hardware design contained within source file of program 7.4 revolves around the design of the two state machines. The state machine SMO (State Machine One) tracks the number of consecutive logic-one bits in the pseudo-noise (PN) sequence. The state machine SMZ (State Machine Zero) tracks the number of consecutive logic-zero bits in the pseudo-noise sequence. The counters, Exact4Zeroes and Exact4Ones, are incremented with the information from the two state machines. These two counters contain, respectively, at any point in the PN sequence generation, the number of runs of exactly four ones and exactly four zeroes which are subsequences of the maximal length sequence. Some primary components of the source file hardware design are defined directly below.

1. **Exact4Ones:** A six-bit counter which enumerates the number of runs exactly 4 ones.

2. **Exact4Zeroes:** A six-bit counter which enumerates the number of runs exactly 4 zeroes.

3. **SMO:** A state machine which continuously tracks the runs of logic ones.

4. **SMZ:** A state machine which continuously tracks the runs of logic ones.

5. **Poly:** A maximal length sequence generator which serves as a test generator.

6. **The states of the one tracking state machine are:**
   o_zero → no consecutive ones state
   o_one → one isolated one found
   o_two → two consecutive ones found
   o_three→ three consecutive ones found
   o_four → four consecutive ones found

7. **The states of the zero tracking state machine are:**
   z_zero → no consecutive zeroes state
   z _one → one isolated zero found
   z _two → two consecutive zeroes found
   z _three → three consecutive zeroes found
   z _four → four consecutive zeroes found

8. **Init:** The init signal is used as an input to the asynchronous preset and/or clear signals of the D flip-flops which provide the basic building blocks for each of the sequential circuits. This signal is used for initialization purposes.

Without further discussion, we present the source file which contains (1) the polynomial generator, (2) the two state machines, and (3) counters which are controlled from the state machines.

```
1     Subdesign 'longPN'
2     (
3     clock                    :Input;
4     Init                     :Input;
5     Poly[10..0]              :Output;
6     Count[10..0]             :Output;
7     Exact4Zeroes[5..0]       :Output;
8     Exact4Ones[5..0]         :Output;
9     )

10    Variable
11    Poly[10..0]             :dff;
12    Count[10..0]            :dff;
13    Exact4Zeroes[5..0]      :dff;
14    Exact4Ones[5..0]        :dff;
15    SMZ                     :Machine of bits(machz[2..0])
16                                    with states(
17                                           z_zero=0,
18                                           z_one=1,
19                                           z_two=2,
20                                           z_three=3,
21                                           z_four=4);
22    SMO                     :Machine of bits(macho[2..0])
23                                    with states(
24                                           o_zero=0,
25                                           o_one=1,
26                                           o_two=2,
27                                           o_three=3,
28                                           o_four=4);
29    Begin
30    %clocks%
31    Poly[10..0].clk = clock;
32    Count[].clk = clock;
33    Exact4Zeroes[].clk=clock;
34    Exact4Ones[].clk=clock;
35    SMZ.clk = clock;
36    SMO.clk = clock;

37    %Inits%
38    Poly[10..1].clrn = Init;
39    Poly[0].prn = Init;
40    %ordinal count%
41    Count[].d = Count[] + 1;
```

PROGRAM 7.4   An FSM for Monitoring an M-Sequence Generator

```
42    %Poly operation%
43    Poly[9..0].d = Poly[10..1].q;
44    Poly[10].d = Poly[0] xor Poly[2];

45    %State Mach Four Zeroes%
46          if( SMZ==z_zero and Poly[0]==0) then
47                SMZ = z_one;
48                Exact4Zeroes[].d=Exact4Zeroes[].q;
49          elsif( SMZ==z_one and Poly[0]==0) then
50                SMZ = z_two;
51                Exact4Zeroes[].d=Exact4Zeroes[].q;
52          elsif( SMZ==z_two and Poly[0]==0) then
53                SMZ=z_three;
54                Exact4Zeroes[].d=Exact4Zeroes[].q;
55          elsif( SMZ==z_three and Poly[0]==0) then
56                SMZ=z_four;
57                Exact4Zeroes[].d=Exact4Zeroes[].q;
58          elsif( SMZ==z_four and Poly[0]==1) then
59                SMZ=z_zero;
60                Exact4Zeroes[].d=Exact4Zeroes[].q+1;
61          else
62                Exact4Zeroes[].d=Exact4Zeroes[].q;
63                SMZ=z_zero;
64          end if;

66    %State Mach Four Ones%
67          if( SMO==o_zero and Poly[0]==1) then
68                SMO = o_one;
69                Exact4Ones[].d=Exact4Ones[].q;
70          elsif( SMO==o_one and Poly[0]==1) then
71                SMO = o_two;
72                Exact4Ones[].d=Exact4Ones[].q;
73          elsif( SMO==o_two and Poly[0]==1) then
74                SMO=o_three;
75                Exact4Ones[].d=Exact4Ones[].q;
76          elsif( SMO==o_three and Poly[0]==1) then
77                SMO=o_four;
78                Exact4Ones[].d=Exact4Ones[].q;
79          elsif( SMO==o_four and Poly[0]==0) then
80                SMO=o_zero;
81                Exact4Ones[].d=Exact4Ones[].q+1;
82          else
83                Exact4Ones[].d=Exact4Ones[].q;
84                SMO=o_zero;
85          end if;
86    End;
```

PROGRAM 7.4   *Continued*

We now present details of the source file, program 7.4.

Lines 1–9: These lines define the subdesign section of the file and declare the chip I/O signals. The array Poly[10..0] presents the eleven outputs of the maximal length sequence generator to the chip output terminals. The array Count[10..0] represents the outputs of a binary sequential counter. These outputs, although routed to the chip outputs, are not functionally required for the current design. They merely make the ordinal sequence of the maximal length generator convenient to observe. In a final design, they might be eliminated. The array variables Exact4Ones[] and Exact4Zeroes[] reveal the running totals of the selected run subsequences.

Lines 10–14: This portion of the variable section of the source code instantiates the thirty-four flip-flops required to perform the indicated functions. The instantiation amounts to allocation in the context of a programmable array.

Lines 15–21: This portion of the variable section of the source file declares the state machine which is used for tracking the predefined zeroes subsequences.

Lines 22–28: This portion of the variable section of the source file declares the state machine which is used for tracking the predefined ones subsequences.

Lines 30–36: These source lines of the main body of the source file connect the clock signal to the counters and state machines which will provide the synchronous hardware execution.

Lines 37–38: Here the PN generator is initialized into a *legal* state.

Lines 40–41: provide the control logic for the ordinal tracking counter.

Lines 42–44: provide the logical connections which generate the maximal length sequence.

Lines 45–64: provide the state-machine logic which locates and tracks the run-length-four-zeroes subsequences.

Lines 66–85: provide the state-machine processing which locates and tracks the run-length-four-ones subsequences.

A segment of the simulation for the monitor state machine is shown below. The bottom line of the digital simulation is produced by the least significant bit of the maximal length sequence generator. This bit produces the serial-bit stream which is the object of the current measurement effort. In the simulation, it is clear from the value of the Count[10..0] array that we are approaching the end of the sequence of length 2,047. The data stream is at state zero near the beginning of the timing segment shown. Therefore, state machine one (SMO) is appropriately showing a state value of o_zero (in other words, a current run length of zero ones). Simultaneously, state machine zero (SMZ) is showing a current run of z_one (a single, isolated one). As the state of Poly0 transitions from a zero state to a one state, the two state machines adjust their estimates. Notice that the state machines appear to be a clock time late in their estimates, but recall that the state machines may not adjust their state estimates until they have observed the next bit of the random sequence. That is, if after four consecutive bits at one state, the state does not change on the next state, the respective run counter may not be incremented. Further observe that SMO begins incrementing its state as the clock periods accrue. Finally, after the data line has maintained four bit times at logic-one, SMO increments the value of Exact4Ones (only after detecting the one-to-zero transition of the data line) and the state of the SMO machine returns to the o_zero state.

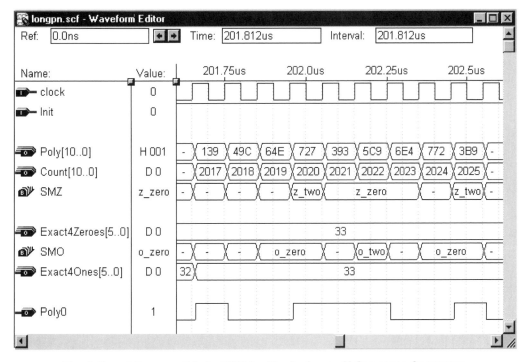

Simulation of Program 7.4: An FSM for Monitoring an M-Sequence Generator

7.5   RETROSPECTIVE

In this chapter, we have examined the concept of a state machine and the constructions within the Altera HDL which facilitate state-machine design in systems. We have further examined the basic definitions of the Moore-style state machine and the Mealy-style state machine as the two primary and contrasting styles in the design and implementation of state machines. We have demonstrated the design of state machines through the use of simple examples using typical fsm (finite-state-machine) sequence detectors. We then employed the use of maximal length sequence generators [also called variously: (1) m-sequence generators, (2) polynomial generators, (3) pseudo-random sequence generators, and (4) pseudo-noise (PN) signal generators, or (5) maximal length code generators]. The use of state machines was demonstrated in realistic, albeit abbreviated applications. Finally, we applied state-machine design concepts to the process of monitoring a particular set of characteristics of a selected pseudo-noise stream.

CHAPTER 7 EXERCISES

1. A state machine is desired to detect the sequence 00001010 (0x0A) whenever it is present in a serial-bit stream. The data rate is 1 MHz and the stream of data is a continuous bit stream.

   a) Develop a finite state machine which will detect the required bit pattern using the minimum number of memory devices. The state machine should use the minimum number of memory elements possible.

   b) Create a simulation which verifies the proper operation of the sequence detector.

   c) Develop and test a PN generator of eleven bits in length. Does the generator ever produce the sequence given above? If so, how many occurrences of the sequence are there over the entire period of $2^{11} - 1$ bits?

2. A "one-hot" state machine is a state machine in which any number of states (say n) are encoded in exactly n flip-flops. For example, a four-state machine might contain the states as shown below. In the example shown, four flip-flops are required to maintain the system state. By contrast, the state may be contained in as few as two flip-flops.

   State Table for One-Hot Encoding

State	State Code
A	0001
B	0010
C	0100
D	1000

   a) Redesign the finite state machine of exercise 1 using a "one-hot" design.

   b) Create a simulation which verifies the proper operation of the system.

   c) Perform timing analyses of the systems as designed in exercise 1 and exercise 2. Compare the two timing analyses and determine which of the two can be run at the maximum execution rate. Can you draw a generalized conclusion from your considerations? Explain.

3. Synchronous, digital data communications systems often depend upon the mean (moving average) energy available in specific spectral lines to recover data timing information. The energy within the requisite spectral locations is produced by state transitions in the binary data stream. To insure an adequate number of data transitions exist in a data stream, a sequence detector is employed at the transmitter end of the system. As a lengthy data stream crosses a given data transportation interface, a sequence detector examines the stream. If an excessive number of consecutive one-bits crosses the interface, a zero-bit is stuffed into the stream. If an excessive number of consecutive zero-bits crosses the interface, a one-bit is stuffed into the data stream. A given system can tolerate a maximum of eight consecutive, identical bits.

   For simulation/testing purposes, use a pseudo-random (m-sequence) generator with a sequence length of 2047.

    a) Design the transmitter fsm "bit-stuffer."

    b) Create a simulation which verifies the performance of your fsm.

4. In communications systems that insert extra bits into the data transmitted data transmission stream, the extra bits must be removed in the receiver (see exercise 3). A complementary, receiver circuit portion of the synchronous digital communication system of exercise 3 is required to remove the excess bits packed into the serial data stream at the transmitter.

    a) Design the receiver fsm and control logic which extracts the extra bits that were inserted at the transmitter. The resulting data stream must be an NRZ (non-return-to-zero) data stream which is a "perfect" replica of the transmitted stream prior to adding the required transition bits.

    b) Create a simulation which verifies the performance of the system.

CHAPTER **8**

APPLICATION OF PARAMETRIC MODULES

8.1 INTRODUCTION

In this chapter, we consider a growing industry standardization method which augments the text-design file approach in a very significant manner. This standardization is evolving around a set of digital system functions which may be readily utilized by the designer. Furthermore, principle parameters of the modules may be specified by the designer at design time. The flexibility this process affords provides additional fuel to the rapid growth which the digital computer and related industries are experiencing. With this methodology, designers may select macrofunctions from a set of significant, powerful, and expanding capabilities provided by a wide array of industrial providers. Specific parameters for each of these modules may be specified by the designer and therefore the designer may obtain state-of-the-art performance while maintaining absolute control over parameters of specific interest for the immediate development solution.

The functions provided by an array of industry providers has been incorporated into designer-accessible design libraries referred to as LPMs (library of parametric modules). The LPM functions are of particular value when rapid access to high-quality, specialized logical functions are required. The situation is analogous to the circumstances presented when a specialized part or subsystem is to be purchased from a manufacturer. The significant difference here is that the required *component* is made accessible in functional rather than physical form. This is particularly valuable when the designer or design team prefers not to spend a disproportionate amount of time developing a highly specialized function but would instead prefer to design at a level incorporating the specialized function into a broader capability that is the primary focus of a particular design effort. The LPM function, in this sense, provides an additional means to higher productivity which the designer may choose to employ as appropriate. We present the material in this chapter to provide designers with the design methods including a set of illustrative examples which may be of value if and when designers prefer to utilize this capability.[1]

To be more specific, the designer may choose from an array of modules including: counters, arithmetic and logic units, latches, flip-flops, memories, phase-lock circuits, encoders, decoders, multiplexors, and a host of other capabilities. We present a relatively small sampling of the available library capabilities in this chapter. The sampling presented here is merely intended to introduce the LPM concept with concrete illustrations. This sampling is intended to demonstrate the concept and some of the mechanisms involved in the process. Because this technology is evolving, the reader may be assured that many more functions and capabilities will be added to the LPM facilities within a relatively short time. For anyone who intends to use this expanding facility, it is incumbent upon him or her to keep abreast of the latest developments.

8.2 AN LPM RANDOM ACCESS MEMORY SYSTEM

In the normal course of digital design, it is usual that the system under development will require the incorporation of a memory system or at least the engagement with a memory system through a process of interconnection or interfacing. This engagement, although quite common, can often be a difficult process. It is especially difficult if the designer must design, develop, and debug a simulation capability which incorporates the memory system. Many integration problems may be uncovered at the simulator level, well before reaching the hardware-integration stage. Of course, without a simulator for preintegration testing, integration may turn out to be quite difficult. Within the Altera design tools, a memory macrofunction is available and may be utilized by the designer. This memory function is incorporated into the tool set as an LPM memory macrofunction. The designer may choose to utilize the *parameterized* memory module from the macrofunction library and then establish the parameters required to perform the desired functions as required by his or her design. We now proceed directly to the design of a sample application which uses the random access memory (RAM) library macrofunction for illustration purposes.

The designer using the Max+PlusII system has the opportunity to select an LPM RAM macrofunction. When the LPM_RAM macrofunction is selected, the user is presented with a parameter data-sheet on which the various alternative parameters relevant to the selected topic may be selected. For example, in dealing with a memory configuration, it is clear that the information such as the width of the data bus and the width of the address bus are key parameters which must be selected. The data-sheet presented to the designer is shown below for the macrofunction named LPM_RAM_DQ.

---

[1]The designer should be aware that in many instances, the LPM function provided constitutes intellectual property of the original designer and/or distributor. In such cases, the LPM function may be employed only as prescribed by appropriate payment or royalty agreements.

```
┌─────────────────────────────────────────────────────────────────────┐
│ Edit Ports/Parameters                                            [X]  │
│                                                                       │
│ Function Name: LPM_RAM_DQ              ┌─────────────────────────┐    │
│                                        │   Help on LPM_RAM_DQ    │    │
│ ┌ Ports ────────────────────────────────────────────────────────┐    │
│ │                          ┌ Port Status ┐ ┌ Inversion ────────┐ │    │
│ │ Port Name:               │  ⦿ Used     │ │ ⦿ None  ○ Pattern/Radix:│
│ │ address[LPM_WIDTHAD-1..0]│  ○ Unused   │ │ ○ All    [      ] [hex ▼]│
│ │                          └─────────────┘ └───────────────────┘ │    │
│ │                                                                │    │
│ │ Name:                         Status:    Inversion:            │    │
│ │ ┌──────────────────────────────────────────────────────────┐▲│    │
│ │ │address[LPM_WIDTHAD-1..0]     Used       None              │ │    │
│ │ │data[LPM_WIDTH-1..0]          Used       None              │ │    │
│ │ │inclock                       Used       None              │ │    │
│ │ │outclock                      Unused     None              │ │    │
│ │ │q[LPM_WIDTH-1..0]             Used       None              │▼│    │
│ │ └──────────────────────────────────────────────────────────┘ │    │
│ └────────────────────────────────────────────────────────────────┘    │
│ ┌ Parameters ────────────────────────────────────────────────────┐    │
│ │ Parameter Name:     [LPM_ADDRESS_CONTROL        ]  ┌ Change ┐  │    │
│ │ Parameter Description: Should the address and control ports be registered? │
│ │ Parameter Value:    [<none>                ▼]      ┌ Clear  ┐  │    │
│ │ Name:                              Value:                      │    │
│ │ ┌──────────────────────────────────────────────────────────┐▲│    │
│ │ │LPM_ADDRESS_CONTROL                 <none>                 │ │    │
│ │ │LPM_FILE                            <none>                 │ │    │
│ │ │LPM_INDATA                          <none>                 │ │    │
│ │ │LPM_NUMWORDS                        <none>                 │ │    │
│ │ │LPM_OUTDATA                         "UNREGISTERED"         │▼│    │
│ │ └──────────────────────────────────────────────────────────┘ │    │
│ └────────────────────────────────────────────────────────────────┘    │
│          ┌────── OK ──────┐              ┌──── Cancel ────┐            │
└─────────────────────────────────────────────────────────────────────┘
```

LPM_RAM_DQ Data-Sheet Presented to the Designer

When presented with this data-sheet, the designer selects the key parameters of interest and may leave others at their default values. The designer may leave the parameters unspecified if they are not required by the particular module under design. For the current illustration, since the primary purpose is to illustrate the concept and then to present a simulation of the resulting implementation, a reasonably small memory is selected. The interested reader may readily implement a much larger memory system in precisely the same manner as that integrated in the following illustration. The selection of parameter values has been made in keeping with the context of manageable illustrations. The parameters of interest were made as follows.

LPM_WIDTH = 4	• specifies that the data bus width is four bits
LPM_WIDTHAD = 4	• specifies that the address bus width is four bits (a total of 16 four-byte data nibbles are contained in the memory)
LPM_NUMWORDS = 16	• verifies that there are 16 addressable nibbles

The remaining parameters are incidental to the current process and will not be discussed further. However, the reader may find the parameters that remain unused here of significant value in practical applications.

Once the designer approves of the parameter definitions, the drawing shown below is placed on the user-selected, open graphic design file (.gdf file) window. Notice that the selected parameters are shown on the graphic design file so that a quick visual inspection may be used to verify parameter selection. If the selections require modification, the data sheet can be reopened by the designer by double-clicking the mouse button when the mouse cursor is within the parameter region shown on the data sheet. The selected RAM system contains separate input and output data buses, an address bus, a clock input signal for input data registration, and a write-enable signal line. The address bus selects the memory word to be read or written and the write-enable signal determines whether the data presented to the input data bus are to be written or not written. If the write-enable line is high, then the data presented to the data bus will be written to the memory. In any event, regardless of the state of the write-enable signal, the data within the memory at the selected address will be presented to the output data bus. Below is the resulting .gdf file which is prepared by the LPM subsystem of the Altera Max+PlusII development software.

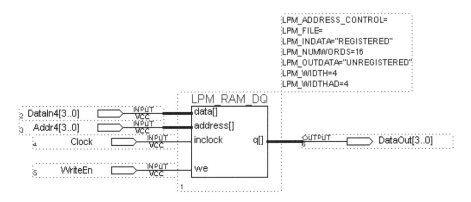

A Graphic-Design (.gdf) File for an LPM_RAM Module

An inspection of the graphic-design file reveals that the selected parameters for the RAM coincide with the desired parameters and the design is accepted. At this point in the design process, the designer has the capability of continuing to design in the graphic-design mode or to switch, so to speak, to the text-design method. Since the current text is essentially based on the text-design method, no further consideration will be given to the graphic-design method as a means of providing system capabilities. In this text, the graphic-design method will be employed primarily as a means of producing individual function capabilities. Integration of components, produced either by graphic-design file or text-design methods, will be accomplished by a text-design methodology.

The graphic-design file is next compiled into an header file (.inc file), named mem1.inc which then contains all of the relevant functional and netlist information contained in the original graphic-design file. This header file is then included in the source file below by the use of the include compiler directive. We now proceed directly to present the source file for program 8.1 which incorporates the memory function discussed above.

```
1    % ** FUNCTION mem1 (datain4[3..0], addr4[3..0], clock,
        writeen) ** %
2    % ** RETURNS (dataout[3..0]); ** %
3    include "mem1.inc";
4    Subdesign 'memory1'
5    (
6    InData[3..0]                        :Input;
7    Addr[3..0], Clock                   :Input;
8    WriteEn                             :Input;
9    OutData[3..0]                       :Output;
10   )
11   Variable
12   MemA                                :mem1;
13   Begin
14   MemA.clock = Clock;
15   MemA.writeen = WriteEn;
16   MemA.datain4[] = InData[3..0];
17   MemA.addr4[] = Addr[];
18   OutData[] = MemA.(dataout[]);
19   End;
```

PROGRAM 8.1   An LPM_RAM Module

The functional capabilities of the RAM module are now accessible to the text-design file, program 8.1, by inclusion of the mem1.inc header file (see line 3 of the subject source file). We now examine program. 8.1 in some detail.

Lines 1–2: These comment lines are incorporated in the source file only to allow the reader a convenient reference for the function prototype which has been made available to the text design file as a result of the inclusion of the header file.

Lines 4–10: These lines declare the I/O signals for program 8.1.

line 6: System input data bus

line 7: Address bus and clock

line 8: Write Enable signal

line 9: System output data bus

Lines 11–12: The variable portion of the source file declares a single instance of the mem1 object which is the four-bit wide by sixteen-word memory system. The single instance of the RAM object is called by the name MemA. By declaring the instance of the memory, MemA inherits all of the ports inherent in the object (in other words, datain4[3..0], addr4[3..0], clock, writeen, dataout[3..0]).

Lines 13–18: The body of the source file contains the operational code which causes the functionality of the memory to be utilized. In the current context, the primary portion of the body is structural (viz. line 14 connects the system clock to the memory, line 15 connects the external write-enable signal to the RAM-write enable, lines 16 and 17 connect the input data and address buses respectively, line 18 connects the output data bus from the RAM to the implementation output chip pins).

The simulation shown below reveals the following RAM operation. During the time period 0 through 2 μsec, writing is enabled (in other words, write-enable is high). Therefore, memory locations 0 through 9 are written with a value equal to double the address modulo 15. From 2 μsec forward, writing is disabled and therefore zeroes are read from the memory locations A through F contain zeroes which are read from the memory. Location zero contains a zero which is also read and finally address-one is reached and a two is read from that location. When the address lines are cycled back to the address sequence 0, 1, 2 . . . , then the values originally written to these locations are read back.

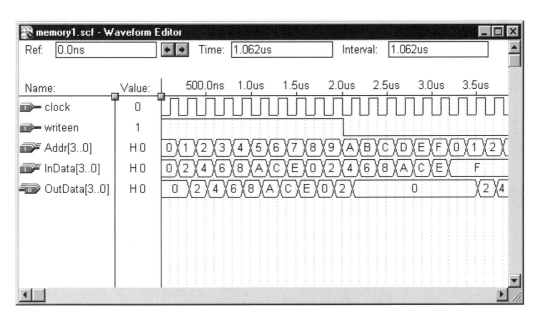

Simulation of Program 8.1: An LPM_RAM Module

In many available memory chips the write-enable is active low. If interface with an off-the-shelf MSI memory system is desired, the sense of the write-enable signal may be inverted. This capability is provided within the LPM macrofunction programmable parameters. Notice that the output data lines reflect the content of the addressed memory area even during write cycles. There is much more that may be demonstrated using RAM systems but for the current time we consider the memory illustration complete.

8.3 A LIBRARY DIGITAL-PHASE DETECTOR

In this section, we examine a digital-phase detector macrofunction. The typical application for a digital-phase detector is within a digital-phase locked loop. In a phase-locked loop (PLL) system, the output of a digital-phase detector would normally be routed to an internal reference oscillator in a manner such that the oscillator is pulled into frequency coherence and possible phase coherence with an externally applied signal. The internal oscillator of the PLL would be either of the voltage-controlled type or the current-controlled type. In the library phase-detector supplied with the Altera MaxPlusII software development environment, there are three input signals. These signals are defined as follows.

nSet	An active-low initialization signal
A	One of two applied signals whose phase will be examined
B	The second of two signals whose phase will be examined

The output signals of the phase detector are:

nDown	An output signal asserted whenever the A input signal leads the B input signal
nUp	An output signal asserted whenever the B input signal leads the A input signal

In addition to the signals described here, a pair of tri-state output signals provide up and down signals for tri-state application, but these will not be discussed further as a part of the current topic. In the Altera-supplied macrofunction, there are no programmable parameters to be selected. When the library function is selected from the macrofunction menu, the graphic-design file symbol shown below is transferred to a graphic-design (.gdf) file. Using the menu-driven graphic-design system supplied with the development environment software, I/O pin symbols are attached to the phase-detector graphic symbol and the editor is employed to modify the pin names for subsequent use. In the graphic design file shown below, the following pin-name modifications have been made.

Library Name	Source File Name
nSet	InSet
A	InA
B	InB
nDown	N_Dn
nUp	N_Up

The graphic-design file is then compiled into a header file named PLL2.inc. This file is sometimes referred to as an include file. The compilation step is required to make the detector circuit accessible to the text-design file which will be utilized for the final implementation step. The include file will be utilized in program 8.2 to provide the functionality of the digital detector.

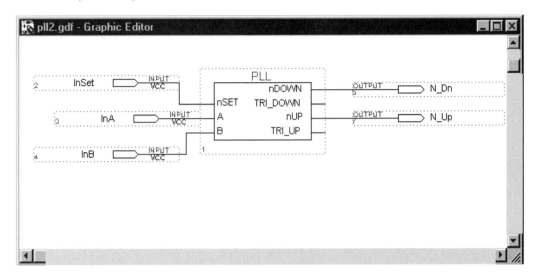

Graphic-Design File for LPM Digital-Phase Detector

The source listing presented below demonstrates the digital-phase detector performance. This source file includes the capability of digital-phase detection through the use of the include file. The include file is a result of processing the graphic-design file which incorporates the invoked library detector. In the source file, externally applied signals are taken from the input pins of the programmable chip and applied to the internally configured digital-phase detector. The two output signals, which indicate whether the A signal or the B signal leads the other in-phase, are brought to output pins. The two output pins also indicate the phase by which one signal leads the other. We now present the source code which provides the phase-detection capability on a programmable array.

```
1     % ** FUNCTION pll1 (inset, ina, inb) ** %
2     % ** RETURNS (n_dn, tridn, n_up, triup); ** %
3     include "PLL2.inc";
4     Subdesign 'PhaseL2'
5     (
6     InA, InB, InSet                          :Input;
7     N_Dn, N_Up   :Output;
8     )
9     Variable
10         Loop1                                :pll2;
11    Begin
12    Loop1.InA = InA;
```

PROGRAM 8.2   A Library Digital-Phase Detector

```
13    Loop1.InB = InB;
14    Loop1.InSet = InSet;
15    N_Dn = Loop1.N_Dn;
16    N_Up = Loop1.N_Up;
17    End;
```

PROGRAM 8.2   *Continued*

The detailed description of the phase detection source code file is presented below.

Lines 1–2: These comment lines are presented as a reminder that the functionality of the library-phase detector is preserved in a function-call format. This function-call format reminds us of the names given the I/O signals in the include file.

Line 3: This command incorporates the functions of the digital-phase detector object into the present source file. The functionality is incorporated as a template from which an instance may be generated.

Lines 4–8: As usual, these lines within the subdesign section of the source file declare the input and output signals of the chip.

Lines 9–10: The variable section of the source file creates a single instance of the phase-detector object. The single instance will be referenced by the name Loop1.

Lines 11–17: The body of the source file contains the processing functions of the implemented hardware. Lines 12, 13, and 14 present the chip input signals to the digital-phase detector. Lines 15 and 16 route the phase-detector outputs to the output pins of the implementation chip.

In the simulation below, the input signal InB leads the signal InA. The subject detector is more appropriately called a rising-falling edge detector in that the phase leading outputs are indicated by the occurrences of edges whether rising or falling. Therefore, the signal n_up is asserted in this condition. Since the percent of time which the signals are in the same state is small, the duty cycle of the n_up signal is also proportionately small.

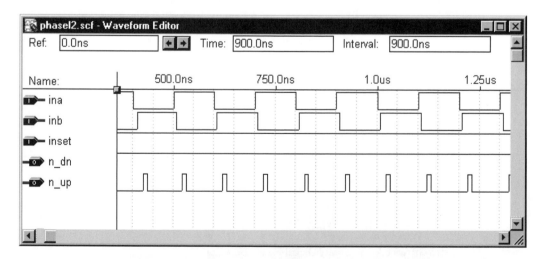

Simulation of Program 8.2: An LPM Digital-Phase Detector

A second simulation of the digital-phase detection system is shown below. In this case the phase-detector inputs have been modified in such a manner that input InA leads input InB. This situation causes the digital-phase detector to assert the output n_dn instead of the output n_up. Furthermore, the A input leads the B input by $\pi/2$ radians which creates a 50% duty cycle on the output waveform.

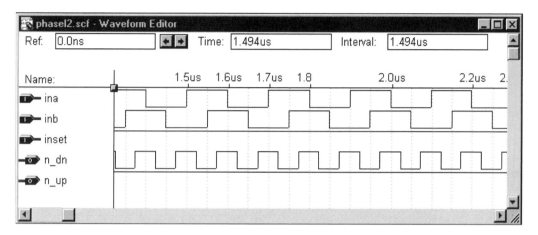

Second Simulation of Program 8.2: An LPM Digital-Phase Detector

In the digital-phase-detector performance, it is clear that the digital-phase detector performs the functions desired. To summarize the functions:

- n_up is asserted whenever input B leads input A
- n_dn is asserted whenever input A leads input B
- The duty cycle of the output signal is proportional to the phase difference of the two signals ($100\% \Rightarrow$ in-phase, $50\% \Rightarrow$)
- The phase detector is more appropriately called a rising-falling edge detector

8.4 AN LPM FOUR-BIT MULTIPLIER

A binary multiplier can be a relatively complex logical building block. The requirements include the widths of the various I/O buses for the multiplier (in other words, multiplicand, multiplier, product) as well as signed or unsigned states of the various arguments. The parametric modules yield a significant advantage in productivity for these examples. The designer is able to make selections for the parameters in question. These parameters are selected by directly interfacing the design environment incorporating the LPM. For the LPM multiplier the designer may choose (1) the width of each of the input data buses, (2) the width of the output data bus, (3) signed or unsigned operation as well as the signed representation to be used (for example, sign-magnitude, 2's complements ... etc.). In the example shown below, the designer has selected parameters for the LPM multiplier which include:

Width of the multiplier	four bits
Width of the multiplicand	four bits
Width of the product	eight bits
Data format	signed, 2's complement

The parameters above have been selected for ease of illustration, but the designer is free to select from a wide availability of parameters. The capability of designer choice for parameters implies that the designer is free to provide optimal parameters for any particular application. This is a superior alternative to either compromising on an existing physical part or creating a custom-designed part. For the selected parameters, the graphic-design file which the Altera digital-design environment produces is shown directly below.

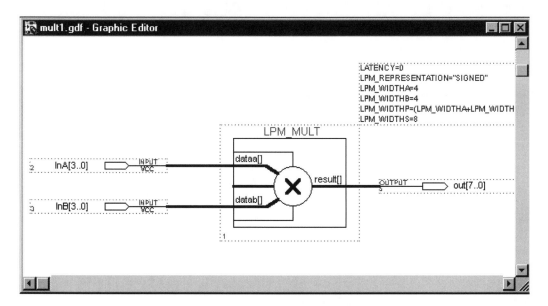

An LPM Multiplier: Graphic-Design File

As in previous LPM illustrations, the graphic-design file is compiled into a header file or an include file. This is accomplished to permit the utilization of the LPM multiplier in a text-file design environment. This is the pattern we have established for previous LPM functions. As before, we continue to utilize the LPM functionality in the text-design files. Without further discussion, we now present the source file, program 8.3, which will serve as the demonstration vehicle for the four-bit 2's complement multiplier shown above.

```
 1    % ** FUNCTION mult1 (ina[3..0], inb[3..0]) ** %
 2    % ** RETURNS (out[7..0]); ** %
 3    include "mult1.inc";
 4    Subdesign 'Multplr'
 5    (
 6    A[3..0], B[3..0]                        :Input;
 7    Product[7..0]                           :Output;
 8    )
 9    Variable
10    Prod1                                   :Mult1;
11    Begin
12    Prod1.ina[3..0] = A[3..0];
13    Prod1.inb[3..0] = B[3..0];
14    Product[7..0] = Prod1.out[7..0];
15    End;
```

PROGRAM 8.3   An LPM Four-Bit Multiplier

In the hardware design of program 8.3, the source code is realized as follows.

Lines 1–2: These lines serve as comment reminders of the multiplier signal definitions.

Line 3: This line includes the multiplier object in the current project.

Lines 4–8: These subdesign section lines declare the chip I/O signals.

Lines 9–10: The variable section of the source code creates an instance, named Prod1, of the object which is named Mult1. The port names, ina[3..0], inb[3..0] and out[7..0] are inherited from the object and may be referenced in the body of the source file.

Lines 11–15: The body of the source file, in the present case, simply connects the input and output signals to the appropriate chip I/O pins. This is referred to as structural implementation.

The simulation below verifies the multiplier implementation. The formation of the product from the initial simulation time ($t = 0$) through $t = 1.50$ µsec is provided for validation purposes. The following table may prove useful in interpreting results.

Multiplier Simulation	Mathematical Interpretation
$(0x0) \times (0x3) = 0x00$	$0 \times 3 = 0_{10}$
$(0x1) \times (0x4) = 0x04$	$1 \times 4 = 4_{10}$
$(0x2) \times (0x5) = 0x0A$	$2 \times 5 = 10_{10}$
$(0x3) \times (0x6) = 0x12$	$3 \times 6 + 2 = 18_{10}$
$(0x4) \times (0x7) = 0x1C$	$1 \times 16 + 12 = 28_{10}$
$(0x5) \times (0x8) = D8$	$5 \times (-8) = -40 = 1101\ 1000 = D8$ where
	$1110\ 1000 \longrightarrow 0010\ 1000$ 2's comp

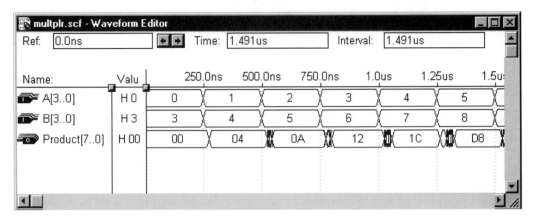

Simulation of Program 8.3: An LPM Four-Bit Multiplier

8.4.1 DIRECT INSTANTIATION OF AN LPM MULTIPLIER

In the design and implementation of the LPM multiplier of the previous section, we first developed an LPM multiplier in a graphic-design format (in other words, with a .gdf file extension). The graphic-design file was compiled and then the LPM multiplier object was incorporated into the multiplier design file with the use of an include file (in other words, .inc format). This method, as shown previously, is one acceptable method of providing and incorporating a parametric multiplier into an HDL text-design file. An additional or alternative method is the use of a direct instantiation of the LPM functionality into the text-design file. The direct instantiation may be employed with most LPM functions. In some sense, the direct instantiation method is preferable from a self-documenting style of design. Recall that one of the objectives of text-design implementation is the documentation which provides for ease of upgrades, product improvements, and maintainability.

We now undertake the design of a second version of a four-bit by four-bit multiplier. The multiplier will be directly instantiated into the source file as contrasted to using the include file or header file method. The multiplier under consideration is capable of accepting signed input data and provides outputs in signed data formats as well. As will be clear shortly, the signed data is provided in 2's-complement data format. We now present, directly below, the source file incorporating the directly instantiated LPM subsystem.

```
1    FUNCTION lpm_mult (dataa[3..0], datab[3..0])
2    RETURNS (result[LPM_WIDTHP-1..0]);

3    Subdesign 'Multplr2'
4    (
5    A[3..0], B[3..0]        :Input;
```

PROGRAM 8.3.1   A Directly Instantiated LPM Multiplier

```
6    Product[7..0]          :Output;
7    )
8    Variable
9    Mult1       :LPM_MULT WITH (LPM_WIDTHA = 4,
10                         LPM_WIDTHB = 4,
11                         LPM_WIDTHP = 8,
12                         LPM_WIDTHS = 8,
13                         LPM_REPRESENTATION = "signed",
14                         LATENCY = 0);
15   Begin
16   Mult1.dataa[3..0] = A[3..0];
17   Mult1.datab[3..0] = B[3..0];
18   Product[7..0] = Mult1.result[7..0];
19   End;
```

PROGRAM 8.3.1   *Continued*

The detailed interpretation of the source file, program 8.3.1, is presented below.

Lines 1 and 2 declare the function prototype of the desired LPM function. The prototype declaration incorporates four-bit data paths for the multiplier and multiplicand. It also incorporates an eight-bit data path for the result or product developed by the multiplier.

Lines 3–7: As in virtually all AHDL source files, the subdesign section of the file contains the declarations of input and output variables. In the present case, this includes multiplier and multiplicand input data paths which are each four-bits wide. Also included is a product output data path which is eight-bits wide.

Line 8–14: These source file lines declare a single instance (direct instantiation) of the multiplier desired. In this variable section of the source file, the parameters of the particular instance are defined. Specifically these parameters are:

LPM_WIDTHA = 4: Defines the parameter which is the data-path width for the multiplier.

LPM_WIDTHB = 4: Parameter which is the data-path width of the multiplicand

LPM_WIDTHP = 8: Parameter defining the data path of the product

LPM_WIDTHS = 8: This parameter sets the sum-port width. Since the sum port is unused in this illustration, the sum parameter is ignored.

LPM_REPRESENTATION = "signed": This parameter sets the data representation for the arithmetic processing as signed (or, alternatively, unsigned).

LATENCY = 0: This input determines the number of clock cycles of latency in the development of the resultant product. A zero latency selects a purely combinational instantiated circuit. The design is more self-documenting in the sense that the source file contains, explicitly, the input and output data-path widths, the information related to the signed nature of the arithmetic processing, and the clocked or combinatorial nature of the data processing.

Lines 15–19: All that remains to complete this design is to provide the structural connections which form the data paths of the current design. Here, the multiplier and multiplicand data paths are connected to the corresponding chip-input pins and the product data path is connected to the corresponding chip output pins.

In the following multiplier simulation, a result is produced every 100 ns. The following information may assist in the process of interpreting the simulation. This provides a computational speed of 10 million multiplies per second.

Simulation Results for Program 8.3.1

Interval (ns)	A Operand	B Operand	Product
0–100	0x0	0x1	0x00
100–200	0x1	0x3	0x03
200–300	0x2	0x5	0xA
300–400	0x3	0x7	0x15
400–500	0x4	0x9 = − 0x7	0xE4 = − 0x1C
500–600	0x5	0xB = − 0x5	0xE7 = − 0x19
600–700	0x6	0xD = − 0x3	0xEE = − 0x18
700–800	0x7	0xF = − 0x1	0xF9 = − 0x07
800–900	0x8 = − 0x8	0x1	0xF8 = − 0x8

The simulation below confirms that the functional performance specifications are achieved. A timing analysis indicates that the LPM multiplier, implemented on a 10K-series Altera part achieves a 65 ns propagation delay. This indicates that the multiplier, as designed, can be pushed to perform in excess of 15 million multiplies per second using the 10K part. Using an Altera 7000-series part, the multiplier is capable of just short of 12 million multiplies per second. The reader is cautioned that no attempt at optimization nor any collateral considerations for system implementation were considered in achieving these estimates. Optimizations, a separate topic, may significantly alter the current estimates.

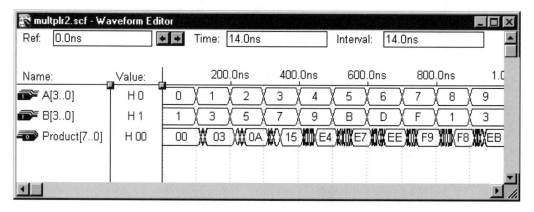

Simulation of Program 8.3.1: A Directly Instantiated LPM Multiplier

The estimates indicating circuit speed developed above are a comparison using the respective architectures of the corresponding parts. However, these estimates do provide a reasonably accurate means of comparison and, in fact, indicate a reasonable estimate of the rates at which these systems may be expected to execute. Clearly, the system above will perform at speeds considerably in excess of those shown in the simulation.

8.5 AN NTSC TELEVISION-SIGNAL GENERATOR

To emphasize that the LPM functions available provide substantial breadth and depth, we now demonstrate the development of a program which generates a National Television Systems Committee (NTSC) standard set of waveforms. Although this chapter concerns the development of parametric modules or LPMs, we include here the NTSC module which, strictly speaking, is not an LPM function. That is, there are no parameters to be set for the module to be demonstrated. Nevertheless, this module provides a macrofunction capability and in general falls into the category of specialized components that the designer may prefer not to design, but instead may prefer to acquire and incorporate.

8.5.1 Introduction

Color television standards defined by the NTSC committee define a set of signals which, for practical purposes, conform sufficiently to the early black and white television standards that synchronize both types of signals provided in both types of receivers. The horizontal sweep rate in color televisions is 15,734.266 Hz. The horizontal oscillator runs at the 15,734.266 Hz rate and at the end of each horizontal sweep, synchronization and blanking signals are generated. During the time period when the horizontal oscillator is retracing (in other words, returning to the left side of the viewing area), blanking signals are generated which deactivate the video signal from the viewing screen. During the latter half of the horizontal blanking period, signals are generated which enable an eight-cycle burst of a color subcarrier signal. The Altera LPM library (and others) contains such a generator which is easily accessible to the digital designer. Vertical trace signals are also generated in a manner similar to the horizontal control signals since the viewing area must be generated in two dimensions.

8.5.2 An LPM NTSC Graphic-Design File

When the NTSC LPM function is invoked from the standard macrofunction library, the graphic-design file below is presented. The I/O pins that the user attaches to the NTSC generator allows the user to modify the names. The names applied in the design are shown in the table on the next page.

LPM Name	Assigned Name	Function	
csync	sync	horizontal sync signal	
hd	horiz	horizontal trace	definition
vd	vert	vertical trace definition	
fld	field	defines odd/even field	
blank	blk	horizontal blanking	
burst	oburst	control of color burst	
clock	clk	digital clock to control sweep timing	
reset	rst	initialization and reset (active low)	

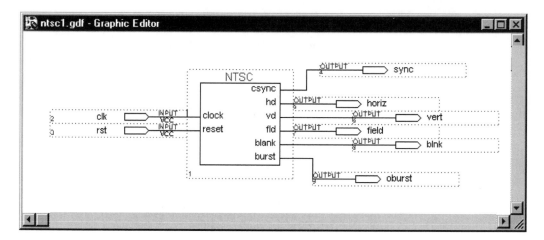

An LPM NTSC Television-Signal Generator Graphic-Design File

8.5.3 Source File for Utilization of NTSC Library Function

The structure of the current program is much like the other programs in this chapter. The current example is presented primarily to demonstrate the breadth of capability increasingly available in this growing standard method of logic design. Therefore, no detailed explanation will be presented for this example. However the reader will easily see that the NTSC program below (program 8.4) is clearly designed with a structural-type design process as are each of the programs in this chapter. It is clear that the most straightforward design method for use with a macrofunction library component is the structural design method.

```
1    % ** FUNCTION ntsc1 (clk, rst) ** %
2    % ** RETURNS (sync, horiz, vert, field, blnk, oburst) ** %
```

PROGRAM 8.4 An LPM NTSC Television-Signal Generator

```
3      include "ntsc1.inc";
4      Subdesign 'ntscgen'
5      (
6      Clock, Reset                        :input;
7      OutSync, Outhoriz, OutVert          :Output;
8      OutField, OutBlnk, OutBurst         :Output;
9      )
10     Variable
11     Gen1                                :ntsc1;
12     Begin
13     Gen1.clk = Clock;
14     Gen1.rst = Reset;
15     OutSync = Gen1.sync;
16     OutHoriz = Gen1.horiz;
17     OutVert = Gen1.vert;
18     OutField = Gen1.field;
19     OutBlnk = Gen1.blnk;
20     OutBurst = Gen1.oburst;
21     End;
```

PROGRAM 8.4   *Continued*

In the simulation result presented below, it is clear that the application of clock signals is essentially all that is required to generate the required NTSC control signals. Earlier in the simulation (not shown), the active-low reset signal was applied. This signal initialized the circuit and the application of a user supplied external clock signal provides the remaining requirement to generate the desired signal.

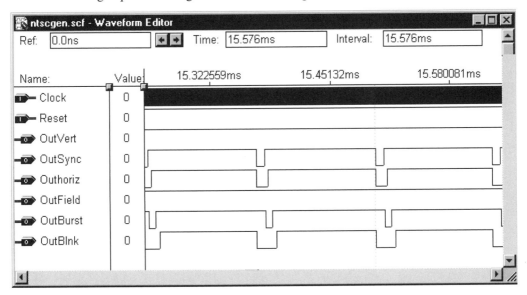

Simulation of Program 8.4: An LPM NTSC Television-Signal Generator

8.6 RETROSPECTIVE

In this chapter, we examined several examples of the growing industry-standard method of employing a library of parametric modules or LPMs. The LPM functions permit the logic designer to leverage enormous capability in the incarnation of software library functions much as software designers have been doing for many years. The innovation in the LPM method is that the technology, especially utilizing programmable logic devices, permits this enormous capability to be leveraged in hardware designs. This design method may be employed, as demonstrated, to achieve a large number of diverse capabilities from various fields of specialization. However, the more usual digital functions such as counters, arithmetic units, decoders, and many others may be achieved with similar ease. In many ways, the use of the LPM library is similar to the use of the 7400 library. An obvious exception is that the LPM library contains programmable parameters instead of accepting the off-the-shelf, built-in capability as is required with most of the 7400-library functions. These user-selectable parameters provide the designer flexibility and optimization capability.

CHAPTER 8 EXERCISES

1. Utilize the LPM phase-detector source file (program 8.2) as a basis to construct a source file with a directly instantiated LPM phase detector. The prototype of the LPM function is:

   ```
   FUNCTION PLL (a, b, nset)
    RETURNS (nup, tri-up, ndown, tri-down);
   ```

   Complete the simulation of the LPM phase detector by running a number of test cases. Use the output of the test cases to make a graph of the duty cycle of the two output waveforms as a function of the time differences in the rising edges of the appropriate input signals.

2. The notion behind parametric-software modules is that the designer can readily adapt basic building blocks with parameters of interest.
   a) Use the basic four-bit adder designs presented earlier as a guide and design an LPM sixteen-bit adder.
   b) Use some of the options such as fast-carry to modify the speed performance of the adder. Compare the performance of the adder with and without fast-carry options.

3. Design a demonstration of a memory read/write tester using a 16K-byte memory. The system should use an LPM_RAM memory system. The test sequence should be to write a checkerboard pattern to the RAM as follows

   ```
   loc 0      01010101
   loc 1      10101010
   loc 2      01010101
   ```

```
loc 3          10101010
. . . . . . . . .
. . . . . . . . .
loc 16382      01010101
loc 16383      10101010
```

The system should then read each memory location and check for the correct pattern.

The memory system must then write the "inverse checkerboard" memory pattern and repeat the check cycle. Following the system test, the memory system must indicate whether there were any bad memory locations and provide error locations to the user. If no errors were found, the system should so indicate.

4. Develop a 16-bit × 16-bit LPM multiplier using the direct instantiation method.

PART II

INTRODUCTION TO APPLICATIONS IN VHSIC HARDWARE DESCRIPTION LANGUAGE

CHAPTER 9

AN INTRODUCTION TO VHDL

9.1 INTRODUCTION

VHDL is arguably the most rapidly growing HDL. It has the benefit of being an IEEE-standard language and is widely recognized as an exemplary method of designing advanced digital systems The VHDL language is much more powerful than any other language utilized for similar purposes today. The power contained in the language is perhaps in some ways a mixed blessing. VHDL is verbose by any standard. On the other hand, the verbosity of the language provides many optional developmental approaches which are perhaps lacking in alternative languages. In this chapter, we present a number of illustrations intended to introduce the VHDL capabilities. The illustrations are selected to present a broad sampling of the semantics rather than to present a carefully structured sequential presentation.

9.2 A SHORT HISTORICAL NOTE

VHDL stands for VHSIC Hardware Description Language. VHSIC, in turn, stands for Very High Speed Integrated Circuits. The language has its origins in a Department of Defense, Tri-Service technology development program which was named the VHSIC program. The primary intent of the VHSIC program was to develop technologies that would permit integrated circuits to be fabricated at or below the 1 μm typical geometry dimension. This objective has been met and surpassed. Typical features in current integrated circuits are well below the 1 μm dimension and continue to be reduced. The VHSIC technology program was eminently successful and surpassed the 0.7 μm barrier before it had completed its course. During the course of the VHSIC program, it was realized that once the physical VLSI geometry hurdles were overcome, the complexity of the resulting circuitry required the development of automation tools with which to develop systems level applications. The most important of the automated tools was properly perceived to be an HDL. The language selected directly resulted in the development of VHDL. The U.S. Air Force accepted the lead role for the defense department and the rest, as they say, is history. This author was pleased to be able to work in the Air Force Avionics Laboratory, within earshot of the VHSIC program office, with some of the key members of that engineering and management team which so successfully produced accomplishments in the presence of overwhelming difficulties. I also had the pleasure of working on the first significant application of the new (at that time) technology in the development of the first VHSIC processor for military airborne applications. My congratulations to Dr. John Hines, Mr. John Blassingame, Mr. William Edwards, and all the others who worked directly on the VHSIC program with the Air Force Avionics Laboratory at Wright Patterson Air Force Base in Dayton, Ohio for a job extremely well done. And a special congratulations to my own former division team-mates who provided research on applications such as the VHSIC data processor. Congratulations especially to Mr. John Garcher, Dr. Mark Michael, and Mr. Mason Friar who worked the technical detail and Mr. Ernest Schelling who worked the international aspects so successfully.

9.3 A PROSPECTIVE GLANCE

As stated earlier, the VHDL language is a powerful and massive language with a myriad of alternative capabilities. We, perhaps, cannot do the language justice in the current text which is designed to introduce advanced digital system design and implementation using HDLs. However, we can cover a reasonable and useful cross-section of the language by exploring example applications. Applications alone are of marginal utility, absent basic principles. Clearly the reader will want to apply the language to new design situations and this consequently requires a knowledge of the language syntax and semantics. Therefore we will, out of necessity, cover some of the formal aspects of the language as required during our exploration. The main theme, however, will be to explore the language and its utility through relatively small although complete applications. The applications in this text are developed using the Altera MAX+plusII software package which contains compilers capable of processing both AHDL and VHDL. We now proceed directly to our first illustrative example which initiates our introduction to VHDL.

9.4 AN INITIAL VHDL COUNTER

We now explore the development of a three-bit counter using the VHDL language. The structure of the language is much more involved than that of the AHDL studied earlier in this text. Therefore, the structure of VHDL design programs is substantially different from the structure of AHDL programs. Rather than discussing the language features in the abstract sense, we choose to discuss them in the context of program 9.1, which is a three-bit (modulo 7) binary counter.

```
1    -- This is a three bit binary counter example in VHDL.
2    -- VHDL comments are preceded by
3    -- two dashes.
4    ENTITY count1 IS
5        PORT
6        (
7            clock            : IN  BIT;
8            enable           : IN  BIT;
9            qa               : OUT INTEGER RANGE 0 TO 7
10       );
11   END count1;
12       -- Architecture Body
13   ARCHITECTURE CountArch OF count1 IS
14   BEGIN
15       PROCESS (clock)
16           VARIABLE  count  :INTEGER RANGE 0 TO 7;
17       BEGIN
18           IF (clock'EVENT AND clock = '1') THEN
19               IF enable = '1' THEN
20                   count := count + 1;
21               END IF;
22           END IF;
23           qa    <= count AFTER 10 ns;
24       END PROCESS;
25   End CountArch;
```

PROGRAM 9.1   An Initial VHDL Counter

We now discuss the details of the VHDL implementation, program 9.1.

Lines 1–3: These comment lines are preceded by a double-dash, which is the VHDL single-line comment indicator.

Lines 4–11: Every VHDL program must have an entity declaration. All designs are described in terms of an entity which is an essential VHDL building block. The entity declaration here describes a counter named count1. The framing of lines 4 and 11 formalize the existence of the entity count1. At the entity level, nothing is known about count1 except that it has input and output ports (can you think of a digital system with no ports?). An analogy between the entity declaration of a VHDL source file and the subdesign section of an AHDL file can easily be made. The entity and subdesign sections of the source files each declare the I/O signals which will occupy pins on the respective implementation chips. The ports statement declares the ports, indicates their names and describes them as either IN (input) or OUT (output). The type of signal the port will carry is also declared as a part of the PORT declaration. BIT means exactly what the reader will think it means, a binary digit. The signals, clock and enable, declared as BIT, are therefore single binary logic lines. The signal, qa, defined as being of data-type integer, is further described as having a RANGE of zero to seven which indicates to the compiler that this is a three-bit value. Integer declarations, in a sense, abstract the underlying mechanisms of the digital implementation. This level of abstraction, convenient as it is, should not be permitted to unduly conceal the underlying digital implementation. The VHDL language differentiates between signals (for example, clock, enable) and integers (for example, qa). The syntax may be inferred from the text of the illustration. For example, the assignment operator, : =, may be used with integers (for example, line 20 of program 9.1). However, signals of type BIT require use of the <= assignment operator (for example, line 23 of program 9.1).

Lines 12–25: These lines describe the architecture body of the entity whose name the architecture declaration contains. In this case, the architecture declaration (line 13) declares the name of the architecture as CountArch and attaches the CountArch architecture to the entity count1. The architecture body is contained between the architecture BEGIN statement (line 14) and the End-architecture-name statement (line 25). If an entity performance or functionality is to be simulated, an architecture declaration is required.

Lines 15–24: In the present example, the architecture body contains a PROCESS, appropriately framed between the PROCESS-END PROCESS statement pair. The signal name, clock, contained within the parentheses forms a sensitivity list (of only one member in this case, but lists of signals are permitted). Whenever any of the signals on the sensitivity list change state, the process is executed. In the current example, whenever the signal, clock, changes state, the corresponding process portion of the design file is invoked.

Line 16: Between the PROCESS statement and the associated BEGIN statement is the declarative portion of the PROCESS section. In this example, a variable (not a signal) named count is declared. Count is declared as an integer with an allowable range from zero to seven. Within a process block, statements execute sequentially, starting with the PROCESS BEGIN statement.

Lines 17–24: The PROCESS block executes in sequential order whenever a change occurs on the clock signal. From line 18, it is clear that whenever the clock signal undergoes a positive transition, and if the enable signal line is true, then the count variable is incremented. The count variable is assigned a new value by the assignment operator, : =. Variables are always updated instantaneously, while signals require a finite time to change. This is the essential difference between a signal and a variable. In line 23, the signal set, qa, is updated from the variable "count." In line 18 of the source code, the program uses the predefined event attribute EVENT. When a signal name is pre-pended to the EVENT attribute, a new signal is formed which is asserted when an event occurs on the corresponding signal. The if statement in line 18 tests for this clock EVENT signal as well as the state of the clock signal.

Below, a simulation of program 9.1 is shown. The digital system works as expected. The counter does not increment while the enable line is false. Counting progresses at the positive clock edge when the enable line is true. Notice that with integers, the constant 1 is used in line 20, whereas the constant '1' is used with variables of type BIT as in lines 18 and 19. The after clause in line 23 is ignored in the PLD implementation.

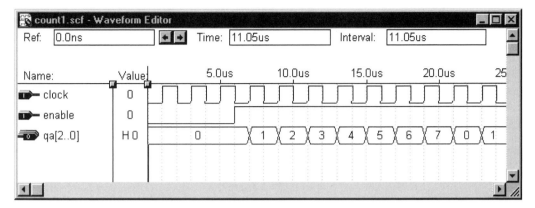

Simulation of Program 9.1: Initial VHDL Counter

9.5 A SIMPLE VHDL D-TYPE FLIP-FLOP

Flip-flops, especially D flip-flops, are important building blocks of integrated digital systems. D-type flip-flops, while an apparently elementary form of memory element (for example as, compared with J-K-type flip-flops), dominate as the choice of memory elements for integrated digital systems. In addition, D flip-flops are simple enough to be utilized in a fundamental example of a complete VHDL system, providing a concrete illustration of some of the syntax and semantics of the VHDL language. Since the D flip-flop readily serves in both capacities, this circuit type will be explored in a variety of circumstances and from slightly differing points of view. We now examine a fundamental exercise in producing a single D-type flip-flop. The flip-flop of program 9.2 has no preset or clear signal. It has only a D-input signal line which is transferred to the output when the positive clock transition occurs.

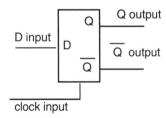

D Flip-Flop Modeled in Program 9.2

We now present the source file of program 9.2 which implements the D-type flip-flop described above.

```
1     -- first the entity declaration
2     ENTITY Dff IS
3          PORT(D     :    IN    BIT;
4               clock :    IN    BIT;
5               q     :    OUT   BIT
6               );
7     END Dff;
8     -- second the architecture body
9     ARCHITECTURE Arch OF Dff IS
10    BEGIN
11         PROCESS(clock)
12         BEGIN
13             if(clock'EVENT AND clock = '1') Then
14                    if(d='1') Then
15                            q <= '1';
16                    else
17                            q <= '0';
18                    end if;
19           end if;
20         END PROCESS;
21    End Arch;
```

PROGRAM 9.2   A Simple VHDL, D Flip-Flop

Lines 2–7 are the entity declaration for this system. As usual, the entity declaration simply declares the I/O terminals (ports, in VHDL terminology) of the associated entity.

Lines 9–21 create the architecture of the flip-flop entity. The only signal in the sensitivity list of the process is the signal, clock, which is contained in the parentheses of the process declaration statement (line 11). The process will be executed only when a clock event has occurred and the clock is in the logic-one state (see line 13). The conditions of line 13 assure that the process will only be executed when a positive edge has occurred on the clock signal. Therefore, the transference of the Boolean value on the D input signal line to the q output signal line will only occur on a positive-clock edge. The D input of the flip-flop is not contained in the sensitivity list of the current circuit and therefore events occurring on the D signal line do not cause the process to be invoked. Consequently, changes on the D input will not be transferred to the q output until a positive edge on the clock signal has been observed.

The performance of the VHDL D flip-flop through a simulation is presented directly below. The flip-flop has only three terminal points, the inputs: (1) clock, (2) D, and (3) the output terminal, q.

The output of the flip-flop designed in program 9.2 responds, as expected, to the positive-edge transition of the clock and the control input. No response is observed to the negative clock transition, again as expected. To demonstrate the design of a negative-edge

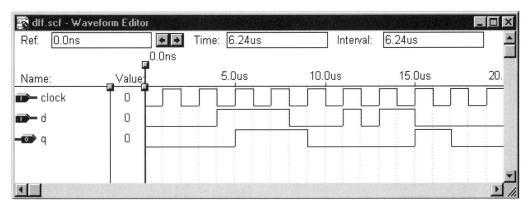

Simulation of Program 9.2: A Simple VHDL D Flip-Flop

triggered flip-flop, we make a slight variation of program 9.2 and show the resulting source listing as program 9.3 below.

9.6   A NEGATIVE-EDGE TRIGGERED FLIP-FLOP

In practice, it is common to utilize both positive-edge triggered flip-flops and negative-edge triggered flip-flops. For a direct comparison with the previous example, we now supply the source code for a negative-edge triggered flip-flop. Since the only difference between the two source files (programs 9.2 and 9.3) is the Boolean argument of the "if" statement, which tests for the state of the clock, we will not dwell on program listing 9.3. We simply present the source code and move on to the associated simulation.

```
1      -- A Negative Edge Triggered
2      -- VHDL, D Type Flip-Flop
3      -- without preset or clear signals
4      -- entity declaration
5      ENTITY Dffneg IS
6          PORT(D                      :    IN   BIT;
7               clock                  :    IN   BIT;
8               q                      :    OUT  BIT
9               );
10     END Dffneg;
11     --architecture body
12     ARCHITECTURE Arch OF Dffneg IS
13     BEGIN
14         PROCESS(clock)
```

PROGRAM 9.3   A Negative-Edge-Triggered VHDL Flip-Flop

```
15          BEGIN
16                  if(clock'EVENT AND clock = '0') Then
17                      if(d='1') Then
18                              q <= '1';
19                      else
20                              q <= '0';
21                      end if;
22              end if;
23          END PROCESS;
24      End Arch;
```

PROGRAM 9.3   *Continued*

Note that the change made to program 9.2 to produce program 9.3 is that line number 13 of program 9.2 is modified to incorporate the negative-edge trigger and becomes line 16 of program 9.3. The simulation of program 9.3 directly below shows that the performance is similar to program 9.2 except for the edge on which the flip-flop makes its decision. Since the performance of program 9.3 is so similar to that of program 9.2, we do not present a detailed description of program 9.3.

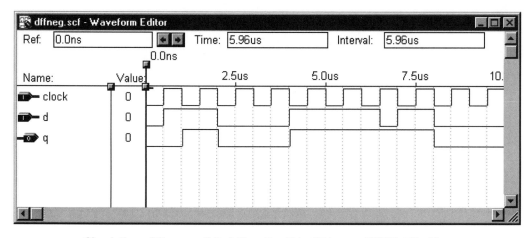

Simulation of Program 9.3: A Negative-Edge-Triggered VHDL Flip-Flop

The reader may observe that the negative-edge triggered flip-flop simulation above exhibits an apparent ANOMALIES at $t = 2.4$ μsec, 2.8μsec, and 7.6 μsec . The d input signal has not met the setup time and consequently the flip-flop should not have changed states. A closer examination reveals that the negative clock transition does not reach the EPLD flip-flop for over 2 ns after the system-clock transition (in other words, the EPLD clock transition is reached at ($t = 2.4$ μsec + 2^+ ns). Therefore, a minimum setup time has been observed for the requisite transition. This delay in the clock permits the flip-flop to transition as shown. This detail can be discovered by utilizing the simulator capability to show the clock transition directly at the flip-flop. The input of the flip-flop is an external node of the system.

9.7 A VHDL D-TYPE FLIP-FLOP WITH SYNCHRONOUS PRESET AND CLEAR

In this section, we elaborate on the previous example by adding preset and clear signals to the requirements for the flip-flop. Although asynchronous preset and clear signals are the more conventionally utilized signals, we present a system with synchronous preset and clear. For contrast, in a later circuit, asynchronous preset and clear will be developed. The source code below does not present an efficient method for processing because of the relatively poor manner in which the if statements are constructed. Assuming that a positive edge has occurred on the clock signal (see line 20), then the if statement in line 21 is executed, and depending upon the value of the d input line, the appropriate signal value is transferred to the output signal, q. Then the if statements in lines 27 and 31 are respectively handled making additional changes to the value of the output signal. Although inefficient, the code performs functionally and we present the source code and simulation results. The design for the system currently being discussed is program 9.4 below.

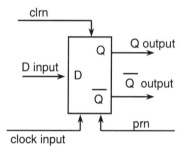

D Flip-Flop with Synchronous Preset and Clear

```
1     -- Source file for a D-type flip-flop with active low
2     -- preset and clear inputs
3     -- The preset and clear are not "conventional" in that
4     -- the prn and clrn signals are asynchronous
5     --------------------------
6     -- first the entity declaration
7     ENTITY Dffpc IS
8         PORT(D                    :    IN    BIT;
9             clock                 :    IN    BIT;
10            q                     :    OUT   BIT;
11            clrn                  :    IN    BIT;
12            prn                   :    IN    BIT
13            );
14    END Dffpc;

15    -- second the architecture body
16    ARCHITECTURE Arch OF Dffpc IS
```

PROGRAM 9.4 VHDL Flip-Flop with Active-Low, Synchronous Preset, and Clear

```
17   BEGIN
18        PROCESS(clock)
19        BEGIN
20            if(clock'EVENT AND clock = '1') Then
21                    if(d='1' and prn='1' and clrn='1') Then
22                            q <= '1';
23                    elsif(d='0' and prn='1' and clrn ='1') Then
24                            q <= '0';
25                    end if;
26        -- handle active low preset
27                    if(prn='0' and clrn='1') then
28                            q <= '1';
29                    end if;
30        -- handle active low clear
31                    if(clrn='0' and prn='1') Then
32                            q <= '0';
33                    end if;
34            end if;
35        END PROCESS;
36   End Arch;
```

PROGRAM 9.4 *Continued*

The simulation shown below verifies that program 9.4 produces a design which incorporates the synchronous signals discussed. From the simulation, we see that as long as the clrn signal is low, the flip-flop remains in the low state (as long as an appropriate clock edge has occurred) even when the D input signal is high over an interval including clock transitions. We also note that as long as the prn signal is low, the q output of the flip-flop remains high regardless of the state of the D input signal. When the clrn and prn signals remain high, the flip-flop behaves in its normal fashion.

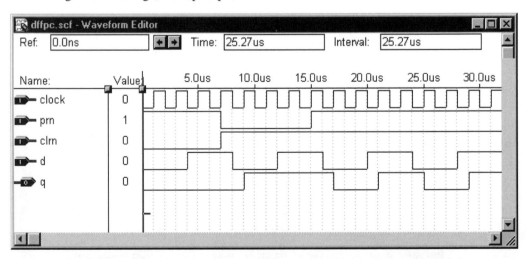

Simulation: VHDL Flip-Flop with Active-Low Synchronous Preset and Clear

9.8 A VHDL FLIP-FLOP WITH ACTIVE LOW ASYNCHRONOUS PRESET AND CLEAR

For a contrast with the previous illustration, we now examine a more traditional D flip-flop which contains active-low asynchronous preset and clear input signal lines (ports in the VHDL vernacular). The performance of the flip-flop is as follows. When the clear (clrn) and preset (prn) lines are high, the flip-flop retains its previous value until a positive clock edge occurs. When a positive clock edge occurs (assuming that clrn and prn remain high), the flip-flop reads the value of D into the stored value, q. If the active-low preset line is low, then the value of q goes high. If the value of the active-low clear line is low, then the value of q goes low. If both preset and clear are low (a condition which should normally be avoided), then the preset input line dominates and the value of the q output goes high. The source file for the design of the flip-flop is shown directly below.

```
1     -- D flip-flop with asynchronous
2     -- preset and clear input ports
3     --------------------
4     ENTITY Dffapc IS
5         PORT(clock          :IN      BIT;
6                             d          :IN      BIT;
7                             q          :OUT     BIT;
8                             prn        :IN      BIT;
9                             clrn       :IN      BIT
10          );
11    END Dffapc;
12    --------------------
13    Architecture Arch1 of Dffapc IS
14    BEGIN
15        PROCESS(clock, clrn, prn)
16            VARIABLE reset, set : INTEGER RANGE 0 to 1;
17            BEGIN
18                if(prn='0') Then
19                    q <= '1';
20                elsif(clrn='0') Then
21                    q <= '0';
22                elsif (clock'EVENT And clock = '1') Then
23                    q<=d;
24                END IF;
25        END PROCESS;
26    End Arch1;
```

PROGRAM 9.5   A VHDL Flip-Flop with Active-Low Asynchronous Preset and Clear

The source code is described in some detail on the next page.

Lines 4–11 constitute the entity declaration for the subject flip-flop. The entity of a VHDL source file declares the I/O ports of the device under consideration.

Lines 13–26 are the architecture definition of the entity. The name of the architecture and the associated entity are explicitly declared in line 13 which is the initial source line of the architecture definition.

Line 16 declares two variables, clrn and prn. The variables are of type integer, each which may take on the values of zero or one as indicated by the RANGE specification.

Lines 15–25 define a process framed by the Process/End-Process statement pair.

Lines 18–25 form the body of the process. Statements within this range are executed sequentially because they are contained in the process body. The variable declarations which occur between the Process and Begin statements have local scope (in other words, local to the process). The variables clock, clrn, and prn which appear in the parentheses of the process statement are considered within the sensitivity list of the process. When events occur on variables within the sensitivity list, the process is invoked and the statements within the process are executed.

A simulation for program 9.5 is shown below. From 0 to greater than 1 μsec, the preset line is held low. This prevents the d input from determining the q output, although several positive clock transitions occur. When the clrn line is asserted (not synchronous with the clock signal . . . around 1.5 μsec), the q output goes low asynchronously (in other words, not on clock transitions). When finally (2.8 μsec) both the prn and clrn signal are set high, the output follows the d input synchronously.

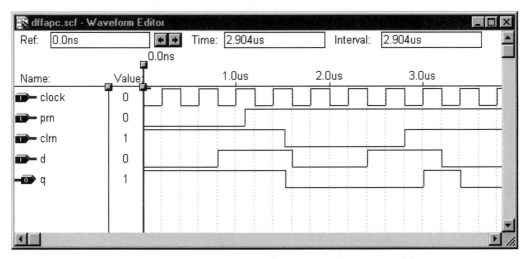

Simulation of Program 9.5: Flip-Flop with Active-Low prn/clrn

Additional simulations could be performed to fully verify the operation of the system at hand but for the current time, the simulation provides a suitable demonstration that the designed flip-flop performs as desired.

9.9 A ONE-BIT VHDL FULL ADDER

We now consider a one-bit VHDL full adder to contrast to the structure and syntax of the VHDL language and the Altera HDL. This comparison is made for the one-bit full adder of chapter 1. However, in addition to a contrast of the two programs, we introduce the use of VHDL libraries. The equations used to implement the full adder are the same as those utilized for the AHDL full adder. The previously derived and implemented equations are repeated below as equations (9.1) and (9.2), for convenience.

$$S = C_{in} \oplus A_1 \oplus A_2 \tag{9.1}$$

$$Cout = A_1 A_2 + C_{in}(A_1 \oplus A_2) \tag{9.2}$$

We now present the source code of the full adder in a VHDL implementation which will be discussed presently. The reader might also notice that both the entity declaration and the architecture body contain have the same name, FullAdd. The Altera compiler graciously accepted the overloaded names and this method of documentation may provide a viable alternative to using the differing architecture names of the previous VHDL examples. It may also interest the reader that the entity FullAdd in program 9.6 has declared as the type of the input and output signals, STD_LOGIC. A brief explanation of these types will be given here, but the reader is directed to the excellent texts by J. Bhasker (Bhasker, 1995),[1] and Douglas L. Perry (Perry, 1994),[2] for a complete explanation of these signals and the associated library.

The VHDL language includes a predefined logic type called, STD_ULOGIC. This logic type is an enumerated data type which contains the following nine members. Whenever more than a single logic driver electrically drives a given logic node, a reasonable question arises as to the resulting logic level. An examination of the associated definitions assists in uncovering the correct result of when multiple drivers drive a single node.

VHDL STD_ULOGIC

Nine-Level Data Type Table	
U	uninitialized
X	unknown
0	logic zero
1	logic one
Z	high impedance
W	weak unknown
L	low or weak logic "0"
H	high or weak logic "1"
—	don't care

Based upon a reasonable set of driver capabilities, a solution to this problem may be achieved. The solution to this problem is referred to as logic resolution. Package STD_LOGIC_1164 defines the STD_ULOGIC and further defines STD_LOGIC as a resolved subtype of data type STD_ULOGIC. The following table has been extracted from the Altera library documentation.

Resolution Table for Std_Logic from Std_uLogic

	'U'	'X'	'0'	'1'	'Z'	'W'	'L'	'H'	'–'
'U'	'U'	'U'	'U'	'U'	'U'	'U'	'U'	'U'	'U'
'X'	'U'	'X'	'X'	'X'	'X'	'X'	'X'	'X'	'X'
'0'	'U'	'X'	'0'	'X'	'0'	'0'	'0'	'0'	'X'
'1'	'U'	'X'	'X'	'1'	'1'	'1'	'1'	'1'	'X'
'Z'	'U'	'X'	'0'	'1'	'Z'	'W'	'L'	'H'	'X'
'W'	'U'	'X'	'0'	'1'	'W'	'W'	'W'	'W'	'X'
'L'	'U'	'X'	'0'	'1'	'L'	'W'	'L'	'W'	'X'
'H'	'U'	'X'	'0'	'1'	'H'	'W'	'W'	'H'	'X'
'—'	'U'	'X'	'X'	'X'	'X'	'X'	'X'	'X'	'X'

The logical variables in the table above are defined as follows

'U' = uninitialized
'X' = unknown
'0' = logic zero
'1' = logic one
'Z' = high impedance
'W' = weak unknown
'L' = weak logic zero
'H' = weak logic one
'—' = don't care

In Table above, the resolution of signals is relatively straightforward. For example, if two logic-one signals drive a common output line (see the '1' row and '1' columns) then the resulting output is clearly a logic '1' as seen by the cell at the intersection of the two driving signals. If a logic '1' and a tri-state driver ('Z') drive a common output line, the clearly the output is a logic '1' (see '1' row and the 'Z' column or the '1' column and the 'Z' row). Note also from the table that a logic '0' and a high impedance ('Z') always results in a logic '0', as would be expected. The resolution table also shows that a weak '1' (in other words, 'H') and a weak '0' (in other words, 'L') result in a weak unknown ('W'). The reader may want to study the resolution table further, but for the current time we progress toward additional examples.

The definitions and resolution logic contained in the tables respectively are defined in the IEEE-1164 standard logic package and table above is essentially a duplicate of the table shown in the standard (extracted from the Altera Max+PlusII files). The upshot, in a nutshell, is that the logic designer may safely use the standard logic definitions and the standard resolution table by simply including these definitions from the IEEE standard library package named ieee.std_logic_1164.all. This package is contained, as recommended in the VHDL standard, in a library named ieee in the Altera development system. Line 2 of the following source file references the correct library and line 3 of the source file includes the package by utilization of the USE clause. The logic signal may be utilized in a manner identical to that which would be done if we had declared the input and output signals to be of type BIT. However, by using the standard library file, we have the benefit of having the resolution of multiple drivers accomplished by the compiler. If we desire an alternate resolution table, one may be defined and utilized by the designer. We now present the source file of a one-bit VHDL full adder using the standard logic types referenced in the IEEE standard.

```
1    -- A VHDL, one bit Full Adder
2    LIBRARY ieee;
3    USE ieee.std_logic_1164.all;
4    Entity FullAdd IS
5            Port(  A1, A2, Cin      :    IN    STD_LOGIC;
6                   Sum, Cout        :    OUT   STD_LOGIC
7                   );
8    End FullAdd;
9    Architecture FullAdd OF FullAdd IS
10   Begin
11                   Process(A1, A2, Cin)
12                   Begin
13                        Sum <= Cin XOR A1 XOR A2;
14                        Cout <= (A1 And A2) OR (Cin And (A1
                              XOR A2));
15                   End Process;
16   End FullAdd;
```

PROGRAM 9.6 A One-Bit VHDL Full Adder

We now describe the functions provided in the source file above.

Lines 2–3: provide the availability of the IEEE standard library to the current source code. The Use clause allows the program to "Use" the standard_logic_1164 definitions.

Lines 4–8: declare the I/O ports of the full adder. These I/O signals will be assigned to I/O pins on the programmable chip which is used for implementation.

Lines 9–16: provide the architecture definition for the entity named FullAdd. In this case, the entity and the associated architecture have the same name. Lines 11 and 15 enclose a defined process. The intervening source lines 13 and 14 provide the processing logic which makes up the full adder. In this case, it is clear that the ordering of the execution of statements 13 and 14 is not necessary. When a file with modified order is compiled and the resulting simulation accomplished, no differences from the previous AHDL adder are observed in the simulation results.

The simulation below was accomplished from the files resulting from program 9.6. A visual inspection of the simulation results verifies that the designed adder works as desired. This concludes our exploration of the one-bit VHDL adder.

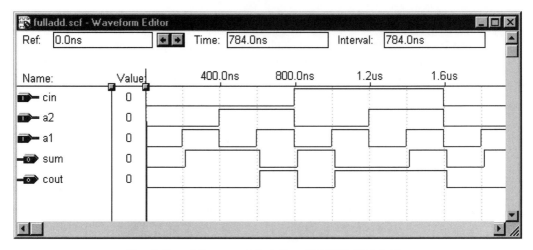

Simulation of Program 9.5: A One-Bit VHDL Full Adder

9.10   A FOUR-BIT VHDL ADDER

We now undertake the design of a four-bit full adder. An obvious alternative is to use the one-bit full adder of the previous section as a component. Four instances of the one-bit full adders could be either individually created or the required four adders could be generated if we so desired. This approach is quite reasonable and might be reasonably taken. However, we leave this alternative as an exercise for the reader. Instead, we take an approach requiring very little source code and present a variation on the structural approach discussed so far. Instead of working the structural details, we utilize the convenience of the integer data types and present program 9.6 as the source file to demonstrate the concept. The source file is now presented.

```
1      -- A VHDL 4 bit adder
2      Entity Fourbadd is
3          Port(Cin        :    IN    Integer Range 0 to 1;
4               Addend1     :    IN    Integer Range 0 to
                                       15;
5               Addend2     :    IN    Integer Range 0 to
                                       15;
6               Sum         :    OUT   Integer Range 0 to 31
7               );
8      End Fourbadd;
9      Architecture A4bitadd of Fourbadd is
10         Begin
11             Sum <= Addend1 + Addend2 + Cin;
12     End A4bitadd;
```

PROGRAM 9.6   A Four-Bit VHDL Adder

As usual, the entity declaration comes first and declares the input and output ports to be utilized on the implementation chip. In the entity declaration above, the carry input, as well as the two addends (in other words, Addend1 and Addend2) are declared as the required inputs. The Sum port is declared as the required output. The ranges of each of the variables is given by the range specification as a pair of decimal numbers. In the associated architecture specification, the input values are simply added using the arithmetic addition operator, since they have been declared as integers.

The simulation shown below clearly shows that the adder works as expected. The reader may consider variations such as extending the word lengths of the addends and/or providing an array of other alternatives.

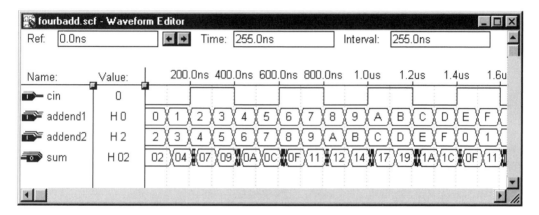

Simulation of Program 9.6: A Four-Bit VHDL Adder

9.11 RETROSPECTIVE

In this chapter, we have covered an informal introduction to the VHDL language. The use of the word informal here implies that a series of case studies has been accomplished without any particular concern as to how the various techniques explored fit into the general scheme of the VHDL landscape. The purpose of this rather ad-hoc approach is to obtain an initial feel for this very large and powerful language prior to incorporating a more complete study. An acquaintance with the general syntax and constructs available is useful for more in-depth examinations. The familiarity gained here will serve well when we begin to examine the language more carefully in the next chapter.

CHAPTER 9 EXERCISES

1. Design an Up-Down VHDL counter, using the VHDL "initial counter" presented in section 9.4 as a starting point:

  a) Add an input control line, "Direction" which controls the counting direction. Direction = '1'=> count up and Direction = '0' => count down.

  b) Create a simulation which demonstrates the correct performance of the Up-Down counter.

2. Modify the VHDL counter of exercise 1 to make an Up-Down-Hold counter.

  a) Add a second control line, Hold, to the counter such that when Hold = '0', then the counter is permitted to count in the direction indicated by Direction. When Hold = '1', then the counter remains in the current state.

  b) Create a simulation demonstrating the correct performance of the Up-Down-Hold counter.

3. Design a VHDL J-K flip-flop. Using the D flip-flop presented in section 9.5:

  a) Design a positive-edge-triggered J-K flip flop

  b) Create a simulation demonstrating the performance of the J-K flip-flop.

  Hint: Remove the D input port and add J and K input ports. Additional signals may be added between the Architecture keyword and the Begin keyword of the Architecture definition section. The signal declarations have the following syntax.

```
SIGNAL  signal_name :  type_name;
```

  The VHDL keyword SIGNAL is followed by the user's choice of signal names. A colon separates the signal name from the signal type. In the current case, the type should be BIT, followed by the usual, line-ending semicolon.

   The Internal logic for the formulation of the translation from D-type to JK-type may be implemented with the additional signals defined.

3. Convert the adder/subtractor presented in chapter 1 (program 1.7) into a VHDL adder/subtractor. Use the methodology developed in chapter 1, which employs 2's complement arithmetic data representation.

4. Design a four-bit VHDL adder using, as a basic component, the VHDL one bit full adder of program 9.6.

REFERENCES

1. J. Bhasker (1995). *A VHDL Primer Revised Edition.* Englewood Cliffs, NJ: Prentice Hall.

2. D. L. Perry (1993). *VHDL Second Edition.* New York: McGraw Hill.

CHAPTER 10

A SEMI-FORMAL INTRODUCTION TO VHDL

10.1 INTRODUCTION

The previous chapter was geared at providing a sudden immersion into a few working VHDL designs. This approach was taken to rapidly familiarize the reader with the general syntax and semantic structure of VHDL. We examined some working programs which immediately supply accurate, if unrefined, information concerning a relatively small number of the fundamental features of the VHDL. We now settle into a more systematic process of examining at least some of the formalized definitions and structures which are the hallmarks of the language. We do this in order to study the language more fully and provide the reader with some of the basics required for additional self-study. Nevertheless, we continue our examination largely by example and attempt to weave the essentials of the language into the context of the examples.

In this chapter, we continue to examine VHDL applications as a vehicle to explore the capabilities of this sophisticated and complex language. The direction of exploration will permit us to re-travel some of the logic design applications explored in previous chapters and to explore additional territories as well. In addition, we will examine the three principle methods available to the VHDL designer to implement the architecture portion of the source file. The three principle methods are (in no particular order):

1. The dataflow method,
2. The behavioral method, and
3. The structural method.

The three methods may be combined into a general design method which is referred to as the mixed-mode method.

In the dataflow method, signal assignment statements are executed concurrently. Statements of the form, $x <= y$, where x and y are both Boolean values (in other words, signals) are typical of the Boolean assignment statement. Formally, the definition assignment statements include both signal assignment and variable assignment statements, but in the present context we usually intend concurrency to be a property of signal assignment statements. Furthermore, in the concurrent signal assignment method, the transfer of Boolean values occurs concurrently, in simulated time (sometimes referred to as non-real-time or non-wall-clock-time). Whenever the designer desires concurrency of execution, he or she simply invokes the concurrent assignment statements.

In the behavioral method, assignment statements (and others) are contained between the Process and End-Process statement pair. When these otherwise-concurrent statements are so contained, the contained statements execute sequentially just as statements in a software programming language (for example, languages such as C , Pascal, or Ada).

In the structural method, the design is specified through the use of structural (in other words, wiring) descriptions. That is to say that the logical interconnection of circuit components is achieved in a notation which is presented by the designer through choices in the source language statements.

In the mixed mode, the designer uses any or all of the three design modes to provide the compiler with a description of the intended design.

We now proceed to a number of complete, if small, illustrative designs, each of which is a complete source file which will compile, generate a corresponding netlist, and will consequently provide a resulting simulation. The source files and corresponding simulation results will be presented.

10.2   THREE DESIGN METHODS

In this section we examine the fundamental design processes through the implementation of essentially the same flip-flop by several means.

10.2.1   A Dataflow D-Type Flip-Flop

The dataflow method utilizes statements of the type

$$x <= y \tag{10.1}$$

where x and y are each Boolean variables. In (10.1), the variable x is updated with the content of the variable y whenever the value of y changes. That is, the simulation monitors the values of all right-hand-side variables (variables are on the right-hand side of the assignment operator) and when these values change, the respective Boolean equations are updated appropriately. We say that equations containing the Boolean assignment operator

<= are concurrent. In this situation, assignments are ordered by the simulator and effectively are performed in a serial fashion in zero simulation time. This zero simulation time, of course, yields the appearance of concurrency in simulated time. More formally, VHDL does not acknowledge a zero-time Boolean assignment but instead refers to the time required as a delta-delay in simulated time. Delta-delay is an infinitesimally small delay in which simulation time is not advanced but the ordering of events is permitted to take place in the simulation. As a illustration of the dataflow modeling method, we now present a dataflow model of a D-type flip-flop. The flip-flop is unclocked and has the following characteristics. The signals clrn and prn are active-low clear and preset signals respectively with prn dominating if both signals are low. When the preset and clear signals are high, the output follows the input (after a suitable delay). The logic equations governing this device are:

$$q = \overline{prn} + (clrn)\, d \tag{10.2}$$

$$qbar = prn\,(\overline{clrn} + \overline{d}) \tag{10.3}$$

The process of deriving (10.2) and (10.3) are left as an exercise for the reader.

We now present the source file for the unclocked flip-flop.

```
1     -- D flip-flop dataflow
2     -- includes preset and clear input ports
3     -------------
4     ENTITY Dff_flow IS
5         PORT(d              :IN      BIT;
6              prn            :IN      BIT;
7              clrn           :IN      BIT;
8              q              :OUT     BIT;
9              qbar           :OUT     BIT
10             );
11    END Dff_flow;
12    -------------
13    Architecture Arch1 of Dff_flow IS
14    BEGIN
15                 q <= not prn Or (clrn And d);
16                 qbar <= prn And (not clrn Or not d);
17    End Arch1;
```

PROGRAM 10.1   An Unclocked D Flip-Flop

Lines 4–11: These lines define the entity with the name Dff_flow. The entity declaration includes the input and output ports as well as the type of the respective signals. In the present case, all signals are of type BIT meaning binary digit. Lines 13–17 define the body of the device architecture. The equations in the body of the architecture (lines 15–16) define the functional behavior of the device and also mean that no physical structure of the flip-flop is implied by the structure of the VHDL program.

In the simulation below, all four combinations of the clrn and prn signals have been used at the beginning of the simulation file (0 through 40 ns). When the clear and preset signals have been deactivated (after 40 ns), the output of the flip-flop follows the input after a 15-ns delay. This is the propagation time of the programmable array element used for the implementation device (in this case, an Altera EPM7032LC44 EPLD). The simulation is carried out using the selected device parameters. In the simulation below, the typical propagation times are of the order of 15 ns.

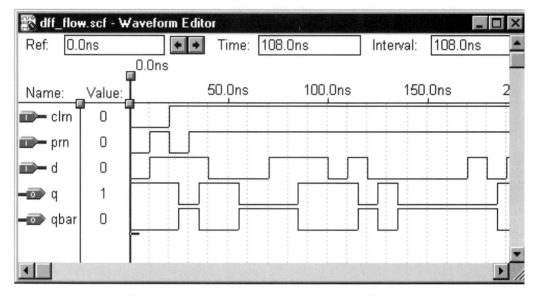

Simulation of Program 10.1: An Unclocked D Flip-Flop

10.2.2 A Structural D-Type Flip-Flop

In this section, we design a single D flip-flop formulated with a structural method as contrasted to the dataflow method of the previous section. We begin by building a primary component of flip-flop which is a two-input Nand gate.

10.2.2.1 A Two-Input Nand Gate The basic building block component of the flip-flop of this section will be a two-input Nand gate. We therefore briefly present this component in a dataflow format.

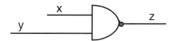

Two-Input Nand for Program 10.2

Without further discussion, we present the source code for the two-input Nand gate.

```
1    -- A two input Nand gate
2    Entity Nandtwo is
3          PORT(x, y      :IN BIT;
4                z          :OUT BIT
5                );
6    End Nandtwo;
7    Architecture Nandtwo of Nandtwo Is
8    Begin
9          z <= not(x And y);
10   End Nandtwo;
```

PROGRAM 10.2   A Two-Input Nand Gate

In the simulation below, all four combinations of the input variables, x and y, are shown along with the resulting output, z. The input variables are toggled every 10 ns. The output is shown to properly follow the logical Nand Boolean function after a 5-ns delay. In program 10.2, lines 1–6 contain the Nand gate entity definition and lines 7–10 define the architecture body of the Nand gate.

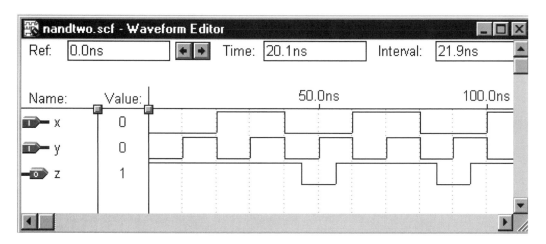

Simulation for Program 10.2: A Two-Input Nand Gate

As in previous simulations, the digital system displays a consistent 15-ns delay. This circuit is capable of producing 100 million decisions per second if the 15-ns delay can be tolerated. The simulation device selected here is the Altera 7032 ELPD. We next proceed to utilized this Nand gate as a component in a slightly larger system.

10.2.2.2 Structural D Flip-Flop Implementation

In contrast to the dataflow flip-flop presented earlier, we now examine a flip-flop implemented in a structural manner. The flip-flop will be specified as a structural element and is based upon the diagram below.

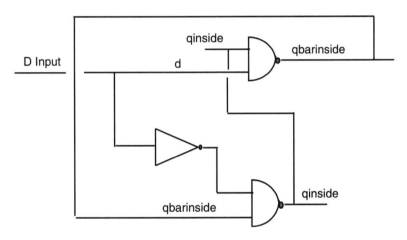

**Schematic Flip-Flip Circuit for the
Structural Representation of Program 10.3**

As indicated, we utilize the basic component studied in the previous section. The structural representation will be documented in the VHDL text style directly, consistent with the logic diagram above. The VHDL source file which implements the required D-type flip-flop is presented directly below. The flip-flop is structurally represented by internal signals and then transferred to the declared ports.

```
1    -- A structural D-Flip-Flip
2    Entity Dff_str Is
3    PORT (d             :IN BIT;
4          q             :OUT BIT;
5          qbar          :OUT BIT
6          );
7    End Dff_str;
8    -------------------
9    -------------------
```

PROGRAM 10.3   A Structural D Flip-Flop

```
10    Architecture ADff_str of Dff_str Is
11    Component Nandtwo
12        Port(x, y          :IN BIT;
13             z             :OUT BIT
14             );
15    End Component;
16    ----
17    Signal qbarinside, qinside          :BIT;
18    Signal dbar                         :BIT;
19    Begin
20        Nandqbar            : Nandtwo Port Map(qinside, d,
                                   qbarinside);
21        Nandq               : Nandtwo Port Map(qbarinside,
                                   dbar, qinside);
22        dbar <= not d;
23        q <= qinside;
24        qbar <= qbarinside;
25        End ADff_str;
26    --------------
27    --------------
28    Entity Nandtwo is
29        PORT(x, y          :IN BIT;
30             z             :OUT BIT
31             );
32    End Nandtwo;
33    Architecture ANandtwo of Nandtwo Is
34    Begin
35        z <= not(x And y);
36    End ANandtwo;
```

PROGRAM 10.3   A Structural D Flip-Flop

In the source file for the structural D flip-flop shown above, a brief review of the code reveals that the architecture of dff_str, which is the structurally implemented flip-flop, is supported with a dataflow architecture for the Nand gate, Nandtwo. In the implementation of the Dff_str, structural architecture, *structure* rather than the *behavior* of the D flip-flop is dictated by the VHDL code. The designer may choose from all of the alternative implementation methods when designing digital systems with the VHDL language. We now examine the source file in some detail.

Lines 1–6 constitute the flip-flop entity. Lines 3–6 of the entity declaration declare the three I/O signals which are each of type bit.

Lines 10–25 make up the architecture definition for the D flip-flop. Lines 17–18 declare the signal lines which make up the internal connection signals for the flip-flop. Lines 20 and 21 each create instances of the Nandtwo gate object. The Nandtwo object used here is the same Nandtwo object of the previous illustration (program 10.2). The first Nandtwo gate is called Nandq and the second has the name Nandqbar. The naming convention here is meant to imply the gates which represent the true side and the false side of the implemented flip-flop respectively. Lines 20 and 21 further define the interconnection of the two Nand gates using the internally defined signal lines. The signal lines of the instantiated Nand gates are mapped to the signal ports of the Nand gate object by ordinal association with the entity port definitions of the port map arguments provided by lines 20 and 21.

Lines 22–24 provide concurrent statements which are used to convey the flip-flop input signals to the internal circuitry and, in turn, convey the internal signals to the output ports.

Lines 28–32 are the source lines used to declare the Nandtwo entity which is the primary component object of the flip-flop. These lines have been described in Program 10.2 above.

Lines 33–36 are the source lines defining the architecture of the constituent Nand gates.

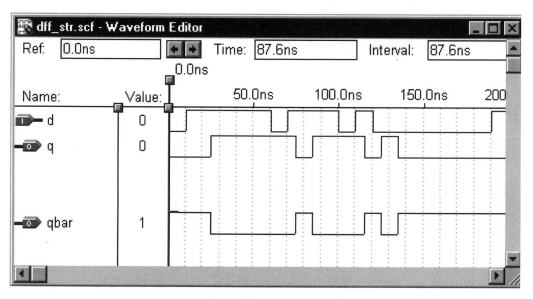

Simulation of Program 10.3: A Structural D Flip-Flop

The simulation of the structural flip-flop, presented above, demonstrates that the memory element works as expected. Furthermore, the propagation delay for the flip-flop is 15 ns which depends upon implementation delay revealed earlier in the investigation of the constituent Nand gates.

10.2.3   A Behavioral (Sequential) Flip-Flop

In the immediately previous sections, we developed two unclocked flip-flops. We now examine a flip-flop structured from sequential statements. In the vocabulary of VHDL, this method is known as a behavioral method. By behavioral here we mean that the statements of the model are executed sequentially (Bhasker, p. 17). Our examination here will continue to concentrate on the contrasts in the various styles or methods of VHDL.

```
1    -- A behavioral D-Flip-Flip
2    Entity Dff_beh Is
3    PORT (d        :IN BIT;
4        q          :OUT BIT;
5        qbar       :OUT BIT
6        );
7    End Dff_beh;
8    ----------------------------
9    Architecture Adff_beh of Dff_beh Is
10   Begin
11   Process(d)
12   Begin
13       q <= d;
14       qbar <= not d;
15   End Process;
16   End ADff_beh;
```

PROGRAM 10.4   A Sequential D Flip-Flop

The general implementation requirements to be met are relatively clear at this point, so we no longer elaborate on the functional requirements but limit our discussion to the essential differences between the current implementation method and the previous implementation methods. It may be of interest to note that there is no explicit memory mechanism specified in the source file of program 10.4. The VHDL language provides for the maintenance the variables (for example, q, qbar) from invocation-to-invocation of the process. This is similar to the static storage-type declaration of the C programming language.

In program 10.4 above, a *process* has been used in the architecture of the Dff_beh flip-flop implementation. Although the process statement itself is considered as a concurrent statement, the statements in the process scope (in other words, the statements framed by the process and end process commands) are executed sequentially. The variable d, which appears in the parentheses following the process statement, is considered to be in the sensitivity list of the process. This implies that the process block is invoked each time the variable, d, exhibits an event. The simulation presented below serves to demonstrate that the system implementation of Program 10.4 performs suitably.

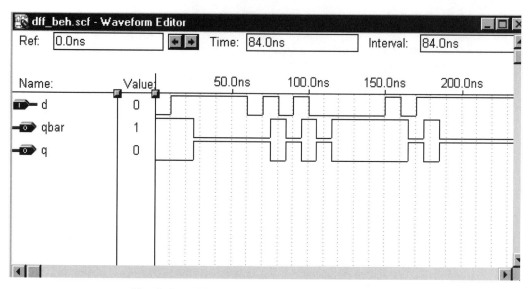

Simulation of Program 10.4: A Sequential Flip-Flop

10.2.4   A Clocked Behavioral D Flip-Flop

In the sequential circuit of the previous section, the full benefits of the sequential processing are not utilized. The constructs such as if statements, case statements, and many others are classified as sequential in nature and are consequently only accessible inside
process blocks. We now provide an example which more fully utilizes the sequential capabilities available inside process blocks. The source listing for a clocked D flip-flop is
shown below. The source file is based upon the design characteristics shown in the following truth table. From the truth table it is clear that the prn and clrn signals should not
be asserted simultaneously. In the final implementation of the K-map solution, the logic is
simplified by making a choice as to the dominance of one of these input signals.

Truth Table, Flip-Flop

prn	clrn	D^n	Q^{n+1}
0	0	0	x
0	0	1	x
0	1	0	1
0	1	1	1
1	0	0	0
1	0	1	0
1	1	0	0
1	1	1	1

K-map for Q^{n+1}

		prn/clrn			
		00	01	11	10
D	0	x	1		
	1	x	1	1	

From the K-map it is clear that the implementing equation should be

$$Q^{n+1} = \overline{prn} + D^n \cdot clrn$$

Note that this is the equation implemented below in the source file of program 10.5.

```
1     -- Source file for a D-type flip-flop with active low
2     -- preset and clear inputs
3     --------------------------
4     -- first the entity declaration
5     ENTITY Dffpc2 IS
6          PORT(D                 :     IN    BIT;
7               clock             :     IN    BIT;
8               clrn              :     IN    BIT;
9               prn               :     IN    BIT;
10              q                 :     OUT   BIT;
11              qbar              :     OUT   BIT
12              );
13    END Dffpc2;

14    -- second the architecture body
15    ARCHITECTURE Arch OF Dffpc2 IS
16    BEGIN
17         PROCESS(clock, clrn, prn)
18         BEGIN
19             if(clock'EVENT AND clock = '1') Then
20                         q <=not prn Or (clrn And d);
21                         qbar <= prn And (not clrn Or not
                           d);
22             end if;
23         END PROCESS;
24    End Arch;
```

PROGRAM 10.5   A Clocked Behavioral (Sequential) Flip-Flop

Lines 5–13: of the source file form the entity and, in turn, define the I/O ports in lines 7–11.

Lines 15–24: form the body of the flip-flop architecture and define the performance in a functional manner.

The simulation below initializes the q and qbar values to zero (this case would be avoided in an actual application). Since the operation of the flip-flop is dependent upon the clock activity, this contradiction in flip-flop states does not correct itself until the occurrence of the first clock pulse or the clrn and prn signals are asserted properly.

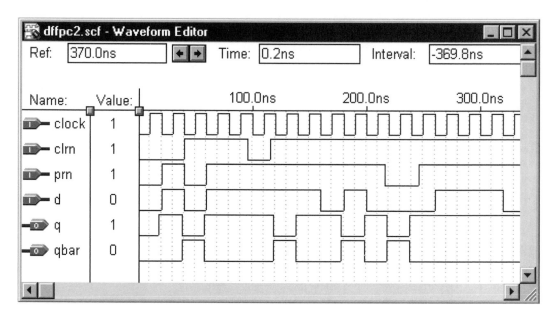

Simulation for Program 10.5: A Clocked Behavioral (Sequential) Flip-Flop

10.3   A VHDL, POSITIVE-EDGE DETECTOR

The positive-edge detector examined in this section is the same type required in the asynchronous serial receiver developed earlier (see chapter 5). The reader may directly compare the digital system implementation of the edge detectors in the AHDL language with the same circuit developed here in VHDL. In the prior investigation, we developed a UART serial receiver function utilizing the AHDL. This application will assist in our elaboration of the capabilities and comparisons of these two very capable languages. The examination here continues to use the VHSIC HDL as a vehicle in our pursuit of advanced logic design, digital system synthesis, and digital system implementation. The system that is the focus of the present design effort is shown in the diagram below.

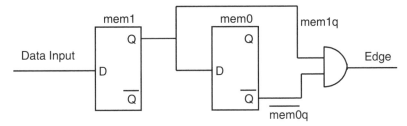

Logic Circuit for Program 10.5

Program 10.1 is the source file that forms the focus of our current discussion. We now examine the source file in some detail.

Lines 3–11: constitute the entity declaration for the positive-edge detector which is named PosEdge. The entity declaration simply defines the I/O relationships of the desired entity. No structural, logical, or behavioral implementation may be inferred from this declaration.

Lines 12–30: describe the architecture of the entity, PosEdge. The corresponding architecture description is named, in turn, PosEdgeArch. These lines of the source file are referred to as the architecture body for the entity PosEdge. The architecture body describes the internal structure of the entity. In this case, the architecture body requires the use of D-type flip-flops. Therefore, the entity definition and architecture body for these components must be available to the compiler.

Lines 33–39: declare the entity which is the D-type flip-flop component to be used. The entity declaration is simply a declaration of existence through the annunciation of the I/O signal characteristics.

Finally, lines 41 through 54 describe the architecture of the D-type flip-flop and are referred to as the architecture body of the D flip-flop.

The four essential portions of the source code which must be available to the compiler are described above. These portions are: (1) the posedge entity, (2) the posedge architecture, (3) the D flip-flop entity, and (4) the D flip-flop architecture. We now present the source file and then describe the content of the source file in some detail.

```
1       -- VHDL positive edge detector
2       ----------------------
3       -- entity declaration for posedge
4       Entity PosEdge IS
5             Port    (        clk         :     IN     BIT;
6                              DataIn      :     IN     BIT;
7                              q1          :     OUT    BIT;
8                              q0          :     OUT    BIT;
9                              Edge        :     OUT    BIT
```

PROGRAM 10.5   A VHDL Positive-Edge Detector

```
10                      );
11    End PosEdge;

12    --architecture body for PosEdge
13    Architecture PosEdgeArch of PosEdge is
14    Component Dff
15            Port(D, clk: IN BIT;
16                  q: OUT BIT);
17    End Component;
18    Signal mem1q, mem0q: BIT;
19    Begin
20            FF1: Dff Port Map(DataIn, clk, mem1q);
21            FF0: Dff Port Map(mem1q, clk, mem0q);
22            Process(clk)
23            Begin
24                if(clk'EVENT And clk='1') Then
25                        q1 <= DataIn;
26                        q0 <= mem1q;
27                        Edge <= mem1q And not mem0q;
28                end if;
29            End Process;
30    End PosEdgeArch;
31    ------------------------
32    ------------------------
33    - entity declaration for Dff
34    Entity dff IS
35    PORT(        D         :      IN     BIT;
36                 clk       :      IN     BIT;
37                 q         :      OUT    BIT
38                 );
39    End dff;
40    -------
41    -- architecture body for Dff
42    ARCHITECTURE DffArch OF Dff IS
43    BEGIN
44        PROCESS(clk)
45        BEGIN
46                if(clk'EVENT AND clk = '1') Then
47                        if(d='1') Then
48                                q <= '1';
49                        else
50                                q <= '0';
51                        end if;
52                end if;
53            END PROCESS;
54    End DffArch;
```

PROGRAM 10.5 *Continued*

The details of source file program 10.1 are now presented.

Lines 4–11: are the entity declaration for the edge detector. In this declaration, the port definitions for the edge detector are given and include two input signals of type BIT, namely clock and DataIn. Also included are two outputs of type BIT, which are made up of output signals from the two flip-flops involved as well as the edge-detection output signal.

Lines 12–30: constitute the architecture body for the edge detector. In lines 14–17 the designer has indicated that a component of type Dff will be employed in the architecture implementation. The entity declaration for the Dff component is contained within the source file in this example. Lines 20 and 21 instantiate two components of type Dff which are named FF1 and FF0, respectively. In these same two instantiation lines, a port map is indicated. The port map provides a port interconnection netlist. Ports can be directly interconnected with other distinct ports that have been defined in the entity declarations. The interconnections may be directly provided in the port map by name reference. Internal connections are made with the assistance of the signals which are defined and appropriately typed in signal statement number 18. Lines 23 through 29 contain the Process-End Process command pair which coerces the enclosed statements to execute sequentially.

In *lines 33–39:* the entity declaration for the component Dff is provided. Dff in this case is a simplified D-type flip-flop. In a practical implementation, a more complete version may be desirable (at least providing a reset input terminal for power on restart conditions). The simplified version has been provided to minimize the already lengthy source code listings. An example of a more complete D-type flip-flop entity declaration was provided in some of the prior illustrations.

Lines 42–54: contain the architecture body for the component Dff. Line 44 contains the process declaration statement and includes the clk signal as a *sensitive* signal. That is, whenever an event occurs on the clk signal, the process in this body is executed. The process body contains lines that are sensitive to the positive clk-signal edge and will be executed sequentially whenever a clk 'EVENT signal is indicated on a positive-clock edge.

The functional performance of the VHDL positive-edge detector is shown below. The simulation was performed on the Altera logic simulator which is a part of the MAX+plusII software package.

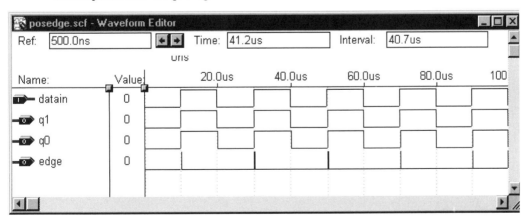

Simulation of Program 10.5: A VHDL Positive-Edge Detector

10.4   A BEHAVIORAL TWISTED-RING COUNTER DESIGN

In this section, we examine the concurrent method of implementation in the development of a twisted ring. In software programming languages, the series of commands or instructions commonly comprise a program that is sequential in nature. That is to say, if one command appears before a second command in the source listing, then the first appearing instruction will be executed before the second. (In advanced parallel hardware architectures and an advanced compiler, this is no longer strictly true, but the notion is sufficiently familiar that we will rely on it in any event.) In digital hardware systems, sequential processing must be carefully structured if desired, since parallelism is the norm. That is, when the appropriate clock edge appears, all circuits connected to that particular clock (usually large numbers of circuits) simultaneously acquire new states. If two processes are to be coerced into a sequential relationship, then that sequential relationship must be carefully established by the control equations governing the processing. In all of the AHDL programs contained in part one of this book, concurrent processing was assumed. VHDL on the other hand contains the semantic mechanisms to provide for concurrent processing, sequential processing, and combinations of such processing. In this section, our sample system will contain concurrent code to implement a twisted-ring counter.

10.4.1   Twisted-Ring Counter Design

To continue to provide a comparison of the syntax and semantics of the AHDL and VHDL hardware design files, we now study a three-bit twisted ring designed in a VHDL design source file. Earlier, in section 2.4, we examined a three-bit twisted ring designed in an AHDL design source file. The current VHDL source file does not contain rectification logic should the counter wander into a so-called *illegal* state. The current design file is presented partly for the purpose of elaborating upon the syntactic and semantic description of VHDL design methods as well as to present subsystem modules that have some utility in pragmatic digital system implantation projects.

   We next present the design of the three-bit twisted ring as program 10.6 below.

```
1     -- entity declaration for twisted ring
2     ENTITY twist3 IS
3         Port(              clk           : IN  BIT;
4                            q2            : OUT BIT;
5                            q1            : OUT BIT;
6                            q0            : OUT BIT
7               );
8     END twist3;
9     -----
10    -- architecture body for twist3
11    Architecture Twist3Arch OF twist3 IS
12    Component D_ff
```

PROGRAM 10.6   A VHDL Three Bit Twisted Ring

```
13              Port(D, clk: IN BIT;
14                   q, qbar: OUT BIT);
15      End Component;
16      Signal FF2q, FF1q, FF0q, FF2qbar, FF1qbar, FF0qbar: BIT;
17      Begin
18              FF2: D_ff Port Map(FF0qbar, clk, FF2q, FF2qbar);
19              FF1: D_ff Port Map(FF2q, clk, FF1q, FF1qbar);
20              FF0: D_ff Port Map(FF1q, clk, FF0q, FF0qbar);
21              PROCESS(clk)
22                  Begin
23                          if(clk'EVENT And clk ='1') Then
24                                  q2 <= FF0qbar;
25                                  q1 <= FF2q;
26                                  q0 <= FF1q;
27                          end if;
28          End Process;
29      End Twist3Arch;
30      -------------------
31      -- entity declaration for d-flip-flop
32      ENTITY D_ff IS
33          PORT(D                   :    IN    BIT;
34              clk                  :    IN    BIT;
35              q                    :    OUT   BIT;
36              qbar                 :    OUT   BIT
37              );
38      END D_ff;
39      -- architecture body for d-flip-flop
40      ARCHITECTURE D_ffArch OF D_ff IS
41      BEGIN
42          PROCESS(clk)
43          BEGIN
44              if(clk'EVENT AND clk = '1') Then
45                      if(d='1') Then
46                              q    <= '1';
47                              qbar <= '0';
48                      elsif(d='0') Then
49                              q <= '0';
50                              qbar <= '1';
51                      end if;
52              end if;
53          END PROCESS;
54      End D_ffArch;
```

PROGRAM 10.6   *Continued*

Lines 1–8: These lines form the entity declaration of the three-bit counter. Only the I/O signals are declared and described as being of type BIT.

Lines 10–29: The architecture of the three-bit twisted-ring is presented in this portion of the source file. Lines 12 through 15 indicate that the architecture of the three-bit twisted-ring incorporates a component of type D_ff. The I/O ports of the component are further declared as a part of the component declaration. As is readily observed, the I/O ports and their respective signal types are given in the argument list. Line 16 provides a signal declaration. The signals declared in this portion of the source file will be used presently as a means of interconnection within the architectures to implement the desired functionality.

Lines 18–20: are used to instantiate three flip-flops of type D_ff. For each of the instantiated flip-flops, the port map, which is contained in the argument list following the instantiation, provides a description of the port utilization for that particular instantiated component. Each component of type D_ff, contains four ports in the current example. In the entity description of the D_ff entity declaration, four ports are declared. These ports are in ordinal conformance with the four ports that are declared in the port map. However, the ordinal port members in the port-map declaration contain the signal names that have been declared in the prior signal declaration statement.

Lines 21–28: complete the architecture description of the counter. The statements are included in the process section (bracketed with the Process-End Process statement pair). Statements in the process section are always executed sequentially. The process statements are executed when an event occurs on the clk signal and the clk signal is at the true level. The statements within the process section implement the process dynamics. That is, the port map interconnections provide the means for the following. (1) The high-order two bits (FF2 and FF1) are shifted to the right. (2) The inverse of the low-order bit (FF0) is shifted into the high-order bit position. The clk'EVENT if-clause fragment provides the data path of the signal to the counter output.

The entity description (lines 32–38) and the architecture description (lines 39–54) for the D-type flip-flop are similar to entity declarations and architecture bodies provided earlier in this chapter.

In the simulation below, the operation of the system is shown. The counter generates 2n states where n is the number of memory elements. Therefore there are 2(3) or six *legal* states in this nonbinary counter.

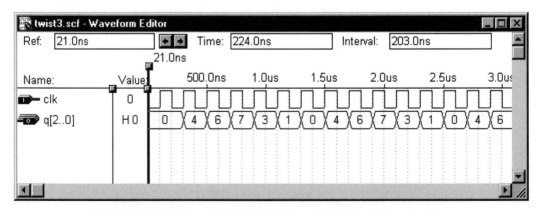

Simulation of Program 10.6: A VHDL, Three-Bit Twisted-Ring Counter

10.5   VHDL STATE MACHINES

In this section, we provide the development of a state machine alongside some basic digital processes studied earlier. We now proceed to design illustrative systems in the VHDL language, which strongly resemble systems designed earlier utilizing the AHDL language.

10.5.1   Ten-Bit VHDL Polynomial and Ordinal Counters

In the current section, we examine the design of a polynomial counter similar to those discussed earlier (for example, see chapter 4), but we now examine an implementation in the VHDL language. The counter is clocked with a single clock which also constitutes the sensitivity list of the associated process. We also implement a collateral, tracking, ordinal counter for the purposes of easing the testing and examination of the system functional performance. Since the examinations of similar systems has been undertaken previously, we proceed directly to the source-level implementation which is provided directly below.

```
1    -- poly counter[9..0]
2    Library IEEE;
3    Use ieee.Std_Logic_1164.all;
4    Entity poly11 is
5            Port(Clock          :In   Bit;
6                    PolyOut     :Out  Bit_Vector(9 downto 0);
7                    CountOut    :Out  Integer Range 0 to 1024
8                    );
9    End Poly11;
10
11   Architecture APoly11 of Poly11 is
12   SIGNAL Poly : Bit_Vector(9 downto 0);
13   Signal Count: Integer Range 0 to 1024;
14   Begin -- architecture
15   Process(clock)
16           Begin -- process
17           if(clock'Event and clock = '1') then
18                   if( Poly(9 downto 0) = ('0','0','0',
                       '0','0','0','0','0','0','0') ) then
19                           Poly(0) <= '1';
20                   else
21                           Poly(8 downto 0) <= Poly(9 downto
                           1);
22                           Poly(9) <= Poly(3) XOR Poly(0);
23                           PolyOut <= Poly;
24                   end if;
25   ------------------
```

PROGRAM 10.7   Matching Polynomial and Ordinal Counters

```
26              Count <= Count + 1;
27              if(Count = 1023) then
28                      Count <= 0;
29          end if;
30          CountOut <= Count;
31          end if;
32      End Process;
33      End Apoly11;
```

PROGRAM 10.7 *Continued*

The input signal is a single-clock signal. The output signals are: (1) PolyOut, which is the ten-bit output of a polynomial counter which is declared of type BIT_VECTOR and (2) CountOut, which is the ten-bit output of a natural binary counter declared as type INTEGER.

Lines 11–33: are the architecture definition associated with the Poly11 entity.

Lines 17–24: implement the control logic for the polynomial generation and are imbedded in the process part of the architecture definition. Lines 18, 19 assure that the illegal state is avoided. Line 22 provides the polynomial generator feedback mechanism.

Lines 26–31: contain the control of the ordinal reference counter which provides a convenient reference for our observations.

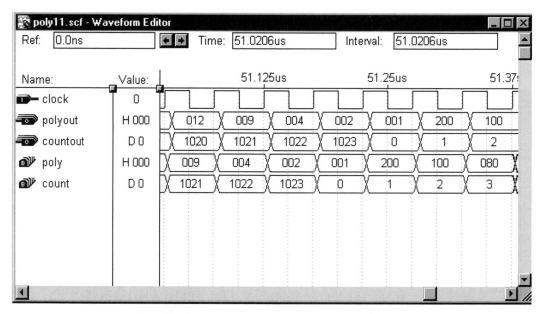

Simulation of Program 10.7: Matching Polynomial and Ordinal Counters

In the system simulation fragment provided above, it is clear that the proper operation of the polynomial counter is likely. As the ordinal reference counter rolls over from the decimal count of 1023 to the next value, which is zero, the polynomial counter rolls over to 0x001. An additional clue concerning the correct operation of the counter is provided by the fact that the poly counter rolls over in a sequence containing the ordered members . . . 0x004, 0x002, 0x001, 0x200, 0x100 . . . which is the expected sequence. The reader may want to implement the counter of program 10.7 and examine an expanded set of simulations to further verify the correct operation of the polynomial sequence generator.

10.5.2 A VHDL FSM State Machine Monitor for an m-Sequence Generator

In chapter 7, we examined a state machine, which was implemented in the AHDL language. That state machine was designed particularly to monitor specific characteristics of an m-sequence generator. Here, we undertake a similar problem for the expressed purpose of studying a slight variation on the original system design, but more fundamentally to examine an implementation of a VHDL state machine.

In the next source file, we include a ten-bit binary ordinal counter and a ten-bit pseudo-random counter as presented in the previous section. We augment the design of the two sequential machines with an fsm machine design which serves to monitor a specific characteristic of the pseudo-random code generator. The subject VHDL file is presented below and is briefly described following the source file listing. In the source listing, note that the function of the system is to track the state of the pseudo-random sequence which is generated from the m-sequence generator. The state machine implemented in VHDL below performs a function much like that of the corresponding AHDL state machine of chapter 7 (fsm monitor for an m-sequence generator). The state machine below keeps track of the number of occurrences of exactly four zeroes in a contiguous sequence.

```
1     ----------------------------
2     -- State Machine entity
3     ----------------------------
4     ENTITY pnState IS
5         PORT(
6                 clock              :IN   BIT;
7                 StateOut           :OUT  Integer Range 0 to 5;
8                 CountRef           :OUT  Integer Range 0 to
                                      1024;
9                 Exact4ZeroesOut    :Out  Integer Range 0 to 64;
10                pnzero             :Out Bit
11                );
12    End pnState;
13    ----------------------
14    --State Machine Architecture
15    ----------------------
```

PROGRAM 10.8   A VHDL FSM for Monitoring an m-Sequence Generator

```
16    ARCHITECTURE ApnState OF pnState IS
17    Component Poly11
18         Port(Clock               :In  Bit;
19         PolyOut                  :Out Bit_Vector(9 downto 0);
20         CountOut                 :Out Integer Range 0 to 1024
21         );
22    End Component;
23    Signal Exact4Zeroes  :Integer Range 0 to 64;
24    Signal pncode        :Bit;
25    ------------
26    Signal PolyOutBus : Bit_Vector(9 downto 0);
27         TYPE STATE_TYPE IS (z_zero,
28                               z_one,
29                               z_two,
30                               z_three,
31                               z_four,
32                               z_GreaterThanFour);
33         SIGNAL NumZeroes: STATE_TYPE;
34    BEGIN — Architecture
35    PolyNew              :   Poly11 Port Map(Clock,
36                                             PolyOutBus,
37                                             CountRef
38                                             );
39         PROCESS (clock)
40         BEGIN
41             IF clock'EVENT AND clock = '1' THEN
42                 pnzero <= PolyOutBus(0);
43    -------------------------------------------
44    -- Beginning of State Machine for detecting zeroes
45    -------------------------------------------
46             CASE NumZeroes IS
47                 WHEN z_zero =>
48                     IF PolyOutBus(0)='0' THEN
49                             NumZeroes <= z_one;
50                     Else
51                             NumZeroes <= z_zero;
52                     END IF;
53         ----------
54         WHEN z_one =>
55             IF PolyOutBus(0)='0' THEN
56                     NumZeroes <= z_two;
57             Else
58                     NumZeroes <= z_zero;
59             END IF;
60         ----------
61         WHEN z_two =>
```

PROGRAM 10.8 *Continued*

```
62                    IF PolyOutBus(0)='0' THEN
63                            NumZeroes <= z_three;
64                    Else
65                            NumZeroes <= z_zero;
66                    END IF;
67                ----------
68            WHEN z_three =>
69                    IF PolyOutBus(0)='0' THEN
70                            NumZeroes <= z_four;
71                    Else
72                            NumZeroes <= z_zero;
73                    END IF;
74                ---------
75            WHEN z_four =>
76                    IF PolyOutBus(0)='1' THEN
77                            Exact4Zeroes <= Exact4Zeroes +1;
78                            Exact4ZeroesOut <= Exact4Zeroes;
79                            NumZeroes <= z_zero;
80                    Else
81                            NumZeroes <= z_GreaterThanFour;
82                    End If;
83            WHEN z_GreaterThanFour =>
84                    IF PolyOutBus(0)='0' THEN
85                            NumZeroes <= z_GreaterThanFour;
86                    Else
87                            NumZeroes <= z_zero;
88                    End if;
89              END CASE;
90           END IF;
91      END PROCESS;
92      -- Output section of State Machine
93      WITH NumZeroes SELECT
94          StateOut <= 0    WHEN    z_zero,
95                       1    WHEN    z_one,
96                       2    WHEN    z_two,
97                       3    WHEN    z_three,
98                       4    WHEN    z_four,
99                       5    WHEN    z_GreaterThanFour;
100     END ApnState;
101     ---------------------------------
102     -- start of poly generator entity
103     ---------------------------------
104     Library ieee;
105     Use ieee.Std_Logic_1164.all;
106     -------------
107     Entity poly11 is
```

PROGRAM 10.8   *Continued*

```
108          Port (
109                    Clock     : In    Bit;
110                    PolyOut   : Out   Bit_Vector(9 downto 0);
111                    CountOut  : Out   Integer Range 0 to 1024
112            );
113  End Poly11;
114  -------------------------------
115  -- start of poly generator architecture
116  -------------------------------
117  Architecture APoly11 of Poly11 is
118  SIGNAL Poly : Bit_Vector(9 downto 0);
119  Signal Count: Integer Range 0 to 1024;
120  Begin -- architecture
123  Process(clock)
124          Begin -- process
125          if (clock'Event and clock = '1') then
126                  if( Poly(9 downto 0) =
                                          ('0','0','0','0','0',
                                           '0','0','0','0','0') )
                                          then
127                          Poly(0) <= '1';
128                  else
129                          Poly(8 downto 0) <= Poly(9 downto
                             1);
130                          Poly(9) <= Poly(3) XOR Poly(0);
131                          PolyOut <= Poly;
132                  end if;
133  --------------------
134                  Count <= Count + 1;
135                  if(Count = 1023) then
135                          Count <= 0;
136                  end if;
137          CountOut <= Count;
138          end if;
139  End Process;
140  End Apoly11;
```

PROGRAM 10.8 *Continued*

In the source listing of program 10.8, the following descriptions apply.

Lines 1–12: describe the entity which is the state machine. The clock is provided to synchronize the state machine. StateOut provides an output indicating the internal state of the system. StateOut is written from the internal bus named state. CountRef is an ordinal output reference for the state machine and is written from the internal signal source named Count. The signal Exact4Zeroes keeps a running record of the number of runs of exactly four zeroes which occur in the ten-bit pseudo-random sequence of length 1023.

Finally, the signal defined as pnzero is the least-significant bit of the ten-bit pn sequence. It is this signal which the state machine examines and is utilized as a pseudo-random serial bit sequence.

Lines 13–100: are the lines establishing the architecture of the monitoring state machine. Within the architecture body, lines 17 through 21 create a template of a ten-bit polynomial counter which is identical to the polynomial counter of Listing 10.7. A copy of the ten-bit polynomial counter is contained in the source listing of program 10.8 as well. Lines 23 through 26 create internal signals which are described as follows:

- Exact4Zeroes is a signal of six binary bits by virtue of its range declaration.
- pncode is the least significant bit of the m-sequence generator. This code is the serial pn sequence being generated.
- PolyOutBus is the bus declared for use in the m-sequence generator instantiation statement, which is lines 35 through 38.

Lines 27–32: define an enumerated variable with an enumerated type declaration statement. The name of the variable selected makes it clear that the variable is to be used for state names. The type being declared is a user-defined type called STATE_TYPE. The state names are:

- z_zero $\longrightarrow$ PolyOutBus(0) = pnzero is a logic '1'
- z_one $\longrightarrow$ one zero detected
- z_two $\longrightarrow$ two consecutive zeroes detected
- z_three $\longrightarrow$ three consecutive zeroes detected
- z_four $\longrightarrow$ four consecutive zeroes detected
- z_GreaterThanFour $\longrightarrow$ five or more consecutive zeroes detected

Line 33: declares a signal named NumZeroes which is of type, STATE_TYPE. This variable is used to keep track of the states of the VHDL state machine.

Lines 35–38: as indicated above, are used to create an instance of the m-sequence generator (or polynomial generator) from the template created by the preceeding component statement (see lines 17–21). The ordering of the variables in the I/O list of the instantiation statement is important to the interpretations of the variables. The mapping made is:

- clock is the state machine input variable, clock;
- PolyOutBus is the ten-bit polynomial produced by the counter; and
- CountRef is the state machine ordinal output variable.

Therefore, PolyOutBus(0) becomes the low-order bit of the pn sequence generator output.

Line 42: writes the serial, pseudo-random code to a machine output pin.

Lines 46–89: contain the state-machine logic. The state machine is attempting to find all runs of exactly four zeroes.

Lines 92–99: write the state information to the machine output.

Lines 101–140: are presented in the current file for readability of the source file. They are identical to program 10.7 and are described in the previous section. They contain the polynomial generator entity declaration and architecture body.

A system simulation segment is shown below. The ordinal count is in the range 968_{10} to 974_{10}. Therefore the simulation is approaching the end of the 1,023 bit cycle of the serial sequence presented by pnzero. The state machine has assumed the state of z_zero each time the value of pnzero is a logic-one. Otherwise, the state machine tallies the number of consecutive zeroes and sets its state accordingly. When exactly four consecutive ones are detected, the tally is incremented. Notice the delay associated with the internal machine tally (in other words, Exact4Zeroes) and the corresponding output (Exact4ZeroesOut).

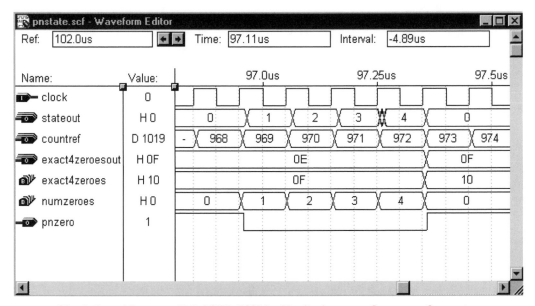

Simulation of Program 10.8: VHDL FSM for Monitoring an m-Sequence Generator

As a final examination of the state machine operation, we show an earlier segment of the simulation.

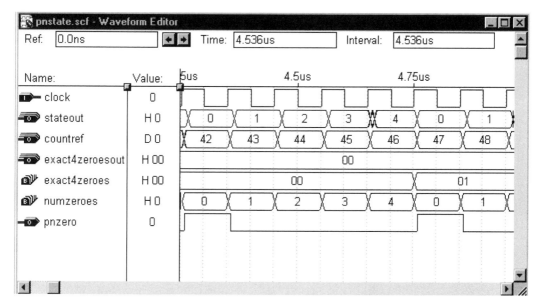

Simulation of Program 10.8: VHDL FSM for Monitoring an m-Sequence Generator

In this second segment, it is clear that the first string of four consecutive zeroes has been detected. Here, when the string of four zeroes is terminated by a one bit, the internal signal Exact4Zeroes is incremented, but the corresponding output, Exact4ZeroesOut, is not incremented simultaneously.

10.6 VHDL AND A CLASSIC 74283 ADDER CIRCUIT

In previous chapters, we discussed the importance of classical 7400-series circuits. The traditional 7400-series functions have been facilitating advanced logic functions and continually improving for a period exceeding a quarter century. These consequential circuits have an esteemed position both in history and modern design practice. The era of 7400 circuits continues in custom, semi-custom, and programmable logic devices through their functional representation in modern computer-aided-design systems. Most VHDL compilers contain some manner of method for the inclusion of the classic 7400-circuit functions. In this section, we examine the inclusion of a 74283 adder circuit using the Altera VHDL compiler. The current example serves not only as a guide for the utilization of the adder circuit considered here, but also as a typical guide for the inclusion of 7400-series functions into a VHDL file in general.

In the digital system considered here, we include a 74283 adder circuit for demonstration purposes. The adder circuit is provided to the source file as an entity using the VHDL component statement. An instance of the adder is then created using a component instantiation statement. The source file along with a simulation segment is shown below.

Lines 1 through 10 make up the entity declaration. The VHDL entity declaration is much like the AHDL subdesign section in which the input and output signals are declared. Although the format or syntax of the AHDL and VHDL input/output declarations differs substantially, there is significant similarity in interpretation.

```
1      -- VHDL and Adder Macrofunction
2      ENTITY MAdder IS
3         PORT(
4             ArgAIn                :IN  Bit_Vector(4 downto 1);
5             ArgBIn                :IN  Bit_Vector(4 downto 1);
6             PortCin               :IN  Bit;
7             PortCout              :OUT Bit;
8             SumOut                :OUT Bit_Vector(4 downto 1)
9             );
10     END MAdder;
11     -------------------------
12     Architecture A_MAdder of MAdder is
13     -------------------------
14     -- Macrofunction definition
15     --FUNCTION 74283 (a[4..1], b[4..1], cin)
16     --RETURNS (cout, sum[4..1]);
17     -------------------------
18     COMPONENT a_74283
19        PORT(
20            A, B                  :IN   Bit_Vector(4 downto 1);
21            Cin                   :IN   BIT;
22            Cout                  :OUT  BIT;
23            Sum                   :OUT  Bit_Vector(4 downto 1)
24            );
25     END COMPONENT;
26     SIGNAL A      :Bit_Vector(4 downto 1);
27     SIGNAL B      :Bit_Vector(4 downto 1);
28     Signal Cin    :Bit;
29     Signal Cout   :BIt;
30     Signal Sum    :Bit_Vector(4 downto 1);
31     Begin -- architecture
32     Adder1: a_74283 PORT MAP (A, B, Cin, Cout, Sum);
33         Process(ArgAIn, ArgBIn, Cin)
34             Begin
35                 A <= ArgAIn;
36                 B <= ArgBIn;
37                 Cin <= PortCin;
38                 PortCout <= Cout;
39                 SumOut <= Sum;
```

PROGRAM 10.9   A VHDL Design Including a 74283 Adder Circuit

```
40                    End Process;
41   End A_MAdder;
```

PROGRAM 10.9 *Continued*

Lines 12- 41: constitute the architecture definition of the MAdder entity.

Lines 14–16: are comment lines which include the function declaration for the 74283 logic circuit function. These comment lines are to recall the ordering of the argument terms.

Lines 18–24: make up the component declaration statement and provide the 74283 entity availability to the current source file.

Lines 26–30: declare signals internal to the MAdder architecture with which internal connection are made.

Line 32: provides an instance of the subject 74283 adder circuit, named Adder1. Adder1 is the single adding circuit utilized in this illustration.

Lines 33–40: describe a process within which the main processing occurs. The sensitivity list for the process includes port signals ArgAIn, ArgBIn, and Cin. Whenever any of these signals change state, the process is invoked. The process body contains logical statements which carry the input signals to the adder instance and, in turn, carry the output signals to the entity output ports.

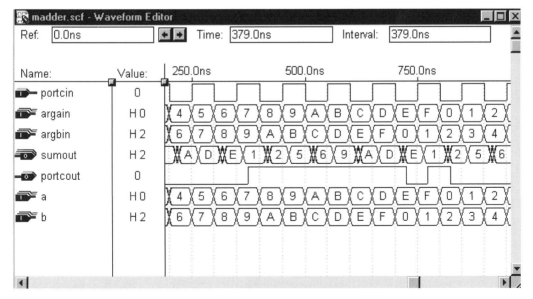

Simulation of Program 10.9, A VHDL Design Including a 74283 Adder Circuit

The simulation above is mostly self-explanatory. The content of the two argument-input buses are summed and placed onto the sumout output bus. The carry input and carry output signals take part in the arithmetic operations in the usual manner.

10.7 RETROSPECTIVE

In this chapter, we examined some of the contrasting methods that may be employed to create and build VHDL hardware designs. The basic design of flip-flop elements has been used primarily to explore quintessential methods of VHDL design. In addition, we examined some applications of common interest. Included are some applications involving a binary counter, a polynomial-sequence generator, and also a VHDL state machine which demonstrates a number of language features useful in VHDL applications. The concluding illustration provided the means for incorporating classical 7400-series logic templates in a VHDL source file.

In this chapter, we have by no means provided a complete set of alternatives, but we have shown some of the more straightforward techniques for the use of VHDL descriptions. Illustrations were developed from source files through to system simulation. The developed systems may then easily be implemented using programmable logic devices.

CHAPTER 10 EXERCISES

1. Design a binary up-counter.
   a) Implement a four-bit binary up-counter, identical to the AHDL counter designed in chapter 4. Create a simulation to verify the performance of the system.
2. Design a four-bit binary down-counter using the state table and K-map technique used in chapter 4.
   a) Implement the counter using a VHDL source file. Create a simulation verifying your design.
3. Combine the two counters above into a single, up-down counter. The counter must have a single up/down control line (UpDn = 1, => count up, UpDn = 0, => count down).
   a) Produce a single VHDL source file implementing the desired up-down counter.
4. Modify the design of the twisted ring of program 4.6.
   a) Add the required logic which prevents the twisted ring from being "beached" onto one of the invalid subrings.
   b) Develop a simulation and verify your design.
5. Develop a source file for an HDL five-bit pseudo-random sequence generator (pn generator or maximal length sequence generator). Name the generator PolyA.
   a) Use the D flip-flop with asynchronous preset and clear signals that was developed in chapter 9. Add a simple binary counter to the source file to facilitate the examination of the simulation phase of the testing.

  b) Create a simulation and utilize the asynchronous preset and clear signals to initialize the generator into several different states to validate the generator's operation.

6. Design a second pn generator identical to the generator of exercise 5.

  a) Name the generator PolyB and append the source code to the source file developed in exercise 5 above.

  b) Design logical circuits which will simultaneously compute autocorrelation values $R_{xx}(m)$, $m = 0, 1, 2, 3, 4$, where

$$R_{xx}(m) = \sum_{k=0}^{2^n-1} x(k)x(k+m)$$

Add the source code for the autocorrelation computation to the file containing the pn generators and compile the source file. Design the code such that m may be readily expanded. Develop a simulation or a set of simulations in which the values of $R_{xx}(m)$ are calculated over an entire period of the autocorrelation function. Graph the autocorrelation values over an entire period of the function and compare your results to theoretical values.

  c) Create a simulation which runs the generators and computes the autocorrelation values as the pn generators sequence through their cycles of length, $2^n - 1 = 31$.

7. A maximal length sequence generator consisting of eleven stages, say Poly[10..0], requires only one two-input exclusive-or gate. This gate takes inputs from the Poly[0] and Poly[2].

  a) Design a pn generator consisting of eleven stages. The generator will develop a sequence of length $2^n - 1 = 2,047$. To ease the problem of tracking the m-sequence generator for simulation purposes, design an ordinal, binary counter to run "alongside" the m-sequence generator. Develop a simulation to assure that the m-sequence generator is executing properly.

  b) Design a finite state machine which gathers statistical information concerning the m-sequence generator. The fsm is to detect all runs of zeroes and all runs of ones. At the completion of the $2^n - 1$ generation intervals, the fsm is to contain the number and size of runs as follows.

Run Variable	Run Size	Number of Runs
Logic 0	1	xxx
	2	yyy
	3	zzz
	4	www
	......	....
Logic 1	1	x'x'x'
	2	y'y'y'
	3	z'z'z'
	4	w'w'w'
	.....	....

8. Redesign the state machine of program 10.8 so that the value of the output bus Exact4ZeroesOut is synchronized as closely as possible to the value of the internal bus Exact4Zeroes. Verify your design through a simulation.

9. Develop a VHDL ripple counter similar to the ripple counter of chapter 4.

10. Develop a VHDL gray-code counter similar to the gray-code counter of chapter 4.

CHAPTER 11

INTEGER TYPES, USER TYPES, ARRAYS AND FUNCTIONS IN APPLICATIONS

11.1 INTRODUCTION

In this chapter, we examine some applications including integer data types, integer arrays, and functions. Functions employing integer data types are utilized in selected applications. The primary effort here is to examine typical applications. A companion text such as Perry (1994), and/or Bhasker (1995) may be used for a more complete and formal coverage of the VHDL language. Instead here we concentrate on complete, compiled, and simulated results.

11.2 LOGIC VECTORS, INTEGERS, AND COMPANION COUNTERS

In this section, we examine some of the characteristics and operations on standard logic bits, standard logic vectors, and integers. We include the application of a pair of companion counters. The two counters we examine here are (1) a six-bit sequential, binary counter (a modulo-64 counter) and (2) a six-bit polynomial counter. The binary counter is a straightforward sequential counter and the polynomial counter is a pseudo-random sequence generator. Examination in this section includes typical operations (for example, comparisons) performed on both standard logic vectors and integers. The comparison operations are virtually identical but the formats of data types differ. In addition to the comparison of data types, data formats, and operations, we coincidentally examine the differences involved in integer and Boolean mathematical types. As usual, our examination takes place within the context of complete, compiled, and simulated code illustrations. A final bit of value may be achieved by the current example. If the designer wishes to quickly ascertain the relationship between a six-bit linear sequence and six-bit pseudo-random sequence, simulation of the current illustration will yield this relationship. The illustration may be expanded in order to achieve relationships for sequence generators of other lengths.

Without additional discussion, we now present program 11.1, which contains

- integer data types,
- integer arithmetic,
- standard logic data types,
- standard logic vector data types,
- Boolean arithmetic on standard logic types, and
- companion six-bit sequence generators.


```
1      Library ieee;
2      USE ieee.std_logic_1164.all;
3      Entity Poly6 is
4      Port(clock           :IN  Bit;
5      countpoly            :OUT Std_Logic_vector(5 downto 0);
6      Sequential           :OUT Integer range 0 to 63;
7      cardout              :OUT Integer range 0 to 1;
8      randout              :OUT Std_Logic
9             );
10     End Poly6;
11     Architecture APoly6 of Poly6 is
12           Signal random      :Std_Logic_Vector (5 downto 0);
13           Signal Cardinal    :Integer Range 0 to 63;
14           Signal Card        :Integer Range 0 to 1;
15           Signal Rand        :Std_Logic;
16     Begin
17           Process(clock)
18           Begin
19                 if(clock'event and clock='1') then
20                       if(random(5 downto 0) = ('0','0',
                          '0','0','0','0') )then
21                             random(0) <= '1';
22                 else
23                             random(4 downto 0) <=
                              random(5 downto 1);
24                 end if;
25                 if(random(0) = not random(1) ) then
26                             random(5) <= '1';
```

PROGRAM 11.1   Companion Six-Bit Sequence Generators

```
27                    else
28                                        random(5) <= '0';
29                end if;
30          Cardinal <= Cardinal + 1;
31          end if;
32          countpoly <= random;
33          Sequential <= Cardinal;
34    -- decode for poly code
35          if(Random(5 downto 0) = '0', '0', '0', '1',
                                      '1', '1') ) then
36              Rand <= '1';
37          else
38              Rand <='0';
39          end if;
40    -- decode for sequential counts
41          if(Cardinal = 3) then
42                Card <=1;
43          else
44                card <= 0;
45          end if;
46      RandOut <= rand;
47      CardOut <= card;
48      End Process;
49    End Apoly6;
```

PROGRAM 11.1 *Continued*

A detailed examination of program 11.1 is now undertaken.

Lines 1 and 2 are used to include the standard logic definitions from the appropriate, standard VHDL library files. In the Altera configuration used throughout this text, the library files are delivered with the development system.

Lines 3–9, which make up the entity declaration, define the I/O ports with a number of different logical and mathematical data types. A standard logic vector is a purposely grouped number of signals of the standard logic type. Integer data types represent ordinary mathematical integers. The output port bus of program 11.1, countpoly, defines six output data pins by virtue of the "5 downto 0" subscript notation. The output port bus named sequential also utilizes six output pins because the integer range variable specifies the VHDL range 0 to 63 phrase. Therefore, the countpoly and sequential output port specifications jointly consume twelve output pins of the implementation chip. When designing with VHDL, the integer data abstraction conceals the underlying digital data representation. This is not fundamentally different from the use of integer or floating-point data types in scientific software development. However, the VHDL designer is constantly aware of the underlying binary representation by reason of the physical constraints of chip implementation.

Lines 11–46 specify the architecture body of the poly6 entity.

Lines 12–15 define a set of signal lines which mirror the corresponding port definitions of the entity. Lines 12 and 13 each specify buses of six-bit width. Line 12 is reasonably explicit in its six-bit bus declaration while line 13 is implicit in its declaration of a six-bit data bus through the use of the "0 to 63" VHDL phrase.

Lines 17–48 specify a process that has only a single signal, clock, on its sensitivity list. The statements within the process are executed sequentially whenever the clock signal realizes a positive transition from the 0 state to the 1 state.

Lines 20–29 construct the six-bit pseudo-random sequence generator. Lines 20 and 21 initialize the counter and assure that the counter will not become beached on its only illegal state. Line 23 is the right-shift register portion of the generator while lines 25 to 28 form the feedback potion of the generator logic.

Line 30 implements the entire sequential counter.

Lines 34–39 implement an arbitrarily selected decode state (seven in this case) for the polynomial sequence generator.

Lines 40–45 implement an arbitrarily selected decode state (three in this case) for the linear sequence generator.

Lines 46 and 47 merely connect the selected decode lines to the respective output pins (ports).

The simulation below shows a portion of the generated sequences when each of the generators is "wrapping-around" in its respective cyclic sequence. In the simulation segment shown, the linear sequence displays the partial sequence ... 61, 62, 63, 0, 1, 2 ... which reveals the modulo-64 nature of the generator. The pseudo-random generator observes the sequence ... 0x0F, 0x07, 0x03, 0x01, 0x20, 0x10, 0x08 ... which clearly reveals the random nature of the sequence in which 0x01 not 0x00 is the initial value of the random sequence generator.

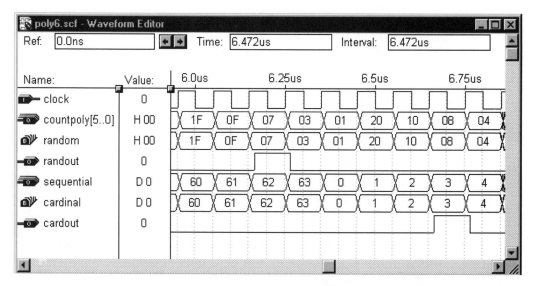

Simulation of Program 11.1: Companion Six-Bit Generators

11.3 A SIMPLE INTEGER PROCESSOR

In this section, we examine the use of integers instead of standard logic vectors or bit vectors to implement a small arithmetic processor. The only signals declared here as standard logic types (or standard logic vectors) are the Opcode and clock signals. All of the arithmetic processing is accomplished with integer declarations and integer arithmetic. In addition, we look at the implementation of a CASE construction in the VHDL language. The specification for our small processor is given in the following table.

Operation Table for Program 11.2

OpCode	Operation/Output
0x0	operand1 + operand2
0x1	operand1 − operand2
0x2	$2 \times$ operand1
0x3	operand1
0x4	operand2
any other opcode	set illegal flag

We now present program 11.2, an example of an integer-implemented processor.

```
1     Library ieee;
2     Use ieee.Std_Logic_1164.all;
3     Entity Proc1 is
4           Port(
5                 clock           :IN  Std_Logic;
6                 OpCode          :IN  Bit_Vector(3 downto 0);
7                 IllegalOp       :OUT Std_Logic;
8                 Operand1        :IN  Integer Range 0 to 31;
9                 Operand2        :IN  Integer Range 0 to 31;
10                Result          :OUT Integer Range 0 to 63
11                );
12    End Proc1;
13    ----------------------
14    Architecture AProc1 of Proc1 is
15    Begin
16          Process(clock)
17          variable arg1, arg2        :Integer range 0 to
                                         31;
18          Begin
19          if(clock'event and clock = '1') then
20          arg1 := Operand1;
21          arg2 := Operand2;
```

PROGRAM 11.2 An Integer Processor

```
22                          CASE Opcode IS
23                              WHEN X"0" =>
24                                Result <= arg1+arg2;
25                                      IllegalOp <='0';
26                              WHEN X"1" =>
27                                Result <= arg1-arg2;
28                                      IllegalOp <='0';
29                              WHEN X"2" =>
30                                Result <= arg1*2;
31                                      IllegalOp <='0';
32                              WHEN X"3" =>
33                                Result <= Operand1;
34                                      IllegalOp <='0';
35                              WHEN X"4" =>
36                                Result <= Operand2;
37                              WHEN others =>
38                                Result <= 63;
39                                      IllegalOp <='1';
40                          END CASE;
41                  end if;
42              End Process;
43      End AProc1;
```

PROGRAM 11.2 *Continued*

In program 11.2, the data elements (buses) have been declared as integers. Certainly the integer declarations and arithmetic yield simple and straightforward code for the processor we demonstrate here. The data buses represented by operand1, operand2, and Result consume sixteen output pins (two five-bit busses and one six-bit bus). The total I/O pins either explicitly or implicitly required by the port declarations of program 11.2 come to twenty-two. In addition to the twenty-two pins required by the port specification, power supply and grounding pins are required on the implementation.

The CASE construction is sufficiently expressive for the current example that we avoid writing detailed descriptions of the processing. However, partial descriptions are offered below and hopefully provide the necessary degree of clarification. Before presenting the detailed descriptions, we note here the extraordinary convenience and conciseness of the VHDL not only for the purposes of design, but also for the purposes of documentation and communication.

The Opcode port input is specified as a standard-logic vector data type. When it is used in a Boolean comparison operation (for example, line 23), the hexadecimal notation X *"value"* may be used as shown. It may be useful to compare this notation with that of the notation shown in program 11.1 for standard-logic vector data types. The arithmetic processor achieves the following results during simulation.

Simulation Results: Program 11.2

OpCode	Operation
0	$3 + 4 = 7$
1	$4 - 5 = 63$
2	$2 \times 5 = 10$
3	6 (operand 1)
4	8 (operand 2)
others	illegal opcode

The reader is encouraged to examine the source code of program 11.2 and verify the solution achieved.

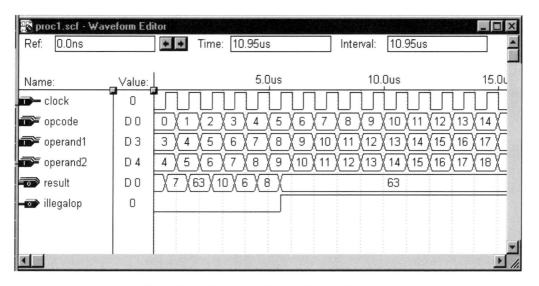

Simulation of Program 11.2: An Integer Processor

11.4 A SIMPLE INTEGER PROCESSOR WITH FUNCTIONS CALLS

In this section, we examine the design of a processor which is much like the processor of the previous section with one principle difference. The processor of this section employs VHDL functions. Functions are one of two subprogram types defined by VHDL. Therefore the principle purpose here is to examine the declaration of functions, their definitions, and the calling semantics. Functions may be defined either in the architecture body, as shown below, or in a package. The package approach is not part of the current examination but has the advantage that the function has visibility to a broader set of application modules. The functions in this illustration are visible only to the entity and architecture within which they are defined.

Lines 15–20 declare and define a function named GetSum(), which returns the sum of the two arguments passed to the function.

Lines 22–27 define a function named GetDiff(), which forms the difference of two arguments passed to it. Similarly lines 29 through 34 define a function named GetDouble-Sum().

Lines 41, 43, and 45 demonstrate the function call syntax. The semantics are very similar to the analogous calls in most modern software analogous such as C, Pascal, and Ada. The return value is rendered to the variable on the left-hand side of the call statement. Consistent typing must be observed through the call semantics.

```
1     --Use of Function declarations and calls
2     Library ieee;
3     Use ieee.Std_Logic_1164.all;
4     Entity Proc3  is
5           Port(
6                clock                :IN  Std_Logic;
7                OpCode               :IN  Integer range 0 to 15;
8                Operand1             :IN  Integer Range 0 to 31;
9                Operand2             :IN  Integer Range 0 to 31;
10               Result               :OUT Integer Range 0 to 63
11                   );
12    End Proc3;
13    -----------------------
14    Architecture AProc3 of Proc3 is
15    Function GetSum(      Operanda: In Integer range 0 to 15;
16                          Operandb: In Integer range 0 to 15)
17          Return Integer is
18    Begin
19          return operanda+operandb;
20    End GetSum;
21    ----------
22    Function GetDiff(     Operanda: In Integer range 0 to 15;
23                          Operandb: In Integer range 0 to 15)
24          Return Integer is
25    Begin
26          return operanda-operandb;
27    End GetDiff;
28    -----------
29    Function GetDoubleSum(Operanda: In Integer range 0 to 15;
30                             Operandb: In Integer range 0 to
                                 15)
31          Return Integer is
32    Begin
33          return (operanda+operandb)*2;
34    End GetDoubleSum;
```

PROGRAM 11.3 An Integer Processor Using Functions

```
35     ------------
36     Begin
37          Process(clock)
38          Begin
39          if(clock'event and clock = '1') then
40                  if(Opcode = 0) then
41                          Result <= GetSum(operand1,
                            operand2);
42                  elsif(OpCode = 1) then
43                          Result <= GetDiff(operand1,
                            operand2);
44                  elsif(OpCode = 2) then
45                          Result <= GetDoubleSum(operand1,
                            operand2);
46                  else
47                          Result <= 63;
48                  end if;
49          end if;
50          End Process;
51     End AProc3;
```

PROGRAM 11.3   *Continued*

The simulation below shows the following simulation segment to assist in verification of the results.

Simulation Results: Program 11.3

OpCode	Operation/Output
0x0	$0 + 6 = 6$
0x0	$1 + 7 = 8$
0x1	$2 - 8 = 26$
0x1	$3 - 9 = 26$
0x2	$2(4 + 10) = 28$
0x2	$2(5 + 11) = 32$
any other opcode	63 (illegal)

Rows three and four may require some investigation for the verification of the processing results, while rows one, two, and five through seven appear relatively self-explanatory. The investigation for the verification of rows three and four is left as an exercise for the reader.

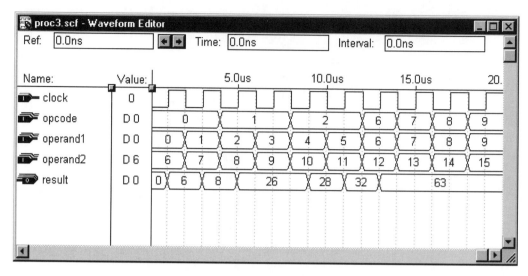

Simulation of Program 11.3: An Integer Processor Using Functions

11.5 AN AVERAGING FILTER

It is well known and often used in digital signal processing that averaging of consecutive, discrete samples of a signal results in a low-pass filtering operation. One possible scenario in which the discrete filter developed in this section might be used is as follows. An analog (continuous signal) is sampled and converted to a digital signal with a resolution of eight bits. The stream of eight-bit samples is then routed into a chip containing a digital signal processor (DSP). The DSP is represented by the VHDL design presented as the source code listing of program 11.4. The samples are clocked into the chip with the signal named clock, which is defined in the port of the entity FIR1 shown below. The eight-bit-wide signal is then clocked through the processing chip represented by the code of program 11.4. The chip contains eight stages of processing that are eight-bits wide (64 flip-flops for this section of the processor alone).

Only the salient differences from previous illustrations will be described in detail for the current example. In program 11.4, below, the DataIn and DataOut port specifications (lines six and seven respectively), each specify eight-bit data paths.

Line 14: A user-defined data type is specified in line 14. In this case, the user-defined type is called RegType and it is declared using the built-in data type *array*. Therefore, the specification of RegType declares a new data type which consists of an array of eight integers with a descending index. The built-in data type, array, may be used with virtually any VHDL data type to create an array of data elements corresponding to any given type.

Line 15: This line creates an instance of the data type, RegType, named Reg. The subscripts "7 downto 0" may now be used to bus data through multiple Reg stages.

Line 19: This arithmetic statement creates the average of all register stages and consequently creates the averaging filter.

Lines 21–28 create a shifting process which is a key part of the finite impulse-response averaging filter. Due to the specification of the process which contains only the clocking signal on its sensitivity list, the register specified processes once for each positive clock transition.

```
1    --FIR1
2    Library ieee;
3    Use ieee.Std_Logic_1164.all;
4    Entity FIR1 is
5          Port(clock            :In Std_Logic;
6                DataIn           :In Integer range 0 to 255;
7                DataOut          :Out integer range 0 to 255
8                );
9    End FIR1;
10
11   Architecture AFIR1 of FIR1 is
12   Begin
13   Process(clock)
14   Type Regtype is array(7 downto 0) of Integer;
15   variable Reg: Regtype;
16          Begin
17          if (clock'event and clock = '1') then
18          --      average of the eight stages
19                DataOut <= (Reg(0)+Reg(1)+Reg(2)+Reg(3)+
20                          Reg(4)+Reg(5)+Reg(6)+Reg(7))/8;
21                Reg(0) := Reg(1);
22                Reg(1) := Reg(2);
23                Reg(2) := Reg(3);
24                Reg(3) := Reg(4);
25                Reg(4) := Reg(5);
26                Reg(5) := Reg(6);
27                Reg(6) := Reg(7);
28                Reg(7) := DataIn;
29          End if;
30          End Process;
31   End AFIR1
```

PROGRAM 11.4   An Averaging Filter

A single simulation of program 11.4 shows a step-function input being applied to the filter. The response that the filter generates gives some insight into the integer processing. The amplitude of the step input is selected at 100 for convenience. Of course the input must be kept within the 0 to 255 integer range which is contained in the port-range constraint (eight bits maximum for those who must continue to think digitally). When the

100-unit step first enters the register, a response value of 12 is achieved. Line 19 of the source code yields

$$\frac{100}{8} = 12.5$$

which is then truncated to 12 by the integer processing. The value of 12.5 could have been retained (within binary, truncated resolution) if the VHDL data type, Real, had been utilized (an obvious alternative to real data types is for the designer to scale the integer values in a so-called fixed-point technique). During the next clock cycle, line 19 of the source file results in

$$\frac{100}{8} + \frac{100}{8} = 12.5 + 12.5 = 25$$

Therefore, the step response of the filter grows linearly (within the bounds of truncated integer arithmetic) to its final value of 100.

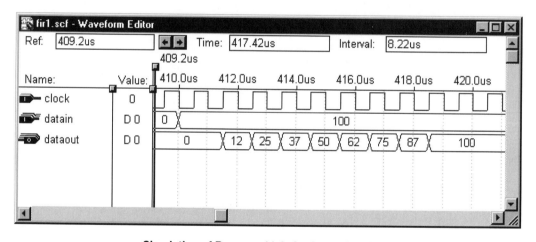

Simulation of Program 11.4: An Averaging Filter

It is clear from the simulation of program 11.4 that we have succeeded in creating a moving average type of finite impulse response filter. Note that the output value takes seven clock times to gradually reach a stable steady-state output after the input undergoes a step change. This is the type of response we expect from a low-pass filter.

11.6 A BINARY COEFFICIENT-WEIGHT FIR FILTER

We now design and simulate a finite impulse response (FIR) filter, implemented with integer data types. The filter also contains binary weighted coefficients. FIR digital filters

are common in signal-processing applications for any number of reasons. They are uncon-
ditionally stable, exhibit predictable performance, and can be readily designed to have a
linear-phase characteristic.

We now briefly review the principles associated with the current filter under design.
The filter consists of eight register stages, each of which is eight bits wide. Therefore, this
design requires 64 flip-flops in the register portion of the system. At each stage, the eight
bit value in the register is to be multiplied by a constant value. Therefore, we must select
eight coefficients, one for each register stage. If the coefficients are selected to be symmetric about the center of the shift register, a linear phase characteristic will be achieved.
We designate the sequence of eight bit output samples as $y(n)$ and the sequence of input
samples as $x(n)$. The output of the FIR filter is achieved by summing as follows.

$$y(n) = a_0 x(n) + a_1 x(n-1) + a_2 (x-2) + \ldots\ldots\ldots + a_{k-1} x(-[k-1]) \qquad (11.1)$$

The register is k stages long and as shown in (11.1) the content of each stage is multiplied
by a selected coefficient. In our current illustration, we let $k = 8$. Since multiplication by
powers of two may be achieved simply by shifting, we select coefficients which are powers of two. We now arbitrarily select a set of coefficients for demonstration. In a later
chapter, we will elaborate on a method for selecting coefficients in a more reasoned fashion. For the current time we select

$$
\begin{aligned}
a_0 &= 2^{-3} \\
a_1 &= 2^{-2} \\
a_2 &= 2^{-1} \\
a_3 &= 1 \\
a_4 &= 1 \\
a_5 &= 2^{-1} \\
a_6 &= 2^{-2} \\
a_7 &= 2^{-3}
\end{aligned}
\qquad (11.2)
$$

Therefore, (11.1) becomes

$$
\begin{aligned}
y(n) = {} & 2^{-3} x(n) + 2^{-2} x(n-1) + 2^{-1} x(n-2) + x(n-3) \\
& + x(n-4) + 2^{-1} x(n-5) + 2^{-1} x(n-6) + 2^{-2} x(n-7)
\end{aligned}
\qquad (11.3)
$$

We state without proof, that the steady state transfer function produced by the implemen-
tion of (11.3) is given by the cosine series

$$H(f) = [2 \cos(\pi fT) + \cos(3\pi fT) + .5 \cos(5\pi fT) + .25 \cos(7\,\pi fT)]e^{-j7\pi fT} \qquad (11.4)$$

where T is the sampling interval.

The validity of this type of equation will be explored more fully in a later chapter.
For the present, we will proceed to VHDL digital implementation.

Equation (11.9) is a typical FIR filter response displaying characteristics which are periodic with foldover occurring at $1/2T$, where T is the sampling interval.

Program 11.5 implements the FIR filter and is presented directly below. It has exactly the same form as the averaging FIR filter but the coefficients have been modified to sequential powers of two. Since the program is virtually identical in essential structure to program 11.4, we provide no additional discussion and will proceed to the simulation results.

```
1     --FIR2
2     Library ieee;
3     Use ieee.Std_Logic_1164.all;
4     Entity FIR3 is
5           Port(clock      :In Std_Logic;
6                     DataIn :In Integer range 0 to 255;
7                     DataOut      :Out integer range 0 to
                                         512
8                     );
9     End FIR3;
10    Architecture AFIR3 of FIR3 is
11    Begin
12    Process(clock)
13    Type Regtype is array(7 downto 0) of Integer;
14    variable Reg: Regtype;
15          Begin
16          if (clock'event and clock = '1') then
17                    DataOut <= Reg(0)/8+Reg(1)/4+Reg(2)/
                      2+Reg(3)+ Reg(4)+Reg(5)/2+Reg(6)/
18                                   4+Reg(7)/8;
19                Reg(0)  := Reg(1);
20                Reg(1)  := Reg(2);
21                Reg(2)  := Reg(3);
22                Reg(3)  := Reg(4);
23                Reg(4)  := Reg(5);
24                Reg(5)  := Reg(6);
25                Reg(6)  := Reg(7);
26                Reg(7)  := DataIn;
27          End if;
28          End Process;
29    End AFIR3;
```

PROGRAM 11.5   A Simple FIR Filter

The simulation presented below shows a step input of amplitude 100 applied to the system and the corresponding filter response. The values from the step response demonstrate that the filter responds to the step input as a lowpass filter would be expected to respond. It is perhaps an advantage to see the filter step response in graphical form. A graph of the step response is shown immediately below the digital simulation results.

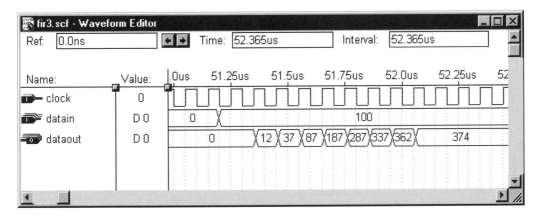

Simulation of Program 11.5: A Simple FIR Filter

The sum of the coefficients for the filter as given in (11.4) is 3.75 which explains why the digital simulation results show the corresponding step response settling to a value of 374 (in other words, $100 \times 3.75 = 375$, but the integer arithmetic has truncated intermediate results resulting to a value of 374 instead of the correct value of 375). In the graphical presentation shown below, emphasis is placed on the discrete nature of the filter input and response. The discrete step-input consists of an initial value of zero followed by a series of inputs of amplitude 100 (constant or step-input). The output responds gradually as would be expected for a lowpass filter. The presentation style was selected for simplicity of comparison and not exact representation. The point made here is that the response is typical of the response that would be expected for a lowpass filter. The step response below has been normalized for convenience.

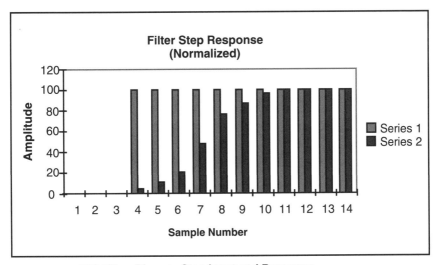

FIR Filter: Discrete Step-Input and Response
Discrete Representation

The continuous function shown on the graph below represents the response of the system to a discrete step function. It may be thought of as the output of the system after being processed through an ideal analog-to-digital converter system. The response curve has been normalized. The correct final step response is 374 as shown in simulation of program 11.5. The final output value is achieved as :

$$\text{Final value} = \left(\frac{100}{8} + \frac{100}{4} + \frac{100}{2} + 100\right) \times 2 = 374 \qquad (11.5)$$

Equation 5 supplies information concerning the integer arithmetic but also supplies insight into an alternative architecture for the FIR processor. The filter may be constructed by folding. The values in Reg(0) and Reg(7) (see program 11.5) may be summed before multiplying by the associated coefficient. Similar symmetric processing may be accomplished throughout.

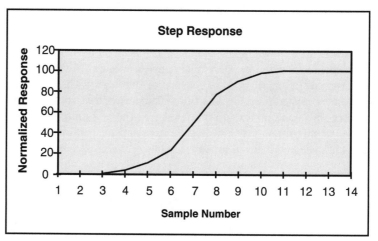

**Program 11.5 FIR Filter Continuous
Representation of Step Response**

The frequency response of the filter is shown in the figure below. This response has been obtained directly from (11.5) using the clock period shown in the diagram as the sampling interval, T. While the frequency response may not appear very impressive, recall that the illustration includes only eight stages of processing and eight arbitrarily selected coefficients. The primary purpose of the example is to demonstrate a VHDL application which utilizes integer processing. Many effective methods exist for designing high performance digital filter coefficients. The reader may find many excellent references in the area of digital signal processing. These references discuss the mathematical basis for determining the desired coefficients. In a later chapter, we very briefly explore the process of obtaining desired coefficients and provide an associated numerical example and design implementation.

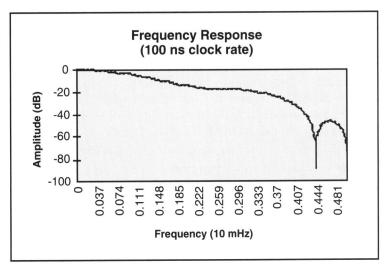

FIR Filter: Steady-State Response

11.7 RETROSPECTIVE

In this chapter, we have examined some applications which deal with integer and array variable types as well as user-defined types. The ease of dealing with the integer data types for arithmetic processing applications have been demonstrated along with some of the limitations. Function declarations, function definitions, and function call semantics have also been described and demonstrated in applications. In addition, we have developed two relatively simple digital filters to demonstrate the use of integer processing in the formulation of shift registers and multiplication. The reader may well have surmised that the form of the equation implementations in the corresponding VHDL source file (program 11.5) has been selected to simplify the multiplication. That is, the coefficients have all been selected as powers of two. This permits multiplication simply by shifting operations. Of course, while this approach simplifies the implementation, it may well not provide the coefficients required for any particular design implementation. This matter is taken up more fully in a subsequent chapter.

CHAPTER 11 EXERCISES

1. For each of the sequence generators of program 11.1, verify the sequence values shown in the simulation by using manual calculations.

2. Verify the simulation results shown for the execution of program 11.2 with manual calculations.

3. Verify the simulation results of program 11.3 using manual calculations.

4. Verify the simulation results of program 11.4 using manual calculations.

5. Examine equation (11.4).

   a) Plot the amplitude of the transfer function in dB. Use the value of T shown in the simulation. Compare your results in the text.

   b) Does the phase term indicate linear phase? Explain.

   c) Design and simulate a folded version of the filter of program 11.5.

6. Redesign the HDL program 11.4, the averaging filter, such that the truncation problem is alleviated. Simulate your design and check the results.

7. Examine the following AHDL program

```
1      Subdesign 'regadd'
2      (
3      clock                          :Input;
4      a[7..0], b[7..0]               :Input;
5      Count[2..0]                    :Output;
6      Reg_a[7..0]                    :Output;
7      Reg_b[7..0]                    :Output;
8      Reg_c[7..0]                    :Output;
9      )
10     Variable
11     Reg_a[7..0]                    :Dff;
12     Reg_b[7..0]                    :Dff;
13     Reg_c[7..0]                    :Dff;
14     Count[2..0]                    :Dff;
15     Begin
16     %*****%
17     Reg_a[].clk=clock;
18     Reg_b[].clk=clock;
19     Reg_c[].clk=clock;
20     Count[].clk=clock;
21     %*****%
22     Count[].d=Count[]+1;
23     %*****%
24     CASE Count[] is
25     WHEN 0 =>
26         Reg_a[].d=a[];
27         Reg_b[].d=b[];
28         Reg_c[].d=Gnd;
29     WHEN 1 =>
30         Reg_a[].d=Reg_a[];
31         Reg_b[].d=Reg_b[];
32         Reg_c[].d=Reg_a[]+Reg_b[];
33     WHEN OTHERS =>
```

PROBLEM 11.7 Source File

```
34        Reg_a[].d=Reg_a[];
35        Reg_b[].d=Reg_b[];
36        Reg_c[].d=Reg_c[];
37   END CASE;
38   %******%
39   End;
```

PROBLEM 11.7   *Continued*

a) The clock starts low and toggles every 500 ns (1 MHz clock rate). The input starts at 0x01 and increments every 500 ns. The b input starts at 0x05 and increments every 500 ns. Predict what a simulation would produce for an interval between 0 and 10 µsec. Describe, in words, the function of this digital system.

b) Compile the source code and check your solution using the simulator.

c) Design a digital system which is functionally equivalent to the AHDL system above using VHDL.

8. Examine the following AHDL program. The program is designed to accomplish multiplication by a shift and add process.

```
1    Subdesign 'shiftadd2'
2    (
3    clock                              :Input;
4    a[7..0]                            :Input;
5    Count[2..0]                        :Output;
6    Reg_a[7..0]                        :Output;
7    Reg_c[7..0]                        :Output;
8    )
9    Variable
10   Reg_a[7..0]                        :Dff;
11   Reg_c[7..0]                        :Dff;
12   Count[2..0]                        :Dff;
13   Begin
14   %******%
15   Reg_a[].clk=clock;
16   Reg_c[].clk=clock;
17   Count[].clk=clock;
18   %******%
19   Count[].d=Count[]+1;
20   %******%
21   CASE Count[] is
22   WHEN 0 =>
23        Reg_a[].d=a[];
24        Reg_c[].d=Gnd;
25   WHEN 1 =>
26        Reg_a[].d=Reg_a[];
```

PROBLEM 11.8   Source File

```
27          Reg_c[].d=Reg_a[];
28      WHEN 2 =>
29          Reg_a[7..1].d=Reg_a[6..0];
30          Reg_a[0].d = Gnd;
31          Reg_c[].d=Reg_c[];
32      WHEN 3 =>
33          Reg_a[].d=Reg_a[];
34          Reg_c[].d=Reg_a[]+Reg_c[];
35      WHEN 4 =>
36          Reg_a[7..1].d=Reg_a[6..0];
37          Reg_a[0].d = Gnd;
38          Reg_c[].d=Reg_c[];
39      WHEN 5 =>
40          Reg_a[].d=Reg_a[];
41          Reg_c[].d=Reg_a[]+Reg_c[];
42      WHEN OTHERS =>
43          Reg_a[].d=Reg_a[];
44          Reg_c[].d=Reg_c[];
45      END CASE;
46      %******%
47      End;
```

PROBLEM 11.8 *Continued*

a) The clock starts low and toggles every 500 ns (1 MHz clock rate). If the input starts at 0x03 and remains constant throughout execution, find the results from 0 through 7 μsec by "manual" analysis. Describe, in words, the operation of this digital system.

b) Compile the source code and check your solution using the simulator.

c) Design a digital system that is functionally equivalent to the AHDL system above using VHDL.

9. Using the shift-and-add multiplication technique of problem 11.8, design a system which will (1) accept a four-bit positive integer input, (2) multiply by the integer constant below (shift-and-add) and finally (3) outputs the 2's complement product from the chip.

a) 25

b) 32

c) 45

d) −45

e) 53

f) −53

Chapter 12

A Simplified VHDL UART/COM Port Receiver

12.1 INTRODUCTION

In this chapter, we continue to examine the VHDL language by developing sample applications. We now undertake the development of a serial communications receiver. To facilitate the language studies that we have been pursuing in earlier chapters, the exploration will focus on the design of a serial digital receiver identical in functionality to the receiver developed earlier using AHDL. The essential information on serial digital transmission is presented in the earlier chapter (chapter 5). A brief review of the material presented earlier may be of value at this time. Therefore, we will simply recount a summary of the requirements here for the sake of convenience.

The receiver, which is the central point of the present design, is for the reception of serial, asynchronous data, transmitted at a rate of 28,800 b/sec. In this chapter, as in the corresponding AHDL chapter, we engage only in the receiver portion of a UART design. No attempt is made here to design the transmitter portion of the system. The data format is seven-bit ASCII data transmitted low-order bit first. The parity bit is attached as bit eight. The eight-bit information is finally framed with a leading start bit and a trailing stop bit. The total transmission is therefore ten bits transmitted synchronously by bit and asynchronously by ten-bit word. A start bit indicates the onset of a received word. Once a word has started into the receiver, all ten bits are received synchronously.

12.2   RECEIVER ARCHITECTURE AND DESIGN

The system is designed with a digital clock frequency of 3.456 MHz. The digital receiver system must generate sampling pulses at the rate of 28.8 kHz. Therefore the digital receiver must generate the sampling signals for the 28,800 b/sec data stream. Program 12.1 below provides the digital receiver function for exploration in the VHDL language. The general architecture employed in this receiver design is identical to the architecture of the HDL implementation utilized in chapter 5. This architecture is repeated here for convenience.

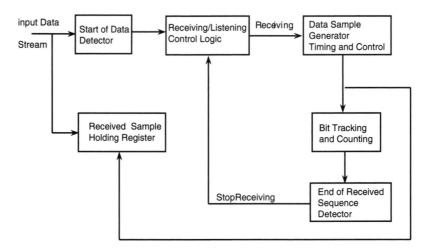

Architecture for VHDL Serial Digital Receiver

We now examine the initial portion of the receiver digital design and implementation. The VHDL receiver is given as program 12.1 on page 269.

Lines 1–2: Line 1 provides the availability of the IEEE library to the current receiver design function. Line 2 specifically selects the standard logic-function definitions for use by the source code. More will be said concerning this below.

Line 4 declares the existence of an entity named Rcvrtest. This is the primary entity with which this entire chapter is concerned.

Lines 7–21 complete the Rcvrtest declaration and the declarations of the constituent I/O ports of the receiver. The signals declared in the I/O ports section all consist of signals of type Std_Logic. These logic types are made available through the use of the IEEE library and Use directives. The port declarations for the receiver that is currently the focus of our design are defined as follows.

clock: The system clock which is routed to the implementation chip.

DataIn: The serial data signal which is the input to the receiver.

DataDelay: A two-bit delay line utilized in positive-edge detection.

PosEdge: An internally generated signal which locates positive data transitions.

Receiving: An internally generated signal set true whenever the receiver is in Receiving mode. This signal is reset when the receiver is in idle mode.

SampleCount: A six-bit logic vector which is the output of a polynomial counter. The counter is utilized to estimate ideal sampling instants of the received signal.

BitEdge: An internally generated signal which estimates the location of bit edges within a given received data word.

BitCounter: An internally generated signal which counts the received bits as they are sampled by the receiver.

BitClock: An internally generated signal which performs the sampling of a received data stream at estimated ideal sampling points (28,800 b/sec only).

StopReceiving: A signal generated by the receiver when the receiver has sampled all of the bits in a received word.

InRegister: This is the register into which received data samples are stored.

SampleCountReset: This internally generated signal reinitializes the register which is estimating ideal sampling instants for each bit to be sampled.

We will next undertake the full description of program 12.1. Program 12.1 is a VHDL source file which implements the simplified serial receiver (simplified meaning that the details of parity checking, multiple received character buffering, interfaces for generating interrupts, and the like are not included in the design. These details are relatively simple to add and have been left as exercises for the reader). The receiver is, on the other hand, fully functional and has been implemented and tested in a hardware implementation. Implementations of the source file as shown in this chapter have been implemented on a 7032 EPLD chip while versions including parity checking and full buffering have been implemented on a 7128 EPLD.

Line 23 is the beginning of the architecture definition for the receiver.

Lines 24–27 declare that the receiver will use a single user-defined flip-flop type as a component in the design and implementation. The flip-flop entity declaration and architecture definition are contained in the current source file. This component is similar to some of the VHDL components developed in earlier chapters and will be discussed later in this chapter.

Lines 65–72 implement a two-bit delay line. The basic components, clocked D flip-flops with asynchronous preset and clear signals, are instantiated and structurally interconnected to form the two-bit delay line. The principle structural signals for the delay-line implementation are declared in lines 29 and 30. The positive-edge detection associated with the delay line is implemented in line 125.

Lines 74–80 implement the input data register. The register is implemented as straightforward shift register. The input data to the chip is routed to InReg(8). The outputs of the eight register stages are named InReg(7) through InReg(0), respectively. The register stages are implemented with the Dffpc2 flip-flop stages. The eight stages are not implemented individually, but instead are generated by the code framed by the Generate-End Generate command pair. The eight stages are implemented with the index, i, and the associated structural connections are collaterally defined. The signal declarations that compose the actual signaling interconnects are declared in lines 35 and 36 and are declared as vectors using the VHDL keyword, downto. If the index of the instantiated stages had been declared as an incrementing rather than a decrementing index, the VHDL keyword, to, would have been used instead. The register stages could have been individually instantiated (in other words, instead of generated).

Lines 82–94 implement the registers used for timing and sampling of the receive data stream. These registers, SampCount(5) through SampCount(0), are partially generated and partially individually instantiated. Since there is no convenient way to express all of the register stages in a common format the individual instantiation becomes necessary. The five stages of the register are formed as a straight-shift register. The high-order input formed counter is as the exclusive-Or of the outputs of the two lowest order stages. This arrangement provides a pseudo-random count sequence which is utilized as a modulo-63. The register content of all zeroes is not a legal member of the pseudo-random sequence. Since a value of 0x11 is the proper decode value to set the sampling interval, this value is decoded in line 119. A control flip-flop output reinitializes the poly counter after each estimation period. This output signal is named SampleCntRstq and is defined in the instantiated flip-flop SampleFF which occurs in line 88 of the source code. The internal data or signal lines utilized for the sampling process are defined in lines 39 and 40.

Lines 100–111 instantiate the register elements for counting the bits within each received word. In this case, there are four flip-flops, BitCount(3) through BitCount(0), in the register used for counting. Only BitCount(2) and BitCount(1) are instantiated by generation. BitCount(3) and BitCount(0) are individually instantiated. Since the four-bit counter is also designed using a pseudo-random or polynomial counter, the input to the high-order bit is the exclusive-Or of the lowest order two bits (Exclusive OR'ing of the two least significant bits is not always required for polynomial counters, but is proper for both six-bit and four-bit counters). The internal signals required for the bit counter are declared in source lines 46 through 48. The count sequence for the four-bit, BitCount function is given in the following table.

Count Sequence of Bit Counter

Count Sequence	BitCount(3–1)	
0	0001	0x1
1	1000	0x8
2	0100	0x4
3	0010	0x2
4	1001	0x9
5	1100	0xC
6	0110	0x6
7	1011	0xB
8	0101	0x5
9	1010	0xA

Count Sequence	BitCount(3–1)
10	1101 0xD
11	1110 0xE
12	1111 0xF
13	0111 0x7
14	0011 0x3
15	0001 (cycle)

Lines 123–127 implement the positive-edge detection and also set the signaling flip-flop called Receiving. Receivingq is the output signal of this flip-flop. The flip-flop with output signal Receivingq is instantiated in line 71 of the source file. The control logic is of the set-or-hold control form and the equation for the control is implemented in line 127 of the source file.

Lines 129–147 are used to transfer information from the internal signals of the chip to the ports of the associated entity (I/O pins of the programmable array in this case).

Lines 151 and 152 indicate the IEEE library, particularly the standard-logic signals, are to be utilized for the flip-flop which directly follows the library declaration and Use clause.

Line 155–163 declare the flip-flop entity which is the sole instantiated component used for this design. Alternate flip-flop entities could have been used for some of the components, but a single flip-flop type suffices in this case. Alternative designs may have reduced the need for signal declarations and other source entries.

Lines 165–180 provide the Dffpc2 architecture definition. This flip-flop is similar to some of the VHDL flip-flops designed in earlier chapters and therefore will not be elaborated upon at the current time.

```
1    LIBRARY ieee;
2    USE ieee.std_logic_1164.all;
3    ----------------
4    Entity Rcvrtest is
5    -- Clock frequency is 3.456 MHz-- clock period is 289.35
       ns
6    -- data rate is 28,800 bps-- DataIn period is 34.72 us
7    Port(clock                 :IN Std_Logic;
8    DataIn                     :IN Std_Logic;
9    PosEdge                    :OUT Std_Logic;
10   DataDelay                  :OUT Std_Logic_VECTOR
                                 (1 downto 0);
11   Receiving                  :OUT Std_Logic;
12   SampleCount                :OUT Std_Logic_VECTOR
                                 (5 downto 0);
13   BitEdge                    :OUT Std_Logic;
```

PROGRAM 12.1 A VHDL RS232/COM Port Receiver

```
14    BitCounter                          :OUT Std_Logic_VECTOR
                                          (3 downto 0);
15    BitClock                            :OUT Std_Logic;
16    StopReceiving                       :OUT Std_Logic;
17    InRegister                          :OUT Std_Logic_VECTOR
                                          (7 downto 0);
18    BitCntfb                            :OUT Std_Logic;
19    SampleCountReset                    :OUT Std_Logic
20    );
21    End Rcvrtest;
22    -------------
23    Architecture ARcvr3 of Rcvrtest IS
24    Component Dffpc2
25        Port(D, Clock, clrn, prn        :IN Std_Logic;
26             q, qbar                     :OUT Std_Logic);
27    End Component;
28    --signals for data delay and egde detection
29    Signal DataDelayn1, DataDelayn0                  :Std_Logic;
30    Signal DataDelayn1bar, DataDelayn0bar            :Std_Logic;
31    Signal PosedgeIn, ReceiveFFd, LogicOne           :Std_Logic;
32    Signal Receivingq, Receivingqbar                 :Std_Logic;
33    -------------------------------
34    --Signals for the input data register
35    Signal InRegq           :Std_Logic_Vector(8 downto 0);
36    Signal InRegqbar        :Std_Logic_Vector(7 downto 0);
37    --------
38    --Signals for the Sampling Counter
39    Signal SampCountq       :Std_Logic_Vector(6 downto 0);
40    Signal SampCountqbar    :Std_Logic_Vector(5 downto 0);
41    --------
42    --Signals for managing sampling counter
43    Signal SampleCntRstq, SampleCntRstqbar      :Std_Logic;
44    ----------------------------
45    -- Signals for Bit Counting
46    Signal BitCountq        :Std_Logic_Vector(3 downto 0);
47    Signal BitCountqbar     :Std_Logic_Vector(3 downto 0);
48    Signal BitCountfb                           :Std_Logic;
49    ----------------------------
50    -- Signals for BitClock and Receiving
51    Signal BitClockFFqbar                       :Std_Logic;
52    Signal BitClockq, BitClockqbar              :Std_Logic;
53    Signal Receivingd                           :Std_Logic;
54    Signal StopReceivingd                       :Std_Logic;
55    Signal StopReceivingq, StopReceivingqbar    :Std_Logic;
56    Signal SampleCntRstd                        :Std_Logic;
```

PROGRAM 12.1 *Continued*

```
57   Signal Nine                                  :Std_Logic;
58   Signal BitClockclk                           :Std_Logic;
59   ---------------------
60   ---------------------
61   Begin
62   -- static logic 1 value
63          LogicOne <= '1';
64   -----------------------------------
65   -- Flip-flops for edge detection
66   DataDelay1: Dffpc2 Port Map(DataIn, Clock, LogicOne,
67                     LogicOne, DataDelayn1, dataDelayn1bar);
68   DataDelay0: Dffpc2 Port Map(DataDelayn1, Clock, LogicOne,
69                     LogicOne, DataDelayn0, DataDelayn0bar);
70   --Receiving
71   ReceivingFF: Dffpc2 Port Map(Receivingd, Clock, LogicOne,
72                     LogicOne, Receivingq, Receivingqbar);
73   ----------------------
74   -- Input Data register
75   InRegq(8) <= DataIn;
76   Gen1:      For i in 7 to 0
77                  Generate
78   InReg:  Dffpc2 Port Map(InRegq(i+1), BitClockq, LogicOne,
79                      LogicOne, InRegq(i), InRegqbar(i) );
80              End Generate;
81   -------------------
82   --SampleCount Register
83   SampleCntRstd <= not (SampCountq(5) And SampCountq(4) And
84          SampCountq(3) And SampCountq(2) And
85          SampCountq(1) And SampCountq(0)) And Receivingq;
86   Gen2: For i in 5 downto 1
87                  Generate
88   SampleFF:    Dffpc2 Port Map(SampCountq(i+1), Clock,
89              SampleCntRstq, LogicOne, SampCountq(i),
90              SampCountqbar(i) ); End Generate;
91   SampCount0: Dffpc2 Port Map(SampCountq(1), Clock,
92              LogicOne, SampleCntRstq, SampCountq(0),
93              SampCountqbar(0));
94   SampCountq(6) <= SampCountq(0) Xor SampCountq(1);
95   ------------------
96   -- Sample Count Reset control
97   SampleCountResetFF: Dffpc2 Port Map(SampleCntRstd, Clock,
98      LogicOne, LogicOne, SampleCntRstq, SampleCntRstqbar );
99   --------------------
100  --BitCounter and control signals
```

PROGRAM 12.1   *Continued*

```
101  BitCountfb <= BitCountq(0) Xor BitCountq(1);
102     BitCount3: Dffpc2 Port Map(BitCountfb, BitClockq,
103  Receivingq,LogicOne, BitCountq(3), BitCountqbar(3));
104  Gen3: For i in 2 downto 1
105                         Generate
106  CountBits:              Dffpc2 Port Map(BitCountq(i+1),
107        BitClockq, receivingq, LogicOne, BitCountq(i),
108                         BitCountqbar(i));
109                         End Generate;
110  BitCount0: Dffpc2 Port Map(BitCountq(1), BitClockq,
111    LogicOne, Receivingq, BitCountq(0), BitCountqbar(0));
112  ------------------------
113  -- Flip-flops for generating bitclock
114  BitClockFF: dffpc2 Port Map (BitClockqbar, BitClockclk,
115          Receivingq, LogicOne, BitClockq, BitClockqbar);
117  StopReceiveFF : dffpc2 Port Map (StopReceivingd, Clock,
118  LogicOne, LogicOne, StopReceivingq, StopReceivingqbar);
119  BitClockclk <= SampCountq(5) And SampCountq(4) And
120                         SampCountq(3) And SampCountq(2) And
121                         SampCountq(1) And SampCountq(0);
122  -----------------------------
123  -- detect a positive edge and set the receiving signal
124  -- start positive edge detection
125          PosEdgeIn <= DataDelayn1 And not DataDelayn0;
126  --set the receiving signal
127          Receivingd <= PosedgeIn Or (Receivingq And not
128                                      StopReceivingq);
128  -----------------------------
129  --Transfer information to output
130          PosEdge <= PosEdgeIn;
131          SampleCount(5 downto 0) <= SampCountq(5 downto 0);
132          DataDelay(1) <= datadelayn1;
133          DataDelay(0) <= datadelayn0;
134          Receiving <= Receivingq;
135  -- binary 111111 is 58 in poly count
136          BitEdge <= SampCountq(5) And SampCountq(4) And
137                         Sampcountq(3) And SampCountq(2) And
138                         SampCountq(1) And SampCountq(0);
139          BitCounter(3 downto 0) <= BitCountq(3 downto 0);
140          BitClock <= BitClockq;
141          Nine <= BitCountq(3) And not BitCountq(2) And
142                 BitCountq(1) And not BitCountq(0);
143          StopReceivingd <= Nine;
144          StopReceiving <= StopReceivingq;
145          InRegister(7 downto 0) <= InRegq(7 downto 0);
```

PROGRAM 12.1 *Continued*

```
146                SampleCountReset <= SampleCntRstq;
147                BitCntfb <= BitCountfb;
148  End ARcvr3;
149  --------------------------------
150  --------------------------------
151  LIBRARY ieee;
152  USE ieee.std_logic_1164.all;
153  -- D flip-flop w/asynch prn and clrn ports
154  --------------------
155  ENTITY Dffpc2 IS
156      PORT(d           :IN          Std_Logic;
157           clock       :IN          Std_Logic;
158           clrn        :IN          BIT;
159           prn         :IN          BIT;
160           q           :OUT         Std_Logic;
161           qbar        :OUT         Std_Logic
162           );
163  END Dffpc2;
164  ------------------
165  Architecture Arch1 of Dffpc2 IS
166  BEGIN
167      PROCESS(clock, clrn, prn)
168          BEGIN
169              if(prn='0') Then
170                      q <= '1';
171                      qbar <='0';
172              elsif(clrn='0') Then
173                      q <= '0';
174                      qbar <= '1';
175              elsif (clock'EVENT And clock = '1') Then
176                      q<=d;
177                      qbar <= not d;
178              END IF;
179          END PROCESS;
180  End Arch1;
181  --------------
```

PROGRAM 12.1 *Continued*

12.3 RECEIVER SIMULATION

In the simulation of the VHDL system shown below, a data signal consisting of the dotting data pattern, 01010101, is provided as input to the receiver. The first seven bits are the ASCII-bit pattern transmitted low-order bit first. Bit eight is a parity bit (sampled, but otherwise ignored in this case). The eight bits are framed with a logical-one start bit and a logical-zero stop bit. The start bit is actually sampled but then walked through the register and eventually is shifted out of the register. After the sampling is completed for the word in question, the register contents are 0xAA which is the correct data received. The received information bits are sampled by the bitclock waveform. Notice that the input data-register contents change appropriately with each sampled bit and the BitCounter also updates its value with each sampled bit. As described in the design process, both the sample counter and the bit counter are initialized to 0x01 and reinitialized to these same values which each cyclic operation. The signal StopReceiving halts the receiving process until the start of a new transmission word is detected. New tranmission words are detected by the processing signal posedge and the receiver is placed into active receive mode by the signal, startreceiving.

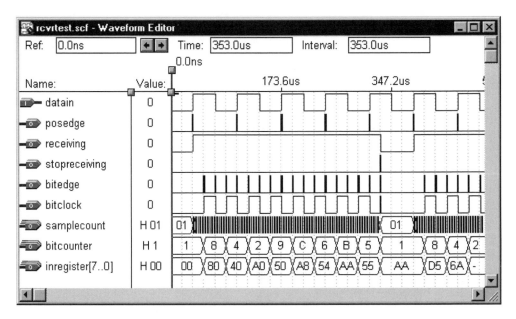

Simulation of Program 12.1: A VHDL UART/COM Port Receiver

The reader is encouraged to compile program 12.1 and to examine receive data patterns other than the receive data pattern shown in the single simulation provided above. Including several bits of dead space between successive data words in addition to modifying the content of the data may also provide insight into the implemented processing. Problems at the end of the chapter provide a means of investigating the receiver design in more detail.

12.4 ALTERNATIVE MEANS OF INSTANTIATING THE INPUT DATA REGISTER

We now examine the mechanism associated with the *generate* function a little more closely. If the generate construct were not available or the designer chose not to employ it, then lines 76–80 of the source file above could have been accomplished with the distinct instantiation statements (a) through (h), shown below. Each of the following entries creates an instance of the flip-flop component. The components are interconnected with the signals enclosed in the parentheses.

```
a) InRegister7: Dffpc2 Port Map(DataIn, BitClockq, LogicOne,
                             LogicOne, InRegq7, InRegq7bar);
b) InRegister6: Dffpc2 Port Map(Inregq7, BitClockq, LogicOne,
                             LogicOne, InRegq6, InRegq6bar);
c) InRegister5: Dffpc2 Port Map(Inregq6, BitClockq, LogicOne,
                             LogicOne, InRegq5, InRegq5bar);
d) InRegister4: Dffpc2 Port Map(Inregq5, BitClockq, LogicOne,
                             LogicOne, InRegq4, InRegq4bar);
e) InRegister3: Dffpc2 Port Map(Inregq4, BitClockq, LogicOne,
                             LogicOne, InRegq3, InRegq3bar);
f) InRegister2: Dffpc2 Port Map(Inregq3, BitClockq, LogicOne,
                             LogicOne, InRegq2, InRegq2bar);
g) InRegister1: Dffpc2 Port Map(Inregq2, BitClockq, LogicOne,
                             LogicOne, InRegq1, InRegq1bar);
h) InRegister0: Dffpc2 Port Map(Inregq1, BitClockq, LogicOne,
                             LogicOne, InRegq0, InRegq0bar);
```

Distinct Instantiation of Input-Register Components

If the direct instantiation method is used, then the appropriate signals also must be declared and the code fragment shown below, (i) through (viii), declares signals that may be used to interconnect the instantiated components.

```
i) Signal      InRegq7, InRegq7bar     :BIT;
ii) Signal     InRegq6, InRegq6bar     :BIT;
iii) Signal    InRegq5, InRegq5bar     :BIT;
iv) Signal     InRegq4, InRegq4bar     :BIT;
v) Signal      InRegq3, InRegq3bar     :BIT;
vi) Signal     InRegq2, InRegq2bar     :BIT;
vii) Signal    InRegq1, InRegq1bar     :BIT;
viii) Signal   InRegq0, InRegq0bar     :BIT;
```

Signals Used to Interconnect Distinct Register Components

Note that although the generate construct is available, the designer is still free to create distinct instances of components. However generate commands often create significant economies in source code. In addition, subscripting variables often facilitates the assignment of signal buses or collections of signals by permitting declaration of multiple signal lines as vectors. The standard logic vectors declared in program 12.1 (lines 10, 12, 14, and 17) are examples of such bit-vector declarations. The appendix of this chapter includes a complete and working source file which provides a complete set of distinct instantiations for comparison.

12.5   RETROSPECTIVE

In this chapter, we developed a complete, albeit simplified, UART receiver using the VHDL language. The simplifications have been made in the interest of presentation clarity, and the omissions are readily incorporated (see chapter exercises). This receiver has been designed with an architecture identical to the previously designed UART receiver (see chapter 5) which was developed using the AHDL language. The approach taken in this chapter was utilized to contrast the VHDL and AHDL semantics in the development of a relatively complete digital system. The subsystem designs and control-logic methodologies utilized (counters, control logic elements, decoders, etc.) were selected from an array of VHDL design methodologies presented independently in earlier chapters. In a sense, the receivers developed in this chapter and chapter 5 serve to focus the applied digital-design process emphasized in this text. The receiver contains registers, counters, and control logic typical of the digital-design requirements of a large cross-section of advanced applications. The receiver also contains a number of VHDL code segments which expose basic VHDL constructs for instantiating components, generating arrays of components, constructing efficient counters, and incorporating standard libraries.

Appendix 12A

An Alternate VHDL Receiver Source File

This appendix provides an alternative source file for implementing the primary receiver of this chapter. In this appendix, the source file does not use any of the generate commands, but instead distinctly instantiates each of the components and declares each of the signals. The structure and variable names of the receiver in this appendix closely track with those of the primary receiver design of the chapter. This may facilitate comparisons in VHDL style.

```
1    Entity Rcvr3 is
2    -- Clock frequency is 3.456 MHz
3    -- clock period is 289.35 ns
4    -- data rate is 28,800 bps
5    -- DataIn period is 34.72 us
6    Port(clock                  :IN BIT;
7          DataIn                :IN BIT;
8          PosEdge               :OUT BIT;
9          DataDelay             :OUT BIT_VECTOR(1 downto 0);
10         Receiving             :OUT BIT;
```

PROGRAM 12 (Appendix) A Structural VHDL COM Port Receiver

```
11              SampleCount             :OUT BIT_VECTOR(5 downto 0);
12              BitEdge                 :OUT BIT;
13              BitCounter              :OUT BIT_VECTOR(3 downto 0);
14              BitClock                :OUT BIT;
15              StopReceiving           :OUT BIT;
16              InRegister              :OUT BIT_VECTOR(0 to 7);
17              BitCntfb                :OUT BIT;
18              SampleCountReset        :OUT BIT
19              );
20      End Rcvr3;
21      Architecture ARcvr3 of Rcvr3 IS
22      Component Dffpc2
23              Port(D, Clock, clrn, prn: IN BIT;
24                      q, qbar          :OUT BIT);
25      End Component;
26      -- signals for datadelay
27      Signal DataDelayn1, DataDelayn0                         :BIT;
28      Signal DataDelayn1bar, DataDelayn0bar                   :BIT;
29      Signal PosedgeIn, ReceiveFFd, LogicOne                  :BIT;
30      Signal Receivingq, Receivingqbar                        :BIT;
31      Signal InRegq7, InRegq7bar                              :BIT;
32      Signal InRegq6, InRegq6bar                              :BIT;
33      Signal InRegq5, InRegq5bar                              :BIT;
34      Signal InRegq4, InRegq4bar                              :BIT;
35      Signal InRegq3, InRegq3bar                              :BIT;
36      Signal InRegq2, InRegq2bar                              :BIT;
37      Signal InRegq1, InRegq1bar                              :BIT;
38      Signal InRegq0, InRegq0bar                              :BIT;
39      Signal SampleCountq0,SampleCountq1                      :BIT;
40      Signal SampleCountq2,SampleCountq3                      :BIT;
41      Signal SampleCountq4,SampleCountq5                      :BIT;
42      Signal SampleCountq0bar,SampleCountq1bar                :BIT;
43      Signal SampleCountq2bar,SampleCountq3bar                :BIT;
44      Signal SampleCountq4bar,SampleCountq5bar                :BIT;
45      Signal SampleCntRstq, SampleCntRstqbar                  :BIT;
46      Signal SampleCount5d                                    :BIT;
47      Signal BitCountq0, BitCountq1                           :BIT;
48      Signal BitCountq2, BitCountq3                           :BIT;
49      Signal BitCountq0bar, BitCountq1bar                     :BIT;
50      Signal BitCountq2bar, BitCountq3bar                     :BIT;
51      Signal BitCountfb                                       :BIT;
52      -- signals for BitClock
53      Signal BitClockFFqbar                                   :BIT;
54      Signal BitClockq, BitClockqbar                          :BIT;
```

PROGRAM 12   *Continued*

```
55    Signal Receivingd                                    :BIT;
56    Signal StopReceivingd                                :BIT;
57    Signal StopReceivingq, StopReceivingqbar             :BIT;
58    Signal SampleCntRstd                                 :BIT;
59    Signal Nine                                          :BIT;
60    Signal BitClockclk                                   :BIT;
61    Begin
62    -- Flip-flops for edge detection
63    DataDelay1: Dffpc2 Port Map(DataIn, Clock, LogicOne,
64                      LogicOne, DataDelayn1, dataDelayn1bar);
65    DataDelay0: Dffpc2 Port Map(DataDelayn1, Clock, LogicOne,
66                      LogicOne, DataDelayn0, DataDelayn0bar);
67    --Receiving
68    ReceivingFF: Dffpc2 Port Map(Receivingd, Clock, LogicOne,
69                       LogicOne, Receivingq, Receivingqbar);
70    -- Input Data register
71    InRegister7: Dffpc2 Port Map(DataIn, BitClockq, LogicOne,
72                       LogicOne, InRegq7, InRegq7bar);
73    InRegister6: Dffpc2 Port Map(Inregq7, BitClockq,
74           LogicOne, LogicOne, InRegq6, InRegq6bar);
75    InRegister5: Dffpc2 Port Map(Inregq6, BitClockq,
76           LogicOne, LogicOne, InRegq5, InRegq5bar);
77    InRegister4: Dffpc2 Port Map(Inregq5, BitClockq,
78           LogicOne, LogicOne, InRegq4, InRegq4bar);
79    InRegister3: Dffpc2 Port Map(Inregq4, BitClockq,
80           LogicOne, LogicOne, InRegq3, InRegq3bar);
81    InRegister2: Dffpc2 Port Map(Inregq3, BitClockq,
82           LogicOne, LogicOne, InRegq2, InRegq2bar);
83    InRegister1: Dffpc2 Port Map(Inregq2, BitClockq,
84           LogicOne, LogicOne, InRegq1, InRegq1bar);
85    InRegister0: Dffpc2 Port Map(Inregq1, BitClockq,
86           LogicOne, LogicOne, InRegq0, InRegq0bar);
87    --SampleCount Register
88    SampleCount5: Dffpc2 Port Map(SampleCount5d, Clock,
      SampleCntRstq,
89             LogicOne, SampleCountq5, SampleCountq5bar);
90    SampleCount4: Dffpc2 Port Map(SampleCountq5, Clock,
      SampleCntRstq,
91             LogicOne, SampleCountq4, SampleCountq4bar);
92    SampleCount3: Dffpc2 Port Map(SampleCountq4, Clock,
93    SampleCntRstq, LogicOne, SampleCountq3,
      SampleCountq3bar);
94    SampleCount2: Dffpc2 Port Map(SampleCountq3, Clock,
95    SampleCntRstq, LogicOne, SampleCountq2,
      SampleCountq2bar);
```

PROGRAM 12 *Continued*

```
96   SampleCount1: Dffpc2 Port Map(SampleCountq2, Clock,
97              SampleCntRstq, LogicOne, SampleCountq1,
                                    SampleCountq1bar);
98   SampleCount0: Dffpc2 Port Map(SampleCountq1, Clock,
99   LogicOne, SampleCntRstq, SampleCountq0, SampleCountq0bar);
100  -- SampleCountReset
101  SampleCountResetFF: Dffpc2 Port Map(SampleCntRstd, Clock,
102    LogicOne, LogicOne, SampleCntRstq, SampleCntRstqbar );
103  --BitCounter
104  BitCount3: Dffpc2 Port Map(BitCountfb, BitClockq,
105  Receivingq, LogicOne, BitCountq3, BitCountq3bar);
106  BitCount2: Dffpc2 Port Map(BitCountq3, BitClockq,
107  Receivingq, LogicOne, BitCountq2, BitCountq2bar);
108  BitCount1: Dffpc2 Port Map(BitCountq2, BitClockq,
109  Receivingq, LogicOne, BitCountq1, BitCountq1bar);
110  BitCount0: Dffpc2 Port Map(BitCountq1, BitClockq,
111  LogicOne, Receivingq, BitCountq0, BitCountq0bar);
112  -- Flip-flops for generating bitclock
113  BitClockFF: dffpc2 Port Map (BitClockqbar, BitClockclk,
114          Receivingq, LogicOne, BitClockq, BitClockqbar);
115  StopReceiveFF : dffpc2 Port Map (StopReceivingd, Clock,
116  LogicOne, LogicOne, StopReceivingq, StopReceivingqbar);
117  -- start positive edge detection
118          LogicOne <= '1';
119          PosEdgeIn <= DataDelayn1 And not DataDelayn0;
120  --set the receiving signal
121          Receivingd <= PosedgeIn Or (Receivingq And not
               StopReceivingq);
122  --
123  SampleCount5d <= SampleCountq0 Xor SampleCountq1;
124  BitCountfb <= BitCountq0 Xor BitCountq1;
125  BitCntfb <= BitCountfb;
126  SampleCntRstd <= not (SampleCountq5 And SampleCountq4 And
127                       SampleCountq3 And SampleCountq2 And
128                       SampleCountq1 And SampleCountq0) And
                          Receivingq;
129  BitClockclk <= SampleCountq5 And SampleCountq4 And
130                       SampleCountq3 And SampleCountq2 And
131                       SampleCountq1 And SampleCountq0;
132  BitEdge <= SampleCountq5 And SampleCountq4 And
133                       Samplecountq3 And SampleCountq2 And
134                       SampleCountq1 And SampleCountq0;
```

PROGRAM 12 *Continued*

```
135  --Transfer information to output
136          PosEdge <= PosEdgeIn;
137          SampleCount(5) <= SampleCountq5;
138          SampleCount(4) <= SampleCountq4;
139          SampleCount(3) <= SampleCountq3;
140          SampleCount(2) <= SampleCountq2;
141          SampleCount(1) <= SampleCountq1;
142          SampleCount(0) <= SampleCountq0;
143          DataDelay(1) <= datadelayn1;
144          DataDelay(0) <= datadelayn0;
145          Receiving <= Receivingq;
146  -- binary 111111 is 58 in poly count (see polygen
                                          software appendix)
148  BitCounter(3) <= BitCountq3;
149  BitCounter(2) <= BitCountq2;
150  BitCounter(1) <= BitCountq1;
151  BitCounter(0) <= BitCountq0;
152  BitClock <= BitClockq;
153  Nine <= BitCountq3 And not BitCountq2 And
154              BitCountq1 And not BitCountq0;
155  StopReceivingd <= Nine;
156  StopReceiving <= StopReceivingq;
157  InRegister(7) <= InRegq7;
158  InRegister(6) <= InRegq6;
159  InRegister(5) <= InRegq5;
160  InRegister(4) <= InRegq4;
161  InRegister(3) <= InRegq3;
162  InRegister(2) <= InRegq2;
163  InRegister(1) <= InRegq1;
164  InRegister(0) <= InRegq0;
165  SampleCountReset <= SampleCntRstq;
166  End ARcvr3;
167  ---------------------------------
168  ENTITY Dffpc2 IS
169      PORT(d        :IN       BIT;
170            clock   :IN       BIT;
171            clrn    :IN       BIT;
172            prn     :IN       BIT;
173            q       :OUT      BIT;
174            qbar    :OUT      BIT
175            );
176  END Dffpc2;
177  --------------------
178  Architecture Arch1 of Dffpc2 IS
```

PROGRAM 12 *Continued*

```
179   BEGIN
180       PROCESS(clock, clrn, prn)
181           VARIABLE reset, set : INTEGER RANGE 0 to 1;
182           BEGIN
183               if(prn='0') Then
184                       q <= '1';
185                       qbar <='0';
186               elsif(clrn='0') Then
187                       q <= '0';
188                       qbar <= '1';
189               elsif (clock'EVENT And clock = '1') Then
190                       q<=d;
191                       qbar <= not d;
192               END IF;
193       END PROCESS;
194   End Arch1;
195   ---------------
```

PROGRAM 12   *Continued*

The simulation on the next page has been developed directly from the source file, program 12-Appendix. This simulation is given to demonstrate the equivalence of the program of this appendix with the primary receiver developed in chapter 12.

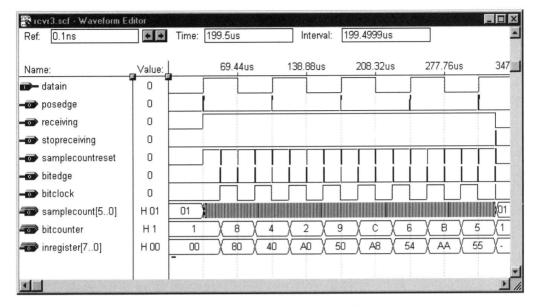

Simulation of Program 12-Appendix

EXERCISES CHAPTER 12

1. The receiver is designed for 28,800 b/sec and utilizes a 3.456 MHz crystal clock.
   a) Redesign the receiver utilizing the same clock, but modify the system for operation at 14,400 b/sec. Create a set of simulation sequences that verify the correctness of your design.
   b) Redesign the system for operation at 9,600 b/sec and a 3.456 MHz clock. Create a simulation verifying the correctness of your design.
   c) Combine the original design with the solution to (a) such that a single input control line will select operation at either 28,800 b/sec or 14,400 b/sec.
   d) Combine the original solution with the solutions to (a) and (b) such that a pair of control lines select operation at 28,800 b/sec, 14,400 b/sec, or 9,600 b/sec.
   e) Another standard crystal oscillator frequency is 3.686 MHz. Redesign the solution in (d) above if system crystal clock operates at 3.686 MHz.

2. The receiver system developed in this chapter utilizes a single sample, optimally placed for each received bit. In the interest of improved error performance, two or three samples of each bit may often be used in digital receivers.
   a) Redesign the receiver to use three samples, symmetrically placed in the interior 33.3% of each bit. Select the value of the bit by a majority voting method and place this sample in the received data register.
   b) Create a simulation verifying the majority voting algorithm sampling process.

If the majority voting algorithm fails to properly certify the start bit, the receiver must be taken out of the active-receiving mode. It must be placed into waiting or listening mode.

3. Modify the receiver design by replacing the D-type receiving flip-flop with a J-K type receiving flip-flop. Compile the design and simulate the performance to assure that the design works properly.

4. Design an m-sequence generator with sequence length 511. The system clock is to be divided by sixteen with a ripple counter. The system clock divided by 16 is to serve as the clock for the m-sequence generator.
   a) Create a source file for the required m-sequence generator. A pn serial bit stream is to be taken from the low-order bit of the generator.
   b) Create a simulation verifying the proper operation of the generator.
   c) Create a positive-edge detector that detects each positive edge of the resulting pn bit stream and produces a positive one (system)-clock pulse duration.
   d) Create an edge detector that produces a one system-clock duration pulse for every edge (positive-going and negative-going) of the pn stream produced by the generator.

5. Given the receiver design of program 12.2:
   a) Redesign the BitCounter design from a polynomial counter to a binary counter.
   b) Redesign the SampleCounter design from a polynomial counter to a binary counter.

6. Modify the receiver program of this chapter to add an eight-byte register file.
   a) The eight-byte register file is to be used to store consecutively received transmission characters. Write consecutive characters to the eight-byte buffer after they have been received and before the next character begins to fill the received data register from the DataIn line.
   b) When the eight-byte buffer is full, raise an interrupt signal. The interrupt signal is to remain high until it is reset by an external input. The external input goes high asserting that the interrupt request has been serviced by a processor that is external to the receiver module.

7. Using standard 7400-series logic modules and/or CMOS 4000-series logic modules:
   a) Estimate the number of such MSI parts required to implement the VHDL receiver designed in this chapter.
   b) Assuming 14 pins per MSI part, calculate the number of device pins that must be interconnected to achieve the receiver function achieved.
   c) Estimate the number of pins that must be externally connected using the VHDL implementation.
   d) Exclude the I/O pins utilized simply to make testing more convenient that would be eliminated in a production design using programmable logic.
   e) Discuss the advantages and disadvantages of the programmable logic implementation when compared with the MSI implementation.

8. The VHDL receiver designed in this chapter contains only a single eight-bit register in which to hold received data. This means that after input data has filled the register, the content must be stored elsewhere (or it will overwritten by the next received character) within little more than a bit time at the transmission rate.

a) Modify the design of the receiver to add a sixteen-character buffer space used for intermediate storage. Assume that when an interrupt service request is processed, it empties the buffer in a single service request.

b) Modify the design of the receiver to a add sixty-four-character buffer space used for intermediate storage.

c) Add a circuit which keeps track of the state of the buffer (in other words, how many characters it contains) for part (a). Repeat for part (c).

d) Add a circuit that raises a flag (requesting interrupt service) when the sixteen-character buffer contains twelve characters. The flag is reset by the processor interface when it services the request.

e) Add a circuit that raises a flag (requesting interrupt service) when the sixty-four-character buffer contains fifty-two characters. The flag is reset by the processor interface when it services the request.

9. The 74180 is a nine-bit parity generator/checker. The 74180 truth table is shown below.

Function Table for Nine-Bit Parity Circuit

Sum of 8 Input 1's	Inputs		Outputs	
	Even	Odd	Even	Odd
Even	H	L	H	L
Odd	H	L	L	H
Even	L	H	L	H
Odd	L	H	H	L
X	H	H	L	L
X	L	L	H	H

The 74180 logic circuit operates as follows. If the eight inputs (usually labeled A through H) sum to an even integer and the Even and Odd input lines are H and L respectively, then the Even and Odd outputs are also H and L respectively. This combination could indicate a "good check" on even parity (see row 1 in the table above). On the other hand, if the A–H input lines are odd and the Even and Odd input lines are H and L respectively, this could be used to indicate an "error" for even parity (see row 2 of the table). Similarly the third and fourth rows could be used to indicate "good parity check" and "parity error" on odd parity, respectively.

Examine the performance of the 74180 part by using a VHDL source file and incorporating the parity checker/generator into the source file by proper instantiation. Then create a simulation to study the performance of the circuit. The function prototype for the parity circuit is shown directly below.

```
FUNCTION 74180 (a, b, c, d, e, f, g, h, evni, oddi)
RETURNS (evns, odds);
```

10. Incorporate the 74180 circuit into the VHDL receiver logic of program 9.2. Modify the receiver to examine parity at the completion of each received data character (ten-bit word containing a seven-bit ASCII data character, one-bit parity, and properly framed by start and stop bits). Create a simulation in which the receiver input contains combinations of correct and incorrect parity for both even and odd parity.

 a) Create a simulation test case for "good" even parity
 b) Create a simulation test case for "bad" even parity
 c) Create a simulation test case for "good" odd parity
 d) Create a simulation test case for "bad" odd parity

CHAPTER 13

VHDL and Digital Filter Design: An Introduction

13.1 INTRODUCTION

In this chapter, we begin by presenting an overview of the theory of digital filter design. The presentation begins with a discussion of the sampling process and the associated transformations (z-transforms) which facilitate the study of digital signal processing. Then a simplified development of both finite impulse response (FIR) and infinite impulse response (IIR) digital filter theory is presented. The current discussion is by no means complete but provides a basis for the development of digital filters provided in the VHDL language in chapter 11 and for the designs presented in the current chapter of this text. Many excellent texts on digital signal processing exist and provide a more complete analysis than can reasonably provided in the current context. The chapter concludes with an illustration of a VHDL FIR digital filter implemented using the well-known Fourier-series method. FIR filter implementation is undertaken in the current chapter primarily to provide an introduction to the implementation mechanics of this popular method.

13.2 SAMPLING OF CONTINUOUS SIGNALS

For the purposes of the current analysis, we define a continuous signal, $x(t)$, such that $x(t)$ exists, is bounded for all time (in other words, $-\infty < t < \infty$), and has bounded derivatives. When the signal, $x(t)$, is sampled, we refer to the resulting signal as, $x^*(t)$. Consider an idealized sampling process in which the sampling is instantaneous and exactly timed at an intervals, T_s. The sampling process can be envisioned with the help of the following diagram.

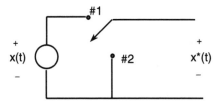

An Idealized Sampling Process

In the diagram above, the switch spends most of its time in position 2. Since this is the common signal reference, we see that the sampled output voltage, $x^*(t)$, is normally zero. At periodic intervals, separated by T_s, the switch instantaneously moves to position 1 where it spends an infinitesimal amount of time. The switch then returns to position 2. During the infinitesimal amount of time that the switch spends in position 1, the output signal, $x^*(t)$, exactly equals the input signal, $x(t)$. We refer to $x^*(t)$ as an ideally sampled signal.

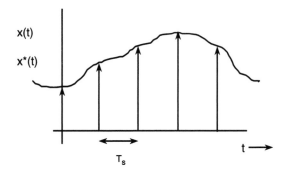

Continuous Signal and Sampled Counterpart

We now seek a mathematical representation that models the conceptual and highly intuitive process described above. Such a representation is available and is easily written in the form

$$x^*(t) = x(t) \sum_{k=-\infty}^{\infty} \delta(t - kT_s) \qquad (13.1)$$

Recall that the delta function is zero whenever its argument is non-zero. The argument of the delta function, namely $(t - kT_s)$, is zero only at instants when

$$t = kT_s \qquad (13.2)$$

Since (13.2) represents the only instants in time for which $x^*(t)$ is non-zero, it is clear that most of the time, $x^*(t)$ is zero. This certainly meets one of the most fundamental notions of our ideally sampled signals. Furthermore, the only instants at which (13.1) indicates a non-zero value of $x^*(t)$ are the instants defined by (13.2). Therefore, equation (13.1) provides a mathematical model for our intuitive notions of ideal sampling. Since this mathematical model provides a means with which to analytically reproduce the effects of ideal sampling, we often refer to (13.1) as an ideal sampling process and similarly often refer to the sequence, $s(t)$ as an ideal sampling waveform or an ideal switching waveform. The ideal switching waveform is shown below as (13.3).

$$s(t) = \sum_{k=-\infty}^{\infty} \delta(t - kT_s) \tag{13.3}$$

A graphical representation of the ideal switching waveform is shown below. From (13.3), we see that $s(t)$ is represented by an infinite sequence of impulses separated in time by intervals of length T_s. This depiction is shown in the figure directly below.

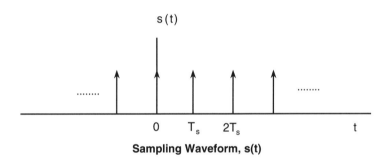

Sampling Waveform, s(t)

We now examine some of the properties of this sampled signal using additional tools.

A frequently examined property of signals is the Fourier transform of the signal. For example, it is common to define the temporal signal and its frequency spectrum as

$$x(t) \longleftrightarrow X(\omega) \tag{13.4}$$

where (13.4) describes a Fourier transform pair and $X(\omega)$ is called the Fourier transform of the temporal signal $x(t)$. $X(\omega)$ is a representation of the frequency spectrum of the signal. The Fourier transform is defined as:

$$X(\omega) = \int_{-\infty}^{\infty} x(t)e^{-j\omega t}\, dt \tag{13.5}$$

Note that the process of sampling is achieved by multiplying the signal and the switching waveform. Applying the definition of the Fourier transform to (13.1), to obtain the spectrum of the sampled signal, we get

$$X*(\omega) = \int_{-\infty}^{\infty} \left[x(t) \sum_{k=-\infty}^{\infty} \delta(t - kT_s) \right] e^{-\omega t} dt \tag{13.6}$$

In any interval where $t \neq kT_s$, the integrand of (13.6) is zero by virtue of the δ function. Therefore, in any interval in which $t \neq kT_s$, there is no contribution to the integral of (13.6) and consequently no contribution to the value of $X*(\omega)$. Since the signal $x(t)$ has bounded derivatives, it remains essentially constant in any infinitesimal interval. When integrating over all intervals for which $t = kT_s$ (the only intervals that contribute non-zero quantities to the integrals), we may write (13.6) as

$$X*(\omega) = \ldots x(-2T_S)e^{j2\omega T_s} \int_{-2T_S^-}^{-2T_s^+} \delta(t + 2T_s)dt + x(-T_s)e^{j\omega T_s} \int_{-T_s^-}^{-T_s^+} \delta(t + T_s)\,dt$$

$$+ x(0) \int_{0^-}^{0^+} \delta(t)dt + x(T_s)e^{-j\omega T_s} \int_{T_s^-}^{T_s^+} \delta(t - T_s)dt + x(2T_s)e^{-j2\omega T_s} \int_{2T_S}^{2T_s^+} \delta(t - 2T_s)dt \ldots \tag{13.7}$$

Since the integrals of (13.7) are each unity, we may write (13.7) as

$$X^*(\omega) = \sum_{k=-\infty}^{\infty} [x(kT_s)e^{-jk\omega T_s}] \tag{13.8}$$

Equation (13.8) can be simplified considerably if we remember that it represents the frequency spectrum of the sampled signal. For the simplification of the notation we now define (strictly for convenience)

$$z = e^{j\omega T_s} \tag{13.9}$$

It is worth noting that (13.9) represents a unity amplitude function with a phase-shift of ωT_s radians or, equivalently, a delay of T_s sec.

With the defining equation provided by (13.9), we rewrite (13.8) as

$$X^*(z) = \sum_{k=-\infty}^{\infty} x(kT_s)z^{-k} \tag{13.10}$$

The interpretation that may now be applied to (13.10) is that the kth sample represented by $x(kT_s)$ is a real number. The multiplying factor, $z^{-k} = e^{-jk\omega T_s}$, represents a delaying factor of kT_s seconds or equivalently a phase retardation of $k\omega T_s$ radians.

Equation (13.10) is called the z transform of the signal, $x(kT_s)$. One final set of simplifications is provided if we drop the T_s in (13.10) and accept the understanding that successive samples of $x(t)$ will be separated at uniform intervals, T_s, and we also drop the asterisk with the further understanding that the representation given by (13.10) is for discrete signals whether or not they are derived from a sampling process. With this set of simplifications, (13.10) may be written in the very convenient, but deceptively simple form given by

$$X(z) = \sum_{k=-\infty}^{\infty} x(k)z^{-k} \tag{13.11}$$

In (13.11), the left-hand side is known as the z-transform of the sequence, $x(k)$. The apparent simplicity of (13.11) stems from the implicit attributes of the variables. For example, the variable z conceals a complex frequency variable term, $e^{j\omega T}$. Furthermore, the variable k contains implicit characteristics of the sampling interval. Writing (13.11) in a less elegant and expanded form, we obtain

$$X(z) = \dots + x(-2)z^2 + x(-1)z + x(0) + x(1)z^{-1} + x(2)z^{-2} + \dots \qquad (13.12)$$

Although the z-transform relationship has been derived through the device of sampling a continuous process, the result is valid whether or not the discrete sequence is obtained by a sampling process on a continuous signal. Equation (13.11) is the final defining relationship for the z transform of the sequence $x(k)$.

13.3 FREQUENCY CONTENT OF THE IDEAL-SWITCHING WAVEFORM

Equation (13.3) is often called the ideal-switching waveform or ideal-sampling waveform. It is clear that $s(t)$ is an even periodic function. The switching function may therefore be expressed as

$$s(t) = \sum_{n=-\infty}^{\infty} C_n e^{-jn\omega_s t} \qquad (13.13)$$

Equation (13.13) is simply an expression for the Fourier series of the switching waveform which is valid because $s(t)$ is an even, periodic function of time. The coefficients C_n are given by

$$C_n = \frac{1}{T_s} \int_{-T_s/2}^{T_s/2} s(t)e^{-jn\omega_s t}dt = \frac{1}{T_s} \int_{-T_s/2}^{T_s/2} \delta(t)e^{-jn\omega_s t}\,dt \qquad (13.14)$$

Completing the indicated integration in equation (13.14) then clearly results in

$$C_n = \frac{1}{T_s} \qquad (13.15)$$

Equation (13.15) effectively indicates that the temporal impulse train given by (13.3) yields a frequency domain impulse train. Substituting (13.15) into (13.13) results in a Fourier expression for the switching waveform that is

$$s(t) = \frac{1}{T_s} \sum_{n=-\infty}^{\infty} e^{-jn\omega_s t} \qquad (13.16)$$

Equation (13.16) says that the ideal-switching waveform $s(t)$ may be represented by an infinite number of sinusoids (in other words, the terms $e^{-jn\omega_s t}$), each with an identical amplitude ($1/T_s$) and each harmonically related to the fundamental frequency ($1/T_s$). Since the amplitude of the resulting frequency components are all identical and they are separated in frequency by an interval ω_s, the frequency spectrum of the switching waveform may be written as

$$S(f) = \frac{1}{T_s} \sum_{n=-\infty}^{\infty} \delta(\omega - n\omega_s) \tag{13.17}$$

where $\omega_s = \dfrac{2\pi}{T_s} = 2\pi f_s$

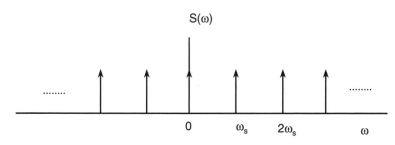

Spectrum of the Sampling Waveform, s(t)

   Relationship (13.17) indicates that the spectral components of the ideal-switching waveform are isolated spectral lines, separated by an interval of length $\omega_s = 2\pi/T_s$ in angular frequency and extending infinitely and periodically in both directions (in other words, $\omega \to \pm\infty$).

13.4 FREQUENCY CONTENT OF THE SAMPLED SIGNAL

The process of sampling is indicated by the product of the continuous signal, $x(t)$, and the switching waveform, $s(t)$ [in other words, a product in the time domain; see equation (13.6)]. This product in the time domain produces a convolution in the frequency domain. That is to say, when two signals are multiplied in the time domain, their spectra are convolved in the frequency domain as shown in (13.18).

$$x(t) \cdot s(t) \longleftrightarrow X(\omega) * S(\omega) \tag{13.18}$$

We assume a bandlimited spectrum of the signal to be sampled. As shown below, the signal to be sampled is bandlimited to a two-sided spectrum of width $2W$ radians per second.

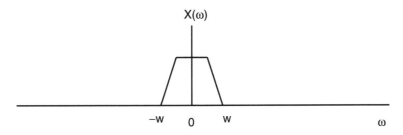

Spectrum of the Signal to be Sampled

When the bandlimited spectrum, $X(\omega)$, is convolved with the infinite impulse train of (13.17), the resulting spectrum, $X^*(\omega)$, is shown in the figure below. From the diagram, it is clear that if $\omega_s \geq 2W$, then the copies or images of the spectrum of the sampled signal are distinct and may readily be separated by linear filtering. If, however, the sampling does not meet this Nyquist criterion, then the images of the original spectrum overlap and no simple means is available for separating them. Directly below, we repeat a portion of this argument in slightly more analytical language.

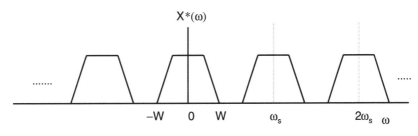

Spectrum of the Sampled Signal

Recall that the convolution of any function with a δ function "sifts" or copies the function. Convolution with an infinite succession of δ functions creates multiple copies of the function in question. The result of (13.18) is that the frequency spectrum, $X(\omega)$, is repeated at intervals in the angular frequency domain separated by $2\pi/T_s$. If the original spectral components of $X(\omega)$ are limited in extent such that

$$|X(\omega)| \equiv 0 \quad \text{for} \quad \omega \leq \frac{W_s}{2} \tag{13.19}$$

then the images of $X(\omega)$ "fit" nicely into a periodic pattern in the frequency domain and each image of the original spectrum of $x(t)$ is clearly discernible (in other words, aliasing does not occur). If, on the other hand, the original spectrum is not limited in extent, then the upper frequencies of the images overlap in the frequency domain and consequently are not distinct. In this case, recovering the original signal from the sampled signal is no longer reasonably possible. This gives rise to the well-known Nyquist sampling criterion which states that the sampling frequency $(1/T_s)$ must exceed twice the upper frequency of the signal to be sampled.

$$\omega_s \geq 2W \qquad\qquad (13.20)$$

When the Nyquist criterion is not met, the resulting overlap of sampled spectrum images occurs and the phenomenon is referred to as aliasing. In the discussions below, we assume that the Nyquist criterion is met and therefore no aliasing of signals results.

13.5   INFINITE AND FINITE IMPULSE RESPONSE SYSTEMS

We now consider a linear discrete system as shown in the diagram below.

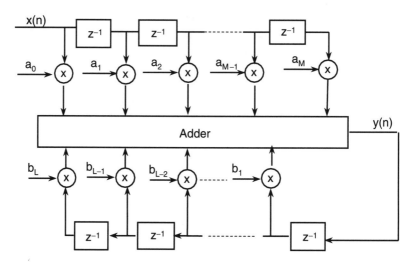

Generalized Discrete Linear System

We write the I/O relationship of the discrete, linear system as a difference equation of the form

$$y(n) = a_0x(n) + a_1x(n) - 1) + ... + a_mx(n - M)$$
$$- b_1y(n - 1) - b_2y(n - 2) - .... -b_1y(n - L) \qquad (13.21)$$

Equation (13.21) indicates that a discrete input data stream, $x(n)$, is presented to the input of the linear system. The input data stream is stored in a shift register. The respective stages of the shift register provide the delay operation represented by the z^{-1} operators in the diagram above. The content of each of the input register stages are multiplied by distinct, discrete coefficients, a_i, and the resulting products are summed. The output,

$y(n)$, is directed through a separate and distinct shift register. Each delayed output sample is multiplied by a coefficient, b_i, and then added to the sum which forms the discrete output. Equation (13.21) may be written as

$$y(n) = \sum_{k=0}^{M} a_k\, x(n - k) - \sum_{k=1}^{L} b_k\, y(n - k) \qquad (13.22)$$

Equation (13.22) is a digital filter which processes input values, $x(n)$, and produces output values, $y(n)$. The input samples may be as many bits in width as desired. If the width of the discrete input data path is W_x, the number of flip-flops required to store input samples for processing is

$$N = W_x M \qquad (13.23)$$

To clarify, if the width of the input data path is eight bits ($W_x = 8$), and the length of the input register is thirty-two stages, then a total of 256 flip-flops is required to implement the input register. If the feedback register path is eight stages long ($L = 8$) and the output data path is eight bits wide, then the feedback path requires an additional sixty-four flip-flops in the mechanization. Using the numbers in this illustration, a total of 320 flip-flops is required simply to implement the two delay-line registers. Not included in this count is the number of register stages required to implement the multipliers and adder. Such a large number of flip-flops seems to present a complex and potentially unwieldy problem for the designer. HDL and programmable arrays render handling of a design responsibility of this magnitude reasonably manageable. For the time being, we examine some special cases of (13.22).

13.6   FINITE IMPULSE RESPONSE FILTERS

If each of the coefficients b_j in (13.22) is made identically zero, then (13.22) may be written as

$$y(n) = a_0 x(n) + a_1 x(n - 1) + \dots + a_m x(n - M) \qquad (13.24)$$

Clearly (13.24) represents an FIR system. If the input data path is assumed eight bits wide (one byte) and the input pulse of amplitude 100_{10} is selected to obtain the single pulse response, we let

$$x(n) = 0x64, \text{ for } n = 0 \qquad (13.25)$$
$$x(n) = 0x00, \text{ otherwise.}$$

The input signal specified by (13.25) provides a discrete, byte-wide pulse with which to stimulate the system. The input signal is clocked into the digital system and subsequently clocked through the registers represented in (13.23), $x(n)$, $x(n - 1)$, $x(n - 2)$ ... $x(n - M)$, respectively. Since the input signal is a single pulse, which walks through the system at the clock rate, the output signal will be, at adjacent clock times, $a_0 x(n)$, $a_1 x(n - 1)$, $a_2 x(n - 2)$ ... $a_M x(n - M)$, respectively.

As stated above, a clocking signal is used to propagate the signal into, and subsequently through, the input register. At each stage, the output signal becomes the product of the coefficient at that stage and the magnitude of the input pulse. Then it is clear that after the Mth clock, the output signal will become zero and remain zero. The system has a single pulse response which is finite in duration, therefore, we say that equation (13.23) represents an FIR filter system.

13.7 A SIMPLE FIR FILTER ILLUSTRATION

We now present a source file, written in VHDL, which implements an FIR system. Program 13.1 performs the requisite processing. The input data path for the FIR filter is eight bits and the filter length is also eight stages. Program 13.1 is a slight variation on the FIR filter of program 11.5.

```
1     Library ieee;
2     Use ieee.Std_Logic_1164.all;
3     Use ieee.Std_Logic_arith.all;
4     Use ieee.Std_Logic_signed.all;
5     Entity FIR131 is
6         Port(clock    :In Std_Logic;
7                 DataIn:In Integer range 0 to 255;
8                 DataOut        :Out Integer range 0 to 511
9                 );
10    End FIR131;

11    Architecture AFIR131 of FIR131 is
12    Begin
13    Process(clock)
14    Type Regtype is array(7 downto 0) of Integer;
15    variable Reg: Regtype;
16        Begin
17        if (clock'event and clock = '1') then
18            DataOut <= -Reg(0)/8+Reg(1)/8+Reg(2)/4+Reg(3)/2+
19                        Reg(4)/2+Reg(5)/4+Reg(6)/8-Reg(7)/8;
20            Reg(0) := Reg(1);
21            Reg(1) := Reg(2);
22            Reg(2) := Reg(3);
23            Reg(3) := Reg(4);
24            Reg(4) := Reg(5);
25            Reg(5) := Reg(6);
26            Reg(6) := Reg(7);
27            Reg(7) := DataIn;
28        End if;
29        End Process;
30    End AFIR131;
```

PROGRAM 13.1   A Demonstration FIR Filter

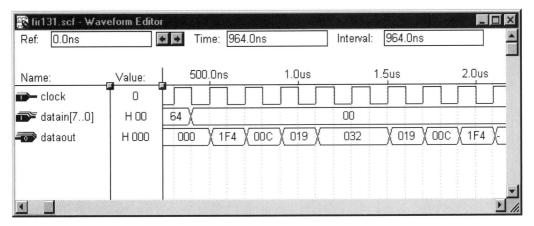

Single Pulse Response of FIR Program 13.1

In the simulation of FIR program 13.1, note that the input is a single pulse of amplitude 0x64 which is a decimal value of 100. Notice that the system clock is running at a period of 100 ns. The following information assists in interpreting the simulation of program 13.1.

The input, single pulse amplitude is $0x64 = 100_{10}$.

1. In the time interval 500 to 700 ns, the output, dataout is

$$\frac{-100}{8} = -12.5_{10} = -0x00C = 0x1F4$$

where the decimal .5 has been truncated by the integer arithmetic.

2. In the interval 700 to 900 ns, the output is:

$$\frac{+100}{8} = 12.5_{10} = 0x0C$$

where the decimal .5 has been truncated by the integer arithmetic.

3. In the interval 900 to 1100 ns, the data output is:

$$\frac{100}{4} = 25_{10} = 0x19$$

4. In the interval 1100 to 1500 ns, the data output is:

$$\frac{100}{2} = 50_{10} = 0x32$$

5. During the next four time intervals, the output is the mirror image of the first four intervals.

Two factors seem clear at this point. First, it is not in our best interest to continue to truncate fractional values and consequently lose accuracy. Second, although we have produced an FIR filter, the objective should be to create a filter with a known frequency response. We consider this problem in the next section.

13.8   THE FOURIER-SERIES METHOD OF FIR DESIGN

We now proceed to show only one method, albeit a very popular method, of a wide variety of available design methods for FIR filters. While many other methods exist, we continue to emphasize the implementation of digital systems rather than the generalized theory of digital signal processing systems. For our present purposes, it is sufficient to demonstrate a single method, since this method typifies the implementation of FIR filters. For the present, we initiate the implementation process. We begin with equation (13.24) which is clearly a finite impulse function. Taking the z-transform of (13.24) we get

$$Y(z) = a_0 X(z) + a_1 z^{-1} X(z) + \dots\dots + a_m z^{-m} X(z) \tag{13.26}$$

where we have observed that a unit delay in the time domain is equivalent to multiplying by a factor of z^{-1} in the z domain. Here the reader might wish to recall equations (13.9) through (13.11) and the related observations relating to the delay factors. If we now factor the common term from the right-hand side of (13.26) and divide both sides by this common factor, we get

$$\frac{Y(z)}{H(z)} \equiv H(z) = a_0 + a_1 z^{-1} + \dots\dots\dots + a_m z^{-m} \tag{13.27}$$

Now, strictly for convenience and with no loss in generality, we assume that m is an even number. If we factor the term $z^{-m/2}$ from (13.27) the result is

$$H(z) = z^{-m/2}[a_0 z^{m/2} + a_1 z^{(m-2)/2} + \dots + a_{m/2} + \dots a_{(m-1)} z^{-(m-2)/2} + a_m z^{-m/2}] \tag{13.28}$$

We now impose the condition that the coefficients in (13.28) be symmetric. This condition obtains the often-sought characteristic of linear phase. That is, we desire that

$$\begin{aligned}
a_0 &= a_m \\
a_1 &= a_{m-1} \\
a_2 &= a_{m-2}
\end{aligned} \tag{13.29}$$

$$\dots\dots$$

etc.

We can now write (13.28) in the form

$$H(z) = z^{-m/2}[a_0(z^{m/2} + z^{-m/2}) + a_1(z^{(m-2)/2} + z^{-(m-2)/2}) + \dots\dots + a_{m/2}] \tag{13.30}$$

Recalling from (13.9) that $z = e^{j\omega T_s}$ and substituting this defining relationship into equation (13.30), we find that (13.30) may be rewritten as

$$H\left(z\right) = e^{-j\omega w T_s m/2}[a_0\left(e^{j\omega T_s m/2} + e^{-j\omega T_s m/2}\right) + a_1\left(e^{j\omega T_s(m-2)/2} + e^{-j\omega T_s(m-2)/2}\right)$$
$$+ .... + a_{m/2}] \tag{13.31}$$

We now recall that Euler's formula states that

$$\cos\theta = \frac{e^{j\theta} + e^{-j\theta}}{2} \tag{13.32}$$

Therefore, we finally write (13.31) in the form

$$H\left(e^{j\omega T_s}\right) = e^{-j\omega T_s m/2}\left[2a_0\cos\left(\frac{\omega T_s m}{2}\right) + 2a_1\cos\left(\frac{\omega T_s\left(m-2\right)}{2}\right) + ... + a_{m/2}\right] \tag{13.33}$$

Equation (13.33) which represents the steady-state response of the digital filter reveals that the steady-state frequency response is a cosine series. Upon closer inspection, (13.33) reveals several additional interesting characteristics.

1. Since the steady-state response is the sum of even functions (cosine terms and a constant), the steady-state response itself must also be an even function.
2. The steady state response has a period equal to the sampling frequency (in other words, at $f_s = 1/T_s$).
3. The steady-state response is said to "fold" at half the sampling frequency.

Therefore the coefficients of the time-domain samples are involved intimately, both in the time-domain and frequency-domain representations. Notice that (13.33) also reveals that the steady-state response of an FIR filter with symmetric coefficients [see (13.29)] has a linear-phase characteristic. This linear-phase also constitutes a fixed-time delay of $mT_s/2$ seconds.

This analysis provides one recipe for designing FIR filters as stated below.

1. Create a function representing the transfer function of the desired filter. The function must necessarily be a compromise between the ideal, desired response, and a reasonably attainable response [see (13.33)].
2. Find the Fourier series coefficients of the function selected.
3. Assign the Fourier coefficients to the appropriate member coefficients of the difference equation [for example, the right-hand side of (13.24), (13.26), or (13.27)].
4. The implemented function will approximate the desired amplitude function as closely as desired based upon the number of Fourier coefficients utilized.

13.8.1 A Rectangular Prototype for Fourier Series Implementation

In this section, we undertake the implementation of a digital filter, following the formulation of the previous section. In accordance with the formulation of the previous section, we first select a simple rectangular prototype. The selected prototype is shown below. We know from the discussion that the filter response is periodic. The response repeats at a frequency interval equal to the sampling frequency, f_s. It is said to fold at the frequency given by $f_s/2$. Such a response is shown below in selected terms. In the analysis below, we assign the value of $f_s = 1000$. Therefore the lowpass filter exhibits a cutoff frequency of $1000/8 = 125$ Hz and the frequency response folds at $1000/2 = 500$ Hz. In the final analysis, the filter will retain its shape and will conform to the provisions of the Fourier representation, but will adjust its period, cutoff frequency, and folding frequency to the selected sampling frequency.

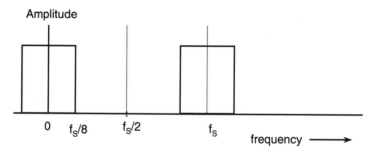

Selected Filter Characteristic

The Fourier coefficients for the function above may be readily found through the standard formulations. The Fourier series for an even function is given by

$$H(\omega) = \alpha_0 + \sum_{n=1}^{\infty} \alpha_n \cos(n\omega_0\omega) \qquad (13.34)$$

The Fourier coefficients for the selected prototype may be found using a formulation for the Fourier coefficients. If we use the Fourier cosine series, the constant or DC term becomes

$$\alpha_0 = \frac{1}{1000} \int_{-125}^{125} 1\, d\omega = \frac{250}{1000} = \frac{1}{4} \qquad (13.35)$$

Since the desired transfer function is even, the Fourier series become a cosine series with coefficients given by

$$\alpha_n = \frac{2}{1000} \int_{-125}^{125} 1 \cos\left(\frac{2n\pi}{1000}\right) \omega\, d\omega \qquad (13.36)$$

Carrying out the indicated operation we get

$$\alpha_n = \left(\frac{2}{1000}\right)\left(\frac{1000}{2n\pi}\right)\left[\sin\left(\frac{2n\pi}{1000}\right)\omega\right]_{-125}^{125}$$

which finally becomes

$$\alpha_n = \frac{2}{n\pi}\sin\left(\frac{n\pi}{4}\right) \text{ for } n \neq 0 \tag{13.37}$$

Evaluating the coefficients and rearranging them to meet the required formulation in (13.33), we finally obtain the following

$$\begin{aligned}
2a_0 &= .06366 \\
2a_1 &= .050 \\
2a_2 &= 0 \\
2a_3 &= -.064 \\
2a_4 &= -.106 \\
2a_5 &= .-09 \\
2a_6 &= 0 \\
2a_7 &= .150 \\
2a_8 &= .318 \\
2a_9 &= .450 \\
a_{10} &= .250
\end{aligned} \tag{13.37a}$$

The coefficients above are twice the values required for the impulse response of the filter as shown below. The implemented filter should contain twenty-one coefficients. Recall that the coefficients of equation (13.33) are the coefficients of the cosine terms. From (13.30) through (13.32), it is clear that the digital filter implementation requires the coefficients of the exponential series. The implementation coefficients can easily be obtained by dividing the coefficients a_0 through a_9 of (13.37a) by two and using the resulting coefficients in a symmetric arrangement where the unmodified value, a_{10}, is the center coefficient. To reinforce this point, we now proceed to evaluate the coefficients of the exponential series directly.

The exponential form of the Fourier series is given by

$$H(\omega) = \sum_{n=-\infty}^{\infty} \eta_n e^{-jn\omega_0\omega} \tag{13.38}$$

In this formulation, the coefficients are given by

$$\eta_n = \frac{1}{1000}\int_{-125}^{125} 1\, e^{-jn\omega_0\omega}\, d\omega \tag{13.39}$$

Performing the indicated integration, we obtain

$$\eta_n = \frac{1}{1000}\left(\frac{1000}{j2n\pi}\right)\left[e^{j\frac{2n\pi\omega}{1000}}\right]_{-125}^{125}$$

If we substitute the limits of integration into the above formulation, we finally get

$$\eta_n = \frac{1}{n\pi} \sin\left(\frac{n\pi}{4}\right) \quad \text{for } n \neq 0 \tag{13.40}$$

Comparing (13.40) and (13.37), we see that $\alpha_n = 2\eta_n$ for $n \neq 0$. This observation corresponds directly with a similar observation that can be made by comparing (13.31) and (13.33). The constant term is easily found from (13.39) by setting $n = 0$ and evaluating the integral which confirms that

$$a_0 = .25 \tag{13.40a}$$

Therefore, the assignment of coefficients to the impulse response, corresponding to equation (13.24), are as follows.

$$\begin{aligned}
a_0 &= a_{20} = .0318 \\
a_1 &= a_{19} = .0250 \\
a_2 &= a_{18} = 0 \\
a_3 &= a_{17} = -.032 \\
a_4 &= a_{16} = -.053 \\
a_5 &= a_{15} = -.045 \\
a_6 &= a_{14} = 0 \\
a_7 &= a_{13} = .075 \\
a_8 &= a_{12} = .159 \\
a_9 &= a_{11} = .225 \\
a_{10} &= .25
\end{aligned} \tag{13.41}$$

After determining the Fourier coefficients and assigning them to the proper positions in the impulse response, we are prepared to implement the filter. The digital processing will be implemented as a binary integer processor so that we must now formulate the binary coefficients. Since we elect here to implement the solution in integer form, we now elect to assign the coefficients as follows

$$\begin{aligned}
a_0 &= a_{20} = 32 \\
a_1 &= a_{19} = 25 \\
a_2 &= a_{18} = 0 \\
a_3 &= a_{17} = -32 \\
a_4 &= a_{16} = -53 \\
a_5 &= a_{15} = -45 \\
a_6 &= a_{14} = 0 \\
a_7 &= a_{13} = 75 \\
a_8 &= a_{12} = 159 \\
a_9 &= a_{11} = 225 \\
a_{10} &= 250
\end{aligned} \tag{13.42}$$

Note that we have taken the original Fourier coefficients, multiplied each of them by 1,000, and rounded them to the nearest integer. Since the integer processing is best accomplished by shift-and-add operations, we now apportion the decimal, integer coefficients as the sum of decimal partial-coefficients which are integral powers of two. We therefore obtain

$$a_0 = a_{20} = 32 = 2^5$$
$$a_1 = a_{19} = 25 = 16 + 8 + 1 = 2^4 + 2^3 + 2^0$$
$$a_2 = a_{18} = 0$$
$$a_3 = a_{17} = -32 = -2^5$$
$$a_4 = a_{16} = -53 = -32 - 16 - 4 - 1 = -2^5 - 2^4 - 2^2 - 2^0$$
$$a_5 = a_{15} = -45 = -32 - 8 - 4 - 1 = 2^5 - 2^3 + 2^2 - 2^0 \qquad (13.43)$$
$$a_6 = a_{14} = 0$$
$$a_7 = a_{13} = 75 = 64 + 8 + 2 + 1 = 2^6 + 2^3 + 2^1 + 2^0$$
$$a_8 = a_{12} = 159 = 128 + 16 + 8 + 4 + 2 + 1 = 2^7 + 2^4 + 2^3 + 2^2 + 2^1 + 2^0$$
$$a_9 = a_{11} = 225 = 128 + 64 + 32 + 1 = 2^7 + 2^5 + 2^5 + 2^0$$
$$a_{10} = 250 = 128 + 64 + 32 + 16 + 8 + 2 = 2^7 + 2^5 + 2^4 + 2^3 + 2^1$$

The implementation of the filter in VHDL follows directly. The source file is shown directly below.

```
1    --Demo3
2    Library ieee;
3    Use ieee.Std_Logic_1164.all;
4    Entity Demo3 is
5        Port(clock    :In Std_Logic;
6              DataIn :In Integer range 0 to 255;
7              DataOut      :Out integer range 0 to 16383
8        );
9    End Demo3;

10   Architecture ADemo3 of Demo3 is
11   Begin
12   Process(clock)
13   Type Regtype is array(20 downto 0) of Integer ;
14   variable Reg: Regtype;
15       Begin
16       if (clock'event and clock = '1') then
17              DataOut <= ((Reg(0)+Reg(20))*32
18                             ---------
19                             +(Reg(1)+Reg(19))*16
20                             +(Reg(1)+Reg(19))*8
21                             +(Reg(1)+Reg(19))
22                             -----------
23                             -(Reg(3)+Reg(17))*32
24                             -----------
25                             -(Reg(4)+Reg(16))*32
26                             -(Reg(4)+Reg(16))*16
```

PROGRAM 13.2 A Fourier-Series Implemented FIR Filter

```
27                                    -(Reg(4)+Reg(16))*4
28                                    -(Reg(4)+Reg(16))
29                                    ------------
30                                    -(Reg(5)+Reg(15))*32
31                                    -(Reg(5)+Reg(15))*8
32                                    -(Reg(5)+Reg(15))*4
33                                    -(Reg(5)+Reg(15))
34                                    ------------
35                                    +(Reg(7)+Reg(13))*64
36                                    +(Reg(7)+Reg(13))*8
37                                    +(Reg(7)+Reg(13))*2
38                                    +(Reg(7)+Reg(13))
39                                    ------------
40                                    +(Reg(8)+Reg(12))*128
41                                    +(Reg(8)+Reg(12))*16
42                                    +(Reg(8)+Reg(12))*8
43                                    +(Reg(8)+Reg(12))*4
44                                    +(Reg(8)+Reg(12))*2
45                                    +(Reg(8)+Reg(12))*1
46                                    ------------
47                                    +(Reg(9)+Reg(11))*128
48                                    +(Reg(9)+Reg(11))*64
49                                    +(Reg(9)+Reg(11))*32
50                                    +(Reg(9)+Reg(11))*1
51                                    ------------
52                                    +(Reg(10))*128
53                                    +(Reg(10))*64
54                                    +(Reg(10))*32
55                                    +(Reg(10))*16
56                                    +(Reg(10))*8
57                                    +(Reg(10))*2);
58              ----------------------
59              Reg(0)  := Reg(1);
60              Reg(1)  := Reg(2);
61              Reg(2)  := Reg(3);
62              Reg(3)  := Reg(4);
63              Reg(4)  := Reg(5);
64              Reg(5)  := Reg(6);
65              Reg(6)  := Reg(7);
66              Reg(7)  := Reg(8);
67              Reg(8)  := Reg(9);
68              Reg(9)  := Reg(10);
69              Reg(10) := Reg(11);
70              Reg(11) := Reg(12);
71              Reg(12) := Reg(13);
```

PROGRAM 13.2 *Continued*

```
72              Reg(13) := Reg(14);
73              Reg(14) := Reg(15);
74              Reg(15) := Reg(16);
75              Reg(16) := Reg(17);
76              Reg(17) := Reg(18);
77              Reg(18) := Reg(19);
78              Reg(19) := Reg(20);
79              Reg(20) := DataIn;
80      End if;
81      End Process;
82 End Ademo3;
```

PROGRAM 13.2   *Continued*

Lines 1–9 declare the entity which is the FIR filter. The filter contains an eight-bit input data bus and a fourteen-bit output bus. These buses are declared as integer values for convenience. However the designer must constantly be aware of the underlying binary implementation.

Lines 10–82 constitute the architecture definition of the FIR filter. Lines 17–58 implement the shift-and-add arithmetic processing of the filter. This shift-and-add processing essentially performs the arithmetic functions of multiply-and-add mathematical processing. In lines 59–79, the source file implements an integer-wide (the default is thirty-two bits or four bytes), twenty-one stage shift register. Note that since the filter contains symmetric coefficients in the difference-equation implementation, the implementation is folded (in other words, symmetric register contents are summed before applying the multiplicative coefficient).

In the simulation below, a portion of the impulse response is shown. The input signal is a value 0x01, an eight-bit value. In the brief segment of the simulation presented below, we see that the first five values of the impulse response are:

$$0x20 = 32_{10}$$
$$0x19 = 25_{10}$$
$$0x00 = 0_{10}$$
$$0xFE0 = -32_{10}$$
$$0xFCB = -53_{10}$$
$$.....................$$
$$\text{etc.}$$

The source code reveals that the current implementation requires a shift register eight-bits wide by twenty-one-stages long. This register requires 168 flip-flops as implemented. The output bus is 16-bits wide.

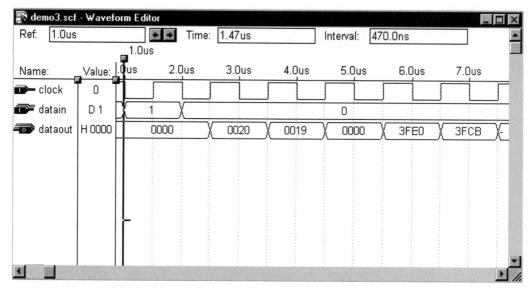

Simulation of Program 13.2: A Fourier-Series Implemented FIR Filter

The frequency response of the implemented filter will now be examined. The amplitude response is achieved through the evaluation of equation (13.33). The coefficients α_n have been found and are presented above as (13.37a). Substituting the coefficients given by (13.37a) into the frequency response given by (13.33) we obtain

$$H(f) = .250 + .06366 \cos\left(\frac{2\pi f \cdot 10^{-6} \cdot 20}{2}\right) + .05 \cos\left(\frac{2\pi f \cdot 10^{-6} \cdot 18}{2}\right)$$

$$-.064 \cos\left(\frac{2\pi f \cdot 10^{-6} \cdot 14}{2}\right) - .106 \cos\left(\frac{2\pi f \cdot 10^{-6} \cdot 12}{2}\right)$$

$$-.09 \cos\left(\frac{2\pi f \cdot 10^{-6} \cdot 10}{2}\right) + .150 \cos\left(\frac{2\pi f \cdot 10^{-6} \cdot 6}{2}\right) \qquad (13.44)$$

$$+.318 \cos\left(\frac{2\pi f \cdot 10^{-6} \cdot 4}{2}\right) + .45 \cos\left(\frac{2\pi f \cdot 10^{-6} \cdot 2}{2}\right)$$

The simulation shown has a sampling interval of 1.0 µsec. With the 1 µsec sampling interval, the frequency response of the system has a period of 1.0 MHz and the response "folds" at 500 KHz. When (13.44) is evaluated (in other words, $20 \log_{10} H(f)$ vs. f) and plotted, then the result is shown directly below. Notice that the abscissa of the resulting graph has been selected as frequency (Hertz) rather than angular frequency in radians per second. In this case, The folding frequency is 500 KHz and the ideal cutoff frequency is 125,000 Hz. The cutoff frequency, folding frequency, and period may be readily confirmed from the figure on the next page.

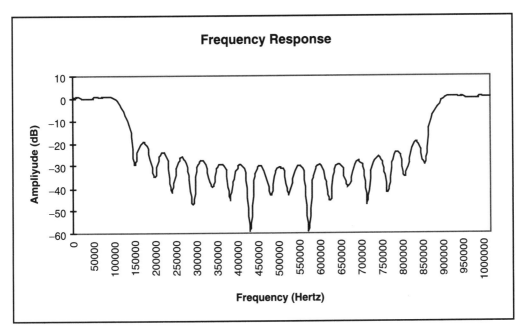

Frequency Response
Sampling Frequency of 1.0 MHz

As stated above, the filter will retain the generalized shape as required by the Fourier representation, but will conform to the selected sampling frequency. That is to say, when the coefficients are maintained exactly the same as above, but the sampling frequency has been selected as 1,000 Hz, the frequency response is evaluated using (13.45).

$$H(f) = .250 + .06366 \cos\left(\frac{2\pi f \cdot 10^{-3} \cdot 20}{2}\right) + .05 \cos\left(\frac{2\pi f \cdot 10^{-3} \cdot 18}{2}\right)$$

$$- .064 \cos\left(\frac{2\pi f \cdot 10^{-3} \cdot 14}{2}\right) - .106 \cos\left(\frac{2\pi f \cdot 10^{-3} \cdot 12}{2}\right)$$

$$- .09 \cos\left(\frac{2\pi f \cdot 10^{-3} \cdot 10}{2}\right) + .150 \cos\left(\frac{2\pi f \cdot 10^{-3} \cdot 6}{2}\right) \quad (13.45)$$

$$+ .318 \cos\left(\frac{2\pi f \cdot 10^{-3} \cdot 4}{2}\right) + .45 \cos\left(\frac{2\pi f \cdot 10^{-3} \cdot 2}{2}\right)$$

Equation (13.45) is (13.44) with the sampling frequency selected as 1×10^3 instead of 1×10^6 as it is in (13.44). Notice that the frequency response retains the same generalized form, but the period of the response is now 1,000 Hz and the response "folds" at

500 Hz and the cutoff frequency is 125 Hz. This is readily observed in the figure below which has been obtained by graphing $20 \log_{10} H(f)$ vs. f in equation (13.45).

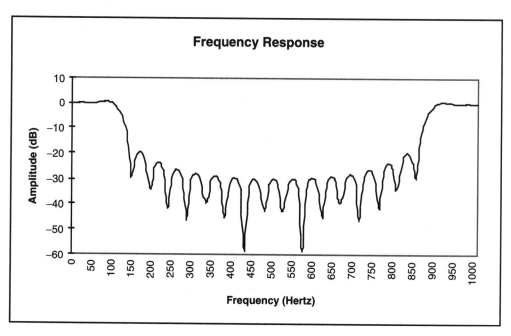

**Frequency Response
Sampling Frequency of 1,000 Hertz**

13.9   RETROSPECTIVE

In the current chapter, we have examined the implementation of digital filters in a manner that is slightly more detailed than in the previous chapters. We also quickly previewed a popular method of designing FIR digital filters, namely the Fourier-series method. In actual practice, the Fourier-series method is combined with the use of window functions to achieve more desirable results. These window functions modify the magnitude of the Fourier coefficients which are employed in the filter implementation and consequently have potentially dramatic effects on the frequency response performance achieved. Nevertheless, the filter implementation process, as covered in this chapter, is not effected. Therefore, the implementation technique explored in the current context is not altered by the process of applying windowing functions. The exploration of windowing functions is beyond the scope of the current text, but the basic implementation of FIR filters VHDL, as shown, encompasses the essential digital design methodology.

CHAPTER 13 EXERCISES

1. Ideal, FIR digital filters that have a passband extending halfway to the folding frequency are sometimes referred to as half-band filters. The ideal frequency response shown below is an example. For the lowpass filter shown, the sampling frequency is 1.0 MHz and the ideal cutoff frequency is 250 KHz.

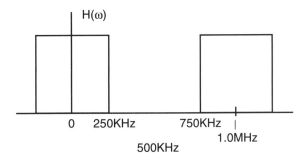

   a) Find the equation of the Fourier coefficients for $H(\omega)$.
   b) List the first eleven coefficients of the Fourier cosine series (including zero valued coefficients and the constant term).
   c) Find the difference equation which represents the implementation of the FIR filter.
   d) Write a VHDL program which implements the half-band filter using a twenty-one-stage filter, eight-bits wide. The VHDL implementation should be a folded FIR implementation (add symmetric register components prior to multiplying by the respective coefficients).
   e) How many flip-flops are required in the filter implementation for the register portion of the design? (Do not count any storage elements included in the arithmetic processing portion of the implementation).
   f) Perform a simulation of the impulse response and verify each of the coefficients by observing the discrete, temporal values of the impulse response.
   g) Perform a simulation of the step response and verify each of the coefficients by observing the discrete, temporal values of the step response.
   h) Find the steady-state frequency response of the twenty-one-stage implementation. Plot a graph of the steady state response for at least one period of the response.

2. Repeat the design of exercise 1, except that the sampling frequency should be set at 10,000 Hz and the cutoff frequency set to 2,500 Hz.

3. Design a twenty-stage VHDL moving average filter.
   a) Design an FIR digital filter implementing the difference equation with the $x(n)$ implemented as eight binary bit values.

$$y(n) = \frac{1}{20}(x(n) + x(n-1) + x(n-2) \dots x(n-18) + x(n-19))$$

  b) Simulate the filter with a unit pulse input and verify that the filter provides the correct impulse response.

  c) Simulate the filter with a unit-step input and verify that the filter provides the correct step response.

  c) Graph the steady-state frequency response of the moving average filter.

4. Repeat the designs above using AHDL.

  a) Repeat 1 above using AHDL.

  b) Repeat 2 above using AHDL.

  c) Repeat 3 above using AHDL.

5. Modify program 13.2.

  a) Apply a scaling multiplier of 1024 to the design given in Section 13.8.1. Re-scale the output to achieve an over-all low frequency gain of approximately 1.0.

  b) Compile and simulate your design to check the results.

INDEX